An Introduction to
Microcomputers

Volume 1
Basic Concepts

An Introduction to
Microcomputers

Volume 1
Basic Concepts

2nd Edition

Adam Osborne

OSBORNE/McGraw-Hill
Berkeley, California

Published by
OSBORNE/McGraw-Hill
630 Bancroft Way
Berkeley, California 94710
U.S.A

For information on translations and book distributors outside of the U.S.A., please write OSBORNE/McGraw-Hill at the above address.

An Introduction to Microcomputers: Volume 1 — Basic Concepts
Second Edition

1234567890 DODO 89876543210

Library of Congress Catalogue Card Number 76-374891

ISBN 0-931988-34-9

Technical editor for this book was Curtis A. Ingraham. Cover design by Joseph Mauro.

Contents

FIGURES

TABLES

1

Microprocessors and Microcomputers

Electronic computers have been with us for 30 years; in that time computers have evolved in various ways. The microcomputer is the most recent evolution, and its impact on the computer industry has been the most profound. Microcomputers are physically smaller than other computers, and in general they do less, but these differences are rapidly disappearing. To a computer programmer a microcomputer does not look like anything very new.

Computer

Computer System

The word computer usually identifies that part of a computer system that actually computes. The rest of the computer system provides an interface between human operators and the computer. Thus, **the computer may be visualized as the "brains" of the computer system.** (See Volume 0 for detailed explanations of computers and computer systems.)

Central Processing Unit

If you look at a computer you will see a box with a lot of electronics inside it. We call this electronic logic. Some of this electronic logic is, in fact, the brains of the computer, while other electronic logic is nothing more than depositories and conduits for information flowing to and from the brains. **The electronic logic that constitutes the brains of the computer is frequently referred to as the Central Processing Unit (CPU).**

Chip

DIP

Electronic logic has itself undergone some remarkable changes during the past few years. **Today vast quantities of electronic logic are created as microscopic circuits on tiny pieces of silicon, referred to as chips. These chips are mounted in Dual In-line Packages (DIPs).** Figure 1-1 illustrates a chip and a DIP.

Microprocessor

Today the word "microprocessor" describes a single chip, packaged in a DIP, containing the logic of a central processing unit, plus various amounts of the "depository and conduit" logic that must surround a CPU. Figure 1-1 illustrates a microprocessor.

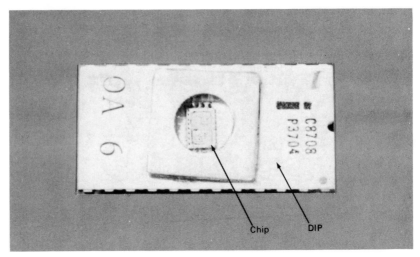

Figure 1-1. A Microprocessor Chip and DIP

Microcomputer

Today the word "microcomputer" describes a product that contains all of the functions found in a computer. This product can be packaged in one of two ways:

One-Chip Microcomputer

1) A microcomputer may be a single chip, packaged in a single DIP. The microcomputer is then referred to as a one-chip microcomputer. A one-chip microcomputer would look just like the DIP illustrated in Figure 1-1.

2) A microcomputer may be configured using a number of DIPs and additional electronic logic. These DIPs and additional electronic logic may fit on a single printed circuit card, or in a box that looks and acts like a small computer. But the microcomputer, whether on a card or in a box, must use a microprocessor for its central processing unit in order to qualify as a microcomputer.

Thus **the word microprocessor has come to describe specific electronic logic and packaging. The electronic logic must be the equivalent of a central processing unit; the package must be a single chip, packaged as a DIP. In contrast, the word microcomputer has come to describe specific electronic logic but a variety of different packages, ranging from a single DIP all the way to a box full of electronics.**

There are indeed striking similarities between microprocessors and central processing units. There are also striking similarities between microcomputers and other computers. In fact, microcomputers look so similar to other computers that any distinction between the two products appears to be a distinction in search of a difference.

However, although microprocessors look remarkably like central processing units, microprocessors have been used in markedly different ways. In consequence, we have had to look at microprocessors as different products. We have had to seek different attributes as advantages, and different omissions as liabilities. Similarities between microprocessors and central processing units have frequently been as much a hindrance to understanding microprocessors as they have been a help.

The purpose of this book is to explain what microprocessors and microcomputers are and, in addition, what sets them apart from computers and central processing units.

Microprocessors, microcomputers, central processing units and computers all share a common ancestry. To acquire a little perspective, therefore, we will begin with a short history of computer evolution.

THE EVOLUTION OF COMPUTERS

Today's smallest microcomputer and largest mainframe computer share a common ancestor — the UNIVAC 1, which was built out of vacuum tubes in 1950. UNIVAC 1 filled a room, yet it had less computing power than most of today's microcomputers. UNIVAC 1 and the **vacuum tube computers** that followed **were used for a very limited number of "expense-is-no-object" applications, frequently to solve mathematical problems that might otherwise have been impossible to solve.**

Bistable Logic Device

The vacuum tube computer's logic was not particularly well suited to scientific applications; its logic **was the immediate and natural consequence of being built out of bistable logic devices** — the building block of every digital computer. A bistable logic device is any device that has two stable states, and the ability to switch on command from one stable state to another.

The basic concepts for the design of a computing machine go all the way back to Charles Babbage, who in 1833 laid out the concepts that can be found, with minor variations, in every digital computer built today. In Chapters 2 and 3 we describe these basic concepts — concepts that allow computing logic to be built out of binary digits, irrespective of how the computer will be used.

Indeed, since the dawn of the computer industry there have been no radical breakthroughs in the basic concepts of computing. **Advances in solid state physics have been the computer industry's evolutionary force. New electronic technology has caused computer prices to fall so rapidly that every few years entire new markets have been engulfed by new waves of radically cheaper, smaller and more powerful computers.** In 1960 computer prices had declined to the point where computers could be used for data processing, and the day of the general purpose computer had arrived.

In 1965 the PDP-8, at $50,000, brought computers into the laboratory and the manufacturing plant's production line, and the minicomputer industry was born. Today minicomputers cost as little as $1,000, and their sphere of influence has spread with this additional price reduction.

But **microcomputer prices range from less than $1 to perhaps $1,000 — and we have entered an era where a computer can control a washing machine or an oven,** or it can be a component in consumer products that are mass merchandised.

This incredible evolution of computers is the direct consequence of some remarkable advances in solid state physics. Let us take a look at these advances.

Transistor   The vacuum tube is a bulky device with expensive internal elements. But it is a bistable logic element; it can be on, allowing current to flow through it, or it can be off, denying current flow. **In the late fifties the vacuum tube was replaced by the transistor,** a small piece of germanium metal, suitably doped with impurities.

Soon an array of discrete, low cost components were available:

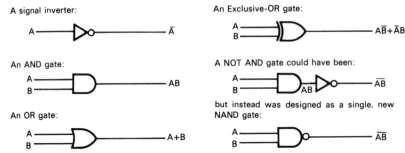

A signal inverter:

An Exclusive-OR gate:

An AND gate:

A NOT AND gate could have been:

but instead was designed as a single, new NAND gate:

An OR gate:

These components combined a number of bistable logic elements to make available more useful functions, such as the ones just illustrated.

But this was just a beginning. Four NAND gates were built into one chip (costing the same as, or little more than, a single NAND gate) to give a quadruple 2-input positive-NAND buffer:

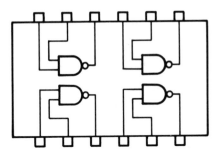

7400 Series Integrated Circuits   Devices such as the quadruple 2-input positive-NAND buffer spawned a whole range of devices, affectionately known, by a generation of logic designers, as 7400 series integrated circuits.

Indeed, the 7400 series integrated circuits, in their day, had as deep an impact on the electronics industry as microprocessors are having today, because 7400 series integrated circuits converted a generation of "circuit designers" into a generation of "logic designers" — and the conversion occurred almost overnight.

Four gates on one chip became ten, and then a hundred, and then a thousand; today one hundred thousand gates worth of logic can be squeezed onto a single silicon chip, and the end is by no means predictable, or even in sight.

Medium Scale Integration   **A chip with a large number of gates on it is called an integrated circuit. If there are approximately 100 to 1000 gates on a chip, we refer to the logic as Medium Scale Integration (MSI). At some ill-defined level, above 1000**

Large Scale Integration   **gates of logic on a chip, we are talking of Large Scale Integration (LSI). At another ill-defined level, above 10,000 gates of logic on a chip, we get Very Large Scale Integration (VLSI).**

The interesting aspect of integrated circuits is that the cost of a chip is a function of physical size — it is not a function of how much logic has been implemented on the chip. Therefore, as chips become more complex, cheaper computers can be built.

Two aspects of the amazingly shrinking computer need to be clarified:

1) Does the whole computer shrink? And, if not, which parts remain the same?
2) If the microcomptuer is so inexpensive, why hasn't it eliminated all other computers?

The whole computer cannot shrink; only the electronics can. What remains is the human interface — display screens and keyboards, means of accepting data inputs and generating results in human readable form.

The microcomputer will never eliminate all other computers, because when computers are used to process data or solve scientific problems, there is a relentless economic need to make the computer more powerful. So with every major advance in solid state electronics technology, you get two new products: a smaller version of yesterday's computer and a more powerful version of today's computer:

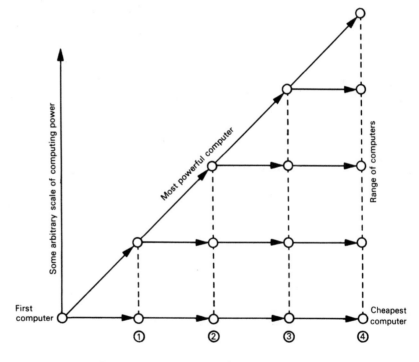

Four major advances in semiconductor technology

As time went by, there developed a considerable spread between the capabilities of the cheapest computer and the most powerful computer. Thus in 1965 the first arbitrary division was made — between minicomputers and large computers. We will not attempt to define what a minicomputer is, as against a large computer. A minicomputer is a minicomputer because the product's manufacturer calls it a minicomputer.

In 1970, a second arbitrary division was made, between minicomputers and microcomputers; but this time the differences between products were easier to define.

A microcomputer was sold as one, or a very few logical devices, destined to become components in a larger logic system.

By way of contrast, all other computers were vehicles for the execution of computer programs, each of which transiently defined the purpose of the computer system.

But differences between minicomputers and microcomputers are rapidly disappearing. In fact, microcomputers are, in many cases, indistinguishable from minicomputers in all ways except their physical construction. However, because of their very small size and low cost, the majority of microprocessors and one-chip microcomputers continue to be used in ways where no minicomputer could ever fit.

THE ORIGIN OF MICROPROCESSORS AND MICROCOMPUTERS

Since this is a book about microprocessors and microcomputers, let us look at the events which culminated in the first true microcomputer.

Datapoint Corporation of San Antonio, Texas, is a manufacturer of "intelligent terminals" and small computer systems. In 1969 they (along with Cogar and Viatron) attempted to make a "great leap forward." **Datapoint engineers designed a very elementary central processing unit and contracted with Intel and Texas Instruments to build the design on a single logic chip.** Intel succeeded, but their product executed instructions approximately ten times as slowly as Datapoint had specified; so Datapoint declined to buy, and built their own central processing unit using existing logic components.

Intel was left with a computer-like logic device whose development had been paid for. They were faced with the choice of manufacturing and selling it, or shelving it. They chose to sell it. **They called it a "microcomputer" and gave it the name "Intel 8008." By today's definitions the 8008 is a microprocessor,** which is the word even Intel now uses to describe the part.

When Datapoint designed the 8008, they intended to use it in simple data processing applications — the traditional job for computers. And some of the earliest Intel 8008 customers did in fact use this microprocessor to build small minicomputers. But **the Intel 8008 also created a market where none had existed: as a programmable logic device.** Let us explore this concept.

In any catalog of logic components, there are perhaps ten thousand different logic devices. The simplest we have already described; simple logic gates may be illustrated as follows:

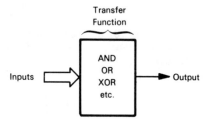

The way in which data inputs are transformed into data outputs is specified by a fixed transfer function. But consider a more interesting logic device, a 2-input multiplexer:

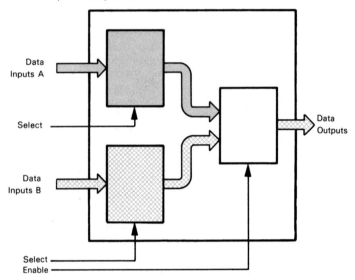

There are two interesting concepts in this multiplexer. First, data is being handled in four parallel line units. Second, there are two non-data signals present: "Select" and "Enable." Select determines which data input will become the data output. Enable determines when it will become an output.

If an LSI chip can contain thousands of gates worth of logic, how about condensing a catalog of logic onto a single, general purpose chip, as follows:

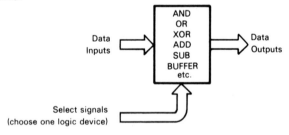

The general purpose chip illustrated above has a good deal of unnecessary, duplicated logic on it. Any one of the ten thousand chips listed in a catalog may be synthesized out of a few "building block" logic functions — AND, OR, XOR, ADD, SUB — plus a few buffers, selects, and enables:

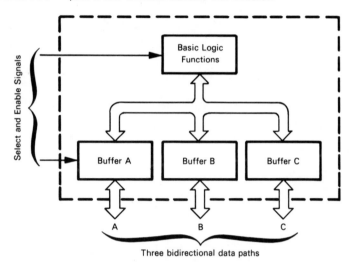

Three bidirectional data paths

This "building block" logic device can synthesize any individual logic device, or any sequence of individual logic devices.
This is the concept of the microprocessor.

ABOUT THIS BOOK

The purpose of this book is to give you a thorough understanding of what microprocessors are and how they differ from other computer products. Basic concepts are covered in considerable detail, and from basic concepts we build the necessary components of a microcomputer system. But if you do find this book hard to follow, stop reading it and first read Volume 0.

This book does not discuss the various technologies which are used to build logic chips, because the type of technology used is usually unimportant to a microprocessor user. Your application may have some key parameters such as the amount of power that you can afford to consume, or the execution speeds that you can tolerate. The various technologies that are used influence power consumption, execution speed and other critical factors, but where these factors are critical, selecting the right microprocessor simply involves looking at product specifications. Understanding whether the product is fabricated using "N-MOS" technology or "C-MOS" technology does not make it significantly easier to understand what a microprocessor is, or how to use it.

How This Book Has Been Printed

Notice that text in this book has been printed in **boldface type** and lightface type. **This has been done to help you skip those parts of the book that cover subject matter with which you are familiar. You can be sure that lightface type only expands on information presented in the previous boldface type.** Therefore, read only boldface type until you reach a subject about which you want to know more, at which point start reading the lightface type.

2
Some Fundamental Concepts

The reason there is no fundamental difference between a microcomputer and any other computer is because all computer products are based on the same fundamental computing concepts, which in turn devolve to one fundamental logical concept — that of the binary digit.

Binary Digit
A binary digit is a number that can have one of two values: 0 or 1. A binary digit can have no other value.

What makes the binary digit so useful is that it can be represented by any bistable device. Anything that can be "on" or "off," "high" or "low," can represent a zero in one state and a one in the other state. Figure 2-1 illustrates a bistable device. And that is all the physics you need to know in order to understand microcomputers.

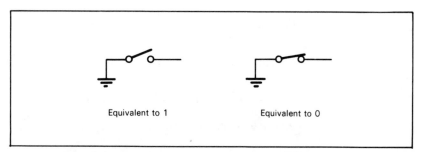

Equivalent to 1   Equivalent to 0

Figure 2-1. A Symbolic Representation of Binary Digits Represented by a Bistable Device

NUMBER SYSTEMS

Any description of number systems makes for dull reading. Unfortunately you must understand how computers count if you want to understand how they work. But number system concepts can be learned slowly, in parallel with other concepts. You do not have to learn one and then the other.

If you already understand binary arithmetic, then you can skip this chapter. If you do not understand binary arithmetic, it may still be a good idea to read only the boldface type on your first pass through this chapter. Move on to Chapter 3, and return to this chapter when you feel the need.

A computer that could count no higher than 1 would not be a very useful machine. Fortunately, **binary digits can be used to represent numbers of any magnitude, just as a string of decimal digits can be used to represent numbers in excess of nine.** Let us therefore consider what numbers really consist of.

Decimal Numbers

When a decimal number has more than one digit, have you ever considered what each digit really represents? The two digits "11" really mean ten plus one:

$$11 = 1 \times 10 + 1$$

Likewise, the number 83 really means eight tens plus three:

$$83 = 8 \times 10 + 3$$

The number 2347 really means two thousands, plus three hundreds, plus four tens, plus seven:

$$2347 = 2 \times 1000 + 3 \times 100 + 4 \times 10 + 7$$

There is nothing unique or special about decimal numbers. The fact that man has ten fingers and ten toes almost certainly accounts for the universal use of base ten numbers, but any other number base would serve just as well.

Binary Numbers

Because decimal digits cease to be unique with the digit 9, ten must be represented by "10," which means 1 times the number base (in this case, ten) plus 0. Using the letter "B" to represent the number base, we have:

$$10 = 1 \times B + 0$$

In the binary numbering system, "B" does not represent ten; it represents two. Therefore, **in the binary system, 10 = decimal 2:**

$$10 = 1 \times 2 + 0$$

Similarly, in the binary system, 11 represents decimal three:

$$11 = 1 \times 2 + 1$$

Stated generally, suppose any numbering system's digits may be represented symbolically by d_i, d_j, d_k, etc. If B represents the number base, then any number can be explained by this equation:

$$d_i d_j d_k d_l \quad = \quad d_i \times B^3 + d_j \times B^2 + d_k \times B + d_l$$

Consider a decimal example (B = 10) and a binary example (B = 2):

$$2174 \quad = \quad 2 \times 10^3 + 1 \times 10^2 + 7 \times 10 + 4$$
$$d_i d_j d_k d_l \quad = \quad d_i \times B^3 + d_j \times B^2 + d_k \times B + d_l$$
$$1011 \quad = \quad 1 \times 2^3 + 0 \times 2^2 + 1 \times 2 + 1$$

Converting Numbers from One Base to Another

Binary to Decimal Conversion

It is easy to convert numbers from one number base to another number base. Since we have only discussed decimal and binary numbers so far, consider the conversion of numbers between these two systems.

$$1011 = 1\times2^3 + 0\times2^2 + 1\times2 + 1$$
$$2^3 = 8 \text{ and } 2^2 = 4, \text{ therefore:}$$
$$1011 = 1\times8 + 0\times4 + 1\times2 + 1$$
$$= 8 + 0 + 2 + 1$$
$$= 11 \text{ (decimal)}$$

Decimal to Binary Conversion

Continuous division by 2, keeping track of the remainders, provides a simple method of converting a decimal number to its binary equivalent; for example, to convert decimal 11 to its binary equivalent, proceed as follows:

	Quotient		Remainder
$\dfrac{11}{2} =$	5	+	1
$\dfrac{5}{2} =$	2	+	1
$\dfrac{2}{2} =$	1	+	0
$\dfrac{1}{2} =$	0	+	1

1 0 1 1   Thus $11_{10} = 1011_2$.

The subscripts 10 and 2 identify the numbers as base ten and base two, respectively.

Converting Fractions

The general equation to convert a fractional binary number to its decimal equivalent may be written as follows:

$$d_i d_j d_k d_l \ldots \text{etc.} = (d_i \times B^{-1}) + (d_j \times B^{-2}) + (d_k \times B^{-3}) + (d_l \times B^{-4}) \ldots \text{etc.}$$

where d_i, d_j, d_k, etc. represent numeric digits and B represents the number base.

For example, to convert 0.1011_2 to its decimal equivalent, proceed as follows:

$$0.1011 = (1\times2^{-1}) + (0\times2^{-2}) + (1\times2^{-3}) + (1\times2^{-4})$$

where $\quad 2^{-1} = \dfrac{1}{2^1} = 0.5; \ 2^{-2} = \dfrac{1}{2^2} = 0.25; \ 2^{-3} = \dfrac{1}{2^3} = 0.125;$

$$2^{-4} = \dfrac{1}{2^4} = 0.0625$$

Thus, $\quad 0.1011_2 = 0.5_{10} + 0 + 0.125_{10} + 0.0625_{10}$
$$= 0.6875_{10}$$

To convert a fractional decimal number to its binary equivalent (e.g., to convert 0.6875_{10} to its binary equivalent), use the following approximation method:

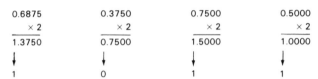

0.6875	0.3750	0.7500	0.5000
× 2	× 2	× 2	× 2
1.3750	0.7500	1.5000	1.0000
↓	↓	↓	↓
1	0	1	1

Unfortunately, binary-decimal fractional conversions are not always exact. Just as a fraction such as $\frac{2}{3}$ has no exact decimal representation, so a decimal fraction that is not the sum of 2^{-n} terms will only approximate a binary fraction.

Consider 0.42357_{10}; the binary representation of this number may be created as follows:

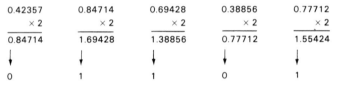

0.42357	0.84714	0.69428	0.38856	0.77712
× 2	× 2	× 2	× 2	× 2
0.84714	1.69428	1.38856	0.77712	1.55424
↓	↓	↓	↓	↓
0	1	1	0	1

The answer is $0.01101\ldots_2$

As a check, let us convert back:

$$0.01101 = 0 \times 2^{-1} + 1 \times 2^{-2} + 1 \times 2^{-3} + 0 \times 2^{-4} + 1 \times 2^{-5}$$
$$= 0 + 0.25 + 0.125 + 0 + 0.03125$$
$$= 0.40625_{10}$$

The difference is $0.42357 - 0.40625$, which equals 0.01732. This difference is caused by the neglected remainder, 0.55424. In other words, the neglected remainder (0.55424) multiplied by the smallest computed term (0.03125) gives the total error:

$$0.55424 \times 0.03125 = 0.01732$$

Other Number Systems

Because binary numbers tend to be very long, binary digits are often grouped into sets of three or four. The numbers are now base 8 (octal) or base 16 (hexadecimal), as shown in Table 2-1. Consider the binary number:

$$110111101100$$

Octal Numbers   By grouping the binary digits into sets of three, the number is converted to octal format:

110	111	101	100	$= 6754_8$
6	7	5	4	

Base 8 (octal) includes only the digits:

$$0, 1, 2, 3, 4, 5, 6, 7$$

Decimal 8 is the same as octal 10.

Table 2-1. Number Systems

Hexadecimal	Decimal	Octal	Binary
0	0	0	0000
1	1	1	0001
2	2	2	0010
3	3	3	0011
4	4	4	0100
5	5	5	0101
6	6	6	0110
7	7	7	0111
8	8	10	1000
9	9	11	1001
A	10	12	1010
B	11	13	1011
C	12	14	1100
D	13	15	1101
E	14	16	1110
F	15	17	1111

Hexadecimal Numbers
By grouping the binary digits into sets of four, the number is converted to hexadecimal base:

$$\underset{D}{1101} \quad \underset{E}{1110} \quad \underset{C}{1100} \quad = DEC_{16}$$

Base 16 (hexadecimal) includes the digits:

0, 1, 2, 3, 4, 5, 6, 7, 8, 9, A, B, C, D, E, F

Decimal 16 is the same as hexadecimal 10.

BINARY ARITHMETIC

Binary numbers can be operated on in the same way as decimal numbers; in fact, binary arithmetic is much easier than decimal arithmetic. Consider binary addition, subtraction, multiplication, and division.

Binary Addition

The possible combinations when adding two binary digits are:

Augend	+	Addend	=	Result	+	Carry
0	+	0	=	0		0
0	+	1	=	1		0
1	+	0	=	1		0
1	+	1	=	0		1

The carry, as in decimal addition, is added to the next higher binary position. For example:

This decimal addition is equivalent to this binary addition.

```
       3                    11        ◄──── carry
      +6                   011
       9               +   110
                        ──────
                          1001
```

This decimal addition is equivalent to this binary addition.

```
      11  ◄──── carry        1   1   ◄──── carry
     208                  11010000
   +  92               +   1011100
    ────                 ─────────
     300                 100101100
```

Binary Subtraction

Microcomputers cannot subtract binary digits; they can only add. Fortunately that is no problem, since subtraction can be converted into addition.

Tens Complement   Subtracting a decimal number is equivalent to adding the tens complement of the number.

The tens complement of a number is generated by subtracting the number from 10.

The final carry, however, must be ignored when performing decimal subtraction via tens complement addition.

Consider the decimal subtraction:

$$9 - 2 = 7$$

The tens complement of 2 is (10−2), which equals 8. The decimal subtraction can therefore be performed via the tens complement addition:

```
              9
           +  8
           ────
    =        17
```

ignore final carry ──┘

Performing decimal subtraction via tens complement addition is silly, since 10−2 is no simpler to evaluate than 9−2 was. **The binary equivalent of a tens complement is a twos complement.** Performing binary subtraction via twos complement addition makes a lot of sense; moreover, twos complement logic is well suited to computers.

Ones Complement

The twos complement of a binary number is derived by replacing 0 digits with 1 digits, and 1 digits with 0 digits, then adding 1. The first step generates the "ones complement" of a binary number. For example, the ones complement of 1011011101 is 0100100010.

Here are some other examples:

Binary number	0101
Ones complement	1010
Binary number	1010100
Ones complement	0101011

Twos Complement

The twos complement of a binary number is formed by adding 1 to the ones complement of that number. For example, the ones complement of 0100 is 1011:

Original number	0100
Ones complement	1011
	+ 1
Twos complement	1100

Now look at how binary subtraction can be performed by adding the twos complement of the SUBTRAHEND to the MINUEND. First consider the following binary subtraction:

Minuend	10001
Subtrahend	− 01011
Difference	00110

The same operation can be performed by taking the twos complement of the subtrahend and adding it to the minuend. The final carry must be discarded, just as it had to be for tens complement subtraction:

Minuend	10001
Twos complement of subtrahend	+ 10101
	100110

discard final carry ⤴

Thus the difference is 00110.

Consider another example:

11001	Minuend	11001	Minuend
− 101	Subtrahend	+ 11011	Twos complement of subtrahend
= 10100		= 110100	

discard final carry ⤴

When a larger number is subtracted from a smaller number, there is no carry to be discarded. Consider the decimal version of this case. $2 - 9$ becomes $2 + (10 - 9)$, or $2 + 1$. The answer, $+3$, is the tens complement of the correct negative result, which is $-(10 - 3) = -7$. Here is a binary example of the same thing:

101	Minuend	101	Minuend
-11011	Subtrahend	$+00101$	Twos complement of subtrahend
-10110	Difference	01010	Negative answer in twos complement form

A larger binary number has been subtracted from a smaller one. The answer on the right is negative, but it is in twos complement form; taking the twos complement of 01010 (twos complement = 10110) and assigning a minus sign provides the same answer as on the left: -10110.

Sign of Answer in Subtraction

When performing twos complement subtraction, the final carry provides the sign of the answer. If the final carry is 1, the answer is positive (the minuend is greater than the subtrahend). If the final carry is 0, the answer is negative (the minuend is smaller than the subtrahend), and is in its twos complement, positive form.

Binary Multiplication

Binary multiplication is actually easier than decimal multiplication, since each partial product, in binary, is either zero (multiplication by 0) or exactly the multiplicand (multiplication by 1). For example:

This decimal multiplication is equivalent to this binary multiplication:

```
        9              1001
      × 5            × 101
      ----           ------
       45             1001
                     0000
                    1001
                    ------
                    101101
```

Binary Division

Binary division can be performed using the same steps as decimal division. Here is an example:

```
                              1011  ◄──── Quotient
            Divisor ──► 101 ) 110111  ◄──── Dividend
                              101
                              ----
                              0011
                              0000
                              ----
                               111  ⎫
                               101  ⎪ Intermediate
                              ----  ⎬ multiplications
                              0101  ⎪ and subtractions
                              0101  ⎭
                              ----
                                 0
```

BOOLEAN ALGEBRA AND COMPUTER LOGIC

Boolean algebra is important in microcomputer applications because it provides the basis for decision making, condition testing, and numerous logical operations.

Boolean algebra uses the binary digits 0 and 1 to define logical decisions. Three Boolean operators, OR, AND, and Exclusive-OR (XOR), combine two binary digits to produce a single-digit result. A fourth Boolean operator, NOT, complements a binary digit.

"OR" Operation

The OR operation is defined, for two integers I and J, by the statement:

If I OR J, or both, equal 1, then the result is 1. Otherwise the result is 0.

A plus sign + is used to represent "OR." While the Boolean symbol for OR is also used to represent arithmetic addition, the two operators should not be confused; they are very similar, but they are not identical. Two binary digits are ORed as follows:

$$0 + 0 = 0$$
$$0 + 1 = 1$$
$$1 + 0 = 1$$
$$1 + 1 = 1$$

Notice that the last OR operation $(1 + 1 = 1)$ is the only OR operation where the result differs from binary addition.

Truth Tables

Logic functions are commonly defined using a Truth Table which lists the output signals associated with allowed input signal combinations. The OR Gate Truth Table is given below:

Truth Table for an OR Gate

Inputs		Output =
I	J	I + J
0	0	0
0	1	1
1	0	1
1	1	1

"AND" Operation

The AND operation may be defined for two integers I and J by the statement:

If I AND J are both 1, then the result is 1. Otherwise the result is 0.

The dot • and Λ symbol are both used to represent the AND operation. The four possible combinations of 0 and 1 for the AND operation are:

$$0 \cdot 0 = 0$$
$$0 \cdot 1 = 0$$
$$1 \cdot 0 = 0$$
$$1 \cdot 1 = 1$$

The AND Gate Truth Table is given below:

Truth Table for an AND Gate

Inputs		Output =
I	J	I · J
0	0	0
0	1	0
1	0	0
1	1	1

"Exclusive-OR" Operation

The Exclusive-OR differentiates between input binary digits which are identical and input binary digits which are different. The output is 1 when the inputs are different and 0 when the inputs are the same. The $\oplus$ or $\veebar$ symbol is used to represent the XOR operation. The four possible combinations of 0 and 1 for the XOR operation are:

$$0 \oplus 0 = 0$$
$$0 \oplus 1 = 1$$
$$1 \oplus 0 = 1$$
$$1 \oplus 1 = 0$$

The XOR Truth Table is given below:

Truth Table for an Exclusive-OR Gate

Inputs		Output =
A	B	A $\oplus$ B
0	0	0
0	1	1
1	0	1
1	1	0

"NOT" Operation

"NOT" complements any binary digit or group of digits.

$$NOT\ 1 = 0$$
$$NOT\ 0 = 1$$

Because of the nature of microcomputer logic, NOT is not a particularly significant logical operation; instead of using the NOT operation, the microcomputer's ability to generate a ones complement is employed.

Combining AND with NOT generates NAND. Combining OR with NOT generates NOR. The results of NAND and NOR are the NOT of AND and NOT of OR, respectively.

A bar is placed over a digit to represent NOT. Therefore:

$$\bar{1} = 0$$
$$\bar{0} = 1$$

Combining Logical Operations

A microcomputer need not have all three of the Boolean operators AND, OR, and Exclusive-OR; some operators may be combined to generate others, as follows:

$A + B$ is reproduced by $\overline{\bar{A} \cdot \bar{B}}$; this is illustrated as follows:

A	B	A + B	$\bar{A}$	$\bar{B}$	$\bar{A} \cdot \bar{B}$	$\overline{\bar{A} \cdot \bar{B}}$
0	0	0	1	1	1	0
0	1	1	1	0	0	1
1	0	1	0	1	0	1
1	1	1	0	0	0	1

The Exclusive-OR may be generated as follows:

$$A \oplus B = (A \cdot \bar{B}) + (\bar{A} \cdot B)$$

This is illustrated as follows:

A	B	A ⊕ B	$\bar{A}$	$\bar{B}$	$A \cdot \bar{B}$	$\bar{A} \cdot B$	$(A \cdot \bar{B}) + (\bar{A} \cdot B)$
0	0	0	1	1	0	0	0
0	1	1	1	0	0	1	1
1	0	1	0	1	1	0	1
1	1	0	0	0	0	0	0

De Morgan's Theorem

Boolean operations can be combined to produce any desired output from a set of known inputs. De Morgan's theorem is a valuable aid in designing such combinations. The theorem can be written in either of these ways:

$$\overline{A \cdot B} = \overline{A} + \overline{B}$$
$$\overline{A + B} = \overline{A} \cdot \overline{B}$$

Therefore a microcomputer needs only two Boolean operators, OR and NOT, to generate all others, since:

$$A \cdot B = \overline{\overline{A} + \overline{B}}$$

generates AND out of OR and NOT. Similarly,

$$A \oplus B = \overline{(\overline{A} + B)} + \overline{(A + \overline{B})}$$

generates XOR out of OR and NOT.

3

The Makings of a Microprocessor Memory and Its Contents

Bits Given that BInary digiTs (referred to as bits) are capable of being manipulated to perform any of the operations described in Chapter 2, how are these basic operations going to be harnessed in order to generate a microprocessor? First let us examine how information is stored as binary data.

MEMORY DEVICES

Binary data are stored in memory elements. Every computer memory consists of an array of bistable elements. Minicomputers used to use "core" memories, which consist of minute metal "donuts" that can hold a clockwise or counterclockwise magnetic charge:

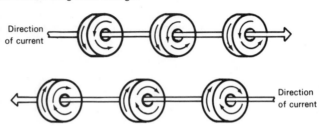

Microcomputers use semiconductor memories, which consist of an array of "gates" that may be conducting or not conducting:

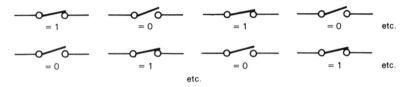

Bubble Memory

Bubble memories represent the latest innovation in memory devices. Bubble memories use a thin film of magnetic material artificially grown on a nonmagnetic base material (generally called a substrate). Microscopic magnetized zones can be created at discrete grid points within the magnetic film. These zones have opposite polarity from the rest of the magnetic film; this may be illustrated as follows:

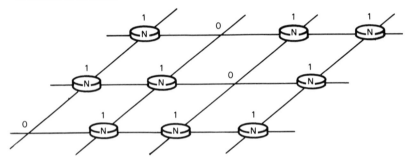

The illustration above arbitrarily shows zones of north polarity in a film of south polarity. These zones of north polarity are referred to as magnetic bubbles; hence the name "bubble memory." The presence of a bubble indicates a 1 bit; the absence of a bubble represents a 0 bit.

Nonvolatile Memory

Core and bubble memories hold their magnetic charge even when disconnected from electric power; you can pull a core memory card out of a computer, plug it into another similar computer, and the contents of the memory should still be intact. **Core memories are therefore said to be "nonvolatile."**

Volatile Memory

Semiconductor memories generally lose all stored data the moment you shut off their power source; therefore they are said to be "volatile."

The type of memory used with a microcomputer is unimportant. It is only necessary that the memory consist of a number of bistable, individually addressable elements, each representing a single binary digit:

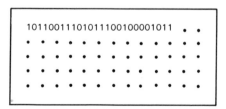

MEMORY TYPES

Every memory device must have these two absolutely necessary properties:

1) Every location that stores a binary digit must be uniquely addressable.
2) It must be possible to read the state of every stored binary digit.

ROM With some memories it is not possible to change the state of binary digits in the memory. If the state of binary digits can be read, but not changed, then the memory is called a Read-Only Memory, or ROM. Of course, by its very nature, any ROM memory is nonvolatile.

RAM You can read the contents of a read/write memory and write into it. Read/write memories are commonly (and inaccurately) referred to as Random Access Memories (RAM).

There is no good reason why a read/write memory, as against a read-only memory, should be referred to as randomly accessible; memory is randomly accessible if individual binary digits can be accessed directly:

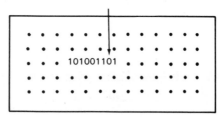

If binary digits within a memory were not randomly accessible, they would be sequentially accessible, which means that the tenth binary digit, for example, could only be accessed by first passing over the nine preceding digits:

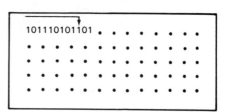

Read-only memories and read/write memories are both randomly accessible. Nevertheless, common terminology refers to read-only memories as ROMs and read/write memories as RAMs.

Bubble Memory Loops

Bubble memories (which we mentioned previously) **are,** in fact, **partially serial and partially random access memories.** Bubbles are located at grid points, as previously illustrated; however, they are configured in "loops," which may be illustrated conceptually as follows:

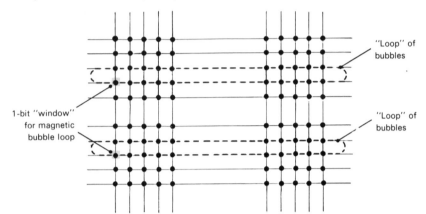

The grid points within a bubble memory can be visualized as depositories where a bubble may or may not reside. A loop of bubbles becomes a loop because structures surrounding the bubble memory rotate the bubbles within the loop. Following a rotation, each grid point in the loop will or will not contain a bubble, depending upon the status of the adjacent grid point before the rotation. This may be illustrated as follows:

Loop before rotation
```
 ,-- 0 1 1 0 0 1 0 0 --,
 |                     | 1   Window
 '-- 1 0 1 1 0 0 1 0 --'
```

Loop after rotation
```
 ,-- 1 1 0 0 1 0 0 1 --,
 |                     | 0   Window
 '--- 1 1 0 1 1 0 0 1 --'
```

Each loop has a 1-bit "window." In order to access any bit position within the loop, either to read or write, you do not directly sense the presence or absence of a magnetic bubble at the selected grid point. Rather, the entire loop is rotated until the required bit is at the loop window. Thus the grid points become depositories that can hold a bit of data, but data is addressed via a loop number and a serial, sequential bit position within the loop. A typical bubble memory device might have many loops of bubbles. In such a device, each loop can be accessed randomly, but within a loop an individual bit must be accessed serially.

Bubble Memory Access

Despite the fact that bubble memories are serial access devices, you will nevertheless see them referred to, inaccurately, as bubble "RAMs."

Bubble memories are not widely used as yet, because they are economical only when they provide very large memory capacities; and being serial access devices, they are (in electronics terms) rather slow. **Microcomputers use semiconductor ROMs and RAMs. All programmable microcomputers have some RAM. Nearly all microcomputers also have some ROM.** A microcomputer that had only RAM would be dangerous; you would lose the entire contents of memory whenever you turned the power off or if there were an inadvertent power failure. Every microcomputer will therefore hold some important, non-varying information in read-only memory. (Every microcomputer has some information of this type, which we will describe as we progress through the book.)

The problem with read-only memory is that information must be built into it when it is manufactured. This presents two problems:

1) The information insertion step costs a fixed sum of money (typically $1000 to $10,000), whether you want a single ROM device or ten thousand of them. If you want ten thousand identical ROMs, then the program insertion cost, spread over all ten thousand parts, does not amount to much of a charge per part. But if you want just one or a few ROMs, they become very expensive memory devices.

2) You had better be absolutely right when you specify the information that is to be stored in the read-only memory. One inaccurate binary digit might result in your having to throw out an entire shipment of ROMs, while you order a new, corrected shipment.

PROM   **If you need relatively few ROMs,** there is **a variation,** which costs more per device but **allows you to insert the information yourself. This device is called a Programmable Read-Only Memory (PROM).** Using special equipment (that is quite inexpensive), you can program a PROM — once. Subsequently you can read the information out of the PROM as often as you wish, but you can never write into it again. Using a PROM, therefore, you will insert the special information that the PROM is to hold, then use it as a ROM in your microcomputer from that point on. Subsequently, if you need to change or correct the information stored in the PROM, you must pull it out, throw it away, and replace it with a fresh unused PROM, writing the new or corrected information into this unused device.

Once you have written information into a PROM, you can read the information as often as you like. The PROM will hold its contents indefinitely.

EPROM   **If you are willing to pay a little more, you can get an Erasable Programmable Read-Only Memory (EPROM).Using special equipment you can write into an EPROM, but you can erase the EPROM contents (usually by shining ultraviolet light on it for twenty minutes or more). Using an EPROM, therefore, you will insert the special information that the EPROM is to hold, then use it as a ROM in your microcomputer. Subsequently, if you need to reuse the EPROM or correct the information stored in it, you take it out of the microcomputer, shine ultraviolet light on it until it is completely erased, then write new information into it.**

An EPROM, like a PROM, holds its information indefinitely once it has been programmed. You can read the contents of an EPROM as often as you like.

EAROM   **There are also Electrically Alterable Read-Only Memories (EAROM).** These are read-only memories you can write into at any time (using special circuits), without erasing prior contents. The problem with EAROMs (at least for now) is that electronically they are relatively difficult to use; also, they slowly lose their information. You can read out of a ROM, PROM, or EPROM as often as anyone has been able to determine and never lose the contents of the memory device. But EAROM contents degrade with every read operation.

MEMORY WORDS

**Word
Size**

Chapter 2 explained how binary digits are combined to represent numbers in excess of 1, just as decimal digits are combined to represent numbers in excess of 9. Table 2-1 gave some binary representations of small numbers. **The primary level at which binary digits are grouped within any computer is one of the most important design characteristics of the computer, and is referred to as the computer's word size.** For example, an "8-bit" computer acquires the "8-bit" label because binary data within the computer will be accessed and processed in eight binary digit units. A memory organized into 8-bit units might be visualized as follows:

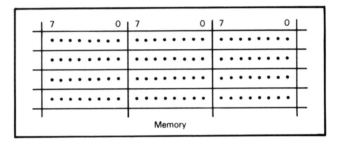

Each dot in the above illustration represents a single binary digit. Each box represents an 8-bit word.

By common convention the bits of a word are numbered from right (0 for the low-order bit) to left (7 for the high-order bit) as illustrated above. Some computer manufacturers reverse the convention, numbering from left to right.

Table 3-1. Computer Word Sizes

Word Size (Bits)	Microcomputers	Minicomputers	Large Computers
4	Many	None	None
6	None	A few obsolete models	None
8	Most common	A few	None
12	A few	A few	None
16	A few	Most common	A few
18	None	A few	A few
24	None	A few	A few
32	None, but expected by 1982	A few	Most common
64	None	None	Common for largest computers

A large number of different word sizes have been used by microcomputer, minicomputer, and mainframe (large computer) manufacturers. Table 3-1 lists the more common word sizes and identifies those word sizes that are used by microcomputers, minicomputers, and large computers.

Most microprocessors use an 8-bit word. There are a number of 4-bit microprocessors that are very much oriented toward digital logic replacement or electronic calculators. There are also a number of 16-bit microprocessors, which tend to compete with minicomputers for their traditional markets. By 1982 there should be some 32-bit microprocessors.

THE BYTE

An 8-bit data unit is called a byte. The byte is the most universally used data unit in the computer industry; it is used even by computers that do not have an 8-bit data word. A 16-bit computer, for example, will often have memory words interpreted as two bytes:

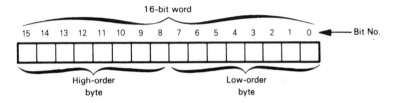

Bytes   When a microcomputer has an 8-bit word size, we can refer interchangeably to "memory bytes" and "memory words"; they mean the same thing.

Words   If a microcomputer's word size is not eight bits, then a memory word and a memory byte do not mean the same thing; a memory byte refers to an 8-bit memory unit, whereas a memory word refers to a unit of the microcomputer's memory word size.

Long   The term "memory word" now frequently refers to 16-bit units, while 32-
Words   bit units are called "long words."

Nibbles   **Many 4-bit microprocessors refer to the 4-bit unit as a "nibble."** Thus each word of 4-bit memory is a nibble, and two 4-bit nibbles constitute a byte.

MEMORY ADDRESSES

Even though every binary digit within a memory must be uniquely addressable, binary digits are not very useful as single entities. Therefore **the smallest unit of information that is usually accessed out of memory is a byte or a word.** For example, when using an 8-bit memory, each time memory is accessed, eight binary digits are referenced.

Each word of memory has a unique memory address. Words within memory have sequential memory addresses, with the first word in the memory having an address of zero, and the last word in the memory having the highest address of any word in that memory. The actual value of this highest address will depend on the size of the memory.

Thus the address of a word is its location in memory. For example, the words of a 1000_{16} (4096_{10}) word memory would be addressed and numbered as follows (in hexadecimal notation):

| End | OFFF | OFFE | OFFD | OFFC | OFFB | OFFA | OFF9 | | • • • |

| • • • | | 09C4 | 09C3 | 09C2 | 09C1 | 09C0 | 09BF | | • • • |

| • • • | | 0005 | 0004 | 0003 | 0002 | 0001 | 0000 | Start |

Conceptually, there are some subtle differences between the way minicomputer and microprocessor programmers use memories. Some of these differences are introduced now, while others are described later, since they will not be meaningful until you understand how microprocessors are used.

Minicomputer Memory Concepts

To the minicomputer programmer, memory is simply a sequence of individually addressable RAM words, with addresses beginning at zero and ending at some large number that depends on the size of the minicomputer's memory. It is only in rare cases that part of the minicomputer's memory will be ROM. Certainly **a minicomputer programmer seldom needs to worry about the physical implementation of memory.** So long as data can be stored and retrieved on demand, where and how this happens is irrelevant.

Microprocessor Memory Concepts

The microprocessor programmer will be very interested in how memory is implemented, because there are many applications where a microprocessor-based product, once developed, will be sold in tens of thousands of units. This being the case, it is very important that the number of discrete components within the microprocessor system be kept to a minimum, since every extra (and therefore unnecessary) component will be multiplied by tens of thousands — thus increasing costs.

The microprocessor programmer has a further interest in memory organization because almost all microprocessor-based products use ROM for some part of memory.

The microprocessor user, if he/she is a logic designer, thinks of memory as semiconductor chips. Figure 3-1 illustrates a 16,384-bit memory device in a dual in-line package.

Figure 3-1. A 16,384-Bit Memory Device

ROM Implementation

Usually ROM is implemented in single chips. For example, a microprocessor may connect to 1024 8-bit words of ROM on a single chip. This single chip will typically have a capacity of 8192 binary digits, divided into (and accessed as) 1024 8-bit units. A microprocessor programmer will be interested in how memory is implemented because moving out of the memory space provided by a single ROM device requires an additional ROM device to be added to the system.

Read/Write Memory Implementation

Read/write memory is commonly implemented on more than one chip. In a very simple case, eight RAM chips may implement 8-bit read/write memory words, with each chip contributing one bit of the word:

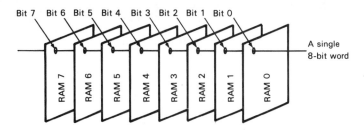

Memory Module

We will refer to this set of eight chips as a memory module.

Small microcomputer systems may use fewer memory chips to implement small read/write memories. For example, two RAM chips may each contribute four bits of an 8-bit word:

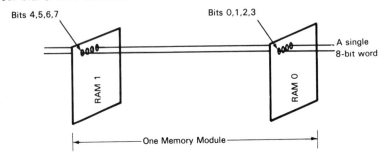

Now there are two memory chips in the memory module.

RAM memory is also available, like ROM, with entire words implemented on a single chip:

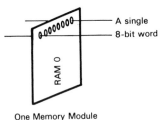

One Memory Module

RAM Chip Memory Size

Commonly a memory chip is described as an "M×N" chip, where M is the number of addressable units on the memory chip and N is the number of bits in each addressable unit. Suppose a RAM chip supplies one bit of an 8-bit word, as shown in the first of the three illustrations above. This device might be described as 4096×1-bit RAM, which means that each device contains 4096 bits of read/write memory, each of which must become one bit of a memory word. Eight 4096×1-bit RAM devices would be needed to build a 4096-byte memory.

A 1024×4 bit RAM would correspond to the second of the preceding illustrations. This RAM would also have 4096 bits of read/write memory, however bits would be addressed four at a time. Two such devices would be needed to build a 1024-byte read/write memory.

If a single 4096-bit RAM were to be organized as 8-bit words, then the device would be described as a 512×8-bit RAM. The third of the preceding illustrations describes such a device.

RAM chips become considerably more expensive as N, the addressable unit width, increases. Thus a 512×8-bit RAM will cost a good deal more than a 1024×4-bit RAM, which in turn will be a lot more expensive than a 4096×1-bit RAM, even though all three devices provide the same total amount of read/write memory, namely 4096 bits. Unless you can save money by using just one M×8 memory device, or two M×4 memory devices, you will achieve lowest cost sticking with M×1 memory devices.

RAM Chip Sizes

Currently 16,384×1-bit RAM chips are the ones most commonly used for large memory systems. 65,536×1-bit RAM chips are becoming increasingly popular. 262,144×1-bit RAM chips will likely start to appear in 1981. 4096×1-bit RAM chips are still widely used, but they are losing favor to 16,384×1-bit RAM chips since they provide a quarter of the memory at half (or more) of the price. 1024×1-bit RAM chips are just about obsolete, since 4096×1-bit RAM chips are available at approximately the same price.

These various memory bit sizes are all powers of two. 16,384, for example, is 2^{14}. 4096 is 2^{12}.

Dynamic RAM

Static RAM

There are two types of RAM memory: dynamic RAM and static RAM. Dynamic RAM, which is cheaper, can only hold data for a few milliseconds; therefore dynamic RAM must constantly be refreshed by having its contents rewritten. Dynamic RAM refresh becomes part of the interface and support logic surrounding the RAM module. It is of great concern to anyone designing a read/write memory module, but it is of no concern to a microprocessor or microcomputer programmer. Static RAM costs more than dynamic RAM, but once data have been written into it, the data will stay there as long as power is being input.

RAM AND ROM ADDRESSES

Anyone designing microprocessor systems will be very interested in knowing exactly which memory addresses have been assigned to what memory. This is because memory addresses translate into ROM and RAM chips. An extra byte of data memory may require eight new RAM chips, which multiplied by 10,000 is very expensive.

Because a microprocessor system designer will be concerned with how memory chips relate to memory addresses, memory addresses will take on a significance that differs markedly from the world of minicomputers and larger computers. Specifically, **every memory address may be visualized as consisting of chip select bits and word address bits.**

The chip select bits select one or more chips that constitute a memory module.

The word address bits identify one memory word within the selected memory module.

Suppose (M×8)-bit memory words are implemented on eight separate M×1-bit memory chips. The chip select bits will select an eight-chip memory module. Memory address bits will identify one memory word, as follows:

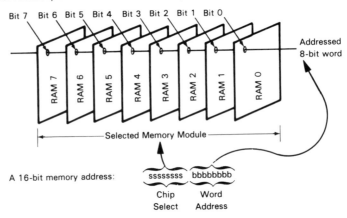

A 16-bit memory address:

Size of Memory Address   **The number of word address bits required by a memory module will depend on chip size.** For example, if a chip contains part or all of 256_{10} memory words, then the word address will consist of eight binary digits:

Smallest word address = 00000000 = 00_{16} = 00_{10}
Largest word address = 11111111 = FF_{16} = 255_{10}

A larger memory chip may have part or all of 16,384 memory words. Then the word address will consist of fourteen binary digits:

Smallest word address = 00000000000000 = 0000_{16} = 0_{10}
Largest word address = 11111111111111 = $3FFFF_{16}$ = $16,384_{10}$

Notice that fourteen binary digits create four hexadecimal digits as follows:

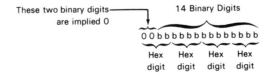

Size of Chip Select

The number of bits used for the chip select will be a function of the microcomputer's architecture, but concatenating the number of chip select bits with the number of word address bits generates the microprocessor's maximum memory capacity. For example, if the microprocessor can address $65,536_{10}$ ($FFFF_{16}$) memory words, 16 binary digits will be required to express the largest allowed memory address.

$$\underbrace{1111}_{F}\underbrace{1111}_{F}\underbrace{1111}_{F}\underbrace{1111}_{F}$$

Now if 16,384-word memory chips are used, the word address consumes fourteen binary digits, which leaves two binary digits for the chip select. In other words, maximum memory will consists of four memory modules, with $16,384_{10}$ words per module, and the 16-bit memory address must be interpreted as follows:

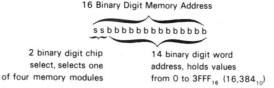

16 Binary Digit Memory Address

$$\underbrace{ss}\underbrace{bbbbbbbbbbbbbb}$$

2 binary digit chip select, selects one of four memory modules

14 binary digit word address, holds values from 0 to $3FFF_{16}$ ($16,384_{10}$)

The important thing to remember is that the microprocessor sets the TOTAL number of memory address binary digits; how they are split between chip select and word address depends on the type of memory chips used — it is entirely up to the logic designer.

Look again at how a total word address is created in a real case. If, as illustrated earlier, the word address within the chip is 01110110101110_2 ($1DAE_{16}$) and the chip select is 10_2 (2), then a 16 binary digit word address is created as follows:

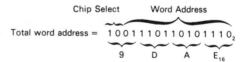

Chip Select   Word Address

Total word address = 1001110110101110_2

$$\underbrace{9}\quad\underbrace{D}\quad\underbrace{A}\quad\underbrace{E}_{16}$$

There is no reason why available memory addresses need to be continuous, or even need to start at zero. For example, a microcomputer system may include one ROM chip implementing 8-bit words and a RAM module made up of two RAM chips, each implementing four bits of an 8-bit word.

If a 1024-by-8 bit ROM chip has a chip select of 000001_2 and a capacity of 1024_{10} memory bytes, then allowed ROM memory addresses will be 0400_{16} through $07FF_{16}$:

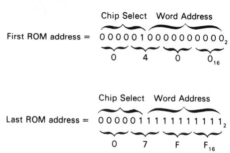

Chip Select   Word Address

First ROM address = 0000010000000000_2

$$\underbrace{0}\quad\underbrace{4}\quad\underbrace{0}\quad\underbrace{0}_{16}$$

Chip Select   Word Address

Last ROM address = 0000011111111111_2

$$\underbrace{0}\quad\underbrace{7}\quad\underbrace{F}\quad\underbrace{F}_{16}$$

Observe that 1024_{10} bytes of memory will now have addresses 1024_{10} through 2047_{10} or 0400_{16} through $07FF_{16}$. **We refer to this range of memory addresses as the memory module's address space. If the RAM module has a select of 00011000_2 and each chip holds 256 by 4 bits,** then the two RAM chips constitute a memory module and provide 8-bit RAM memory words with addresses 1800_{16} through $18FF_{16}$.

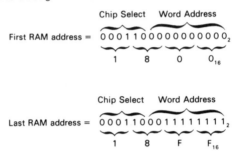

Addresses in the range 1800_{16} through $18FF_{16}$ constitute the RAM module's address space.

INTERPRETING THE CONTENTS OF MEMORY WORDS

A memory word consists of a number of binary digits. Therefore, binary digits are the only form in which information can be stored in a word of memory.

An 8-bit memory word can contain 256 (2_8) different patterns of zeros and ones. The pattern of zeros and ones within a memory word may be interpreted in any one of the following ways:

1) Pure binary numeric data that stand alone.
2) Binary numeric data that must be interpreted as one part of a multiword data unit.
3) A data code; that is, a bit pattern subject to some arbitrary predefined set of interpretations.
4) An instruction code; that is, a bit pattern that is to be transmitted to the microprocessor. The microprocessor will decode the bit pattern and interpret it as identifying the operations that the microprocessor logic must immediately perform.

This is the only important concept to understand at this time:

Upon examining the contents of any word of memory, it is impossible to determine whether the memory word contains numeric data, a code, or an instruction.

In Chapter 4 you will learn how a microprocessor takes care of the fact that the contents of any memory word may be interpreted in a number of different ways. But first we will describe each interpretation of a memory word.

STAND ALONE, PURE BINARY DATA

**Methods of
Representing
Binary Data**

Consider first pure binary data, subject to no special interpretations.
It is important to understand that you can represent pure binary data, on paper, as a binary number, an octal number or a hexadecimal number. The choice is purely a question of reader convenience and has no impact whatsoever on the data word. Here is an example for an 8-bit data word:

```
        4        E   ◄─── Hexadecimal
      ⏜    ⏜⏜⏜
      0 1 0 0 1 1 1 0   ◄─── Binary
      ⏝ ⏝⏝ ⏝⏝⏝
      1    1    6   ◄─── Octal
```

$$01001110_2 = 116_8 = 4E_{16}$$

Here is an example for a 16-bit data word:

```
      D      B      8      B   ◄─── Hexadecimal
    ⏜⏜⏜ ⏜⏜⏜ ⏜⏜⏜ ⏜⏜⏜
    1 1 0 1 1 0 1 1 1 0 0 0 1 0 1 1   ◄─── Binary
    ⏝ ⏝⏝ ⏝⏝⏝ ⏝⏝ ⏝⏝⏝
    1    5    5    6    1    3   ◄─── Octal
```

$$1101101110001011_2 = 155613_8 = DB8B_{16}$$

The choice of binary, octal or hexadecimal representation for a memory word's contents is not data interpretation; it is merely an alternative way of writing the same thing on a piece of paper.

INTERPRETED BINARY DATA

Multiword Binary Data

The contents of a memory word, interpreted as pure binary data, may stand alone, or may be part of a larger numeric unit. For example, an 8-bit memory word standing alone can represent numeric values ranging from 0 to 255_{10}. A 16-bit memory word, on the other hand, can represent numeric values ranging from 0 to $65,535_{10}$. **There is no reason why 8-bit memory words should not be interpreted in pairs.** Now the contents of each 8-bit memory word will be interpreted as the lower-half or the upper-half of a 16 binary digit unit:

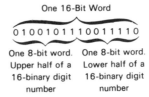

One 16-Bit Word

0 1 0 0 1 0 1 1 1 0 0 1 1 1 1 0

One 8-bit word.   One 8-bit word.
Upper half of a   Lower half of a
16-binary digit   16-binary digit
number   number

There is, in fact, no limit to the number of memory words that may be concatenated to generate very large numbers. Here is an example of a 48-bit number:

One 48-Bit Word

100111011101111010100110001110110101101100101101

Byte 5   Byte 4   Byte 3   Byte 2   Byte 1   Byte 0

Suppose six 8-bit memory words are required to represent a single numeric unit, as illustrated above. Normally, these six memory words would be contiguous; that is, they would have memory addresses adjacent to each other. However, **there is nothing in the logic of a microprocessor that demands the many bytes of a multibyte number to be contiguous; contiguous multibyte numbers are easier to process; that makes contiguous organization desirable.**

Multibyte Binary Addition

What about multibyte arithmetic? Numbers that occupy many memory words can be added, subtracted, multiplied or divided using the rules described in Chapter 2. Nothing was said in Chapter 2 about the number of binary digits associated with any number. Thus if a 16-bit number is stored in two adjacent 8-bit memory words, binary addition rules described in Chapter 2 would still be used, but the 16-bit numbers would have to be added in two steps as follows:

```
                                  Word 1    Word 0

                                  10011101  10000110
                                 +00101010  11010100
Carries from Word 0 and Word 1 ─► 0            1
                                 ─────────────────────
                                 =11001000  01011010

                                  Step 2    Step 1
```

The carry, if any, from each step is added to the low-order digit of the next step.

The logical extension of the above example to numbers stored in three, four, or more memory words is self-evident. Here, for example, is how two numbers, each occupying four 8-bit words, would be added in four steps:

Word 3	Word 2	Word 1	Word 0
10110100	10000101	01101011	11011010
+ 01111010	10111010	01000010	00111001
1	1	0	1

= 00101111	00111111	10101110	00010011
Step 4	Step 3	Step 2	Step 1

Multibyte Binary Subtraction

There is a catch to subtracting multibyte numbers. Recall from Chapter 2 that binary data are subtracted by taking the twos complement of the subtrahend and adding it to the minuend. Consider two 16-bit numbers stored in 16-bit memory words. **The logic associated with subtracting one 16-bit number from another is very straightforward and may be illustrated as follows:**

$$23A6_{16} - 124A_{16} = 115C_{16}$$

$$23A6_{16} = 0010001110100110$$

$$\text{Twos complement of } 124A_{16} = \begin{cases} 1110110110110101 \\ 1 \end{cases}$$

$$\text{Answer} = 0001000101011100$$
$$\phantom{\text{Answer} = 0001}1 \quad 1 \quad 5 \quad C$$

Now consider the same subtraction where the numbers are stored in two adjacent 8-bit memory words. The subtraction may be directly reproduced as follows:

	Word 1	Word 0	
$23_{16} =$	00100011	10100110	$= A6_{16}$
Ones complement of $12_{16} =$	11101101	10110101	$= $ Twos complement of $4A_{16}$
		1	
	00010001	01011100	
	1 1	5 C	
	Step 2	Step 1	

Notice that only the low-order byte of the number is twos complemented. The high-order byte is ones complemented. While this may seem confusing at first, it really is not. If you visualize a multibyte number as a single numeric unit, then it is self-evident that when the twos complement of the multibyte number is generated, 1 will be added to the low-order byte of the multibyte number only:

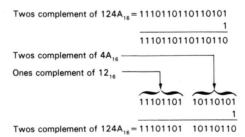

$$\text{Twos complement of } 124A_{16} = 1110110110110101$$
$$\phantom{\text{Twos complement of } 124A_{16} = 1110110110110}1$$
$$1110110110110110$$

Twos complement of $4A_{16}$

Ones complement of 12_{16}

11101101   10110101
1

$$\text{Twos complement of } 124A_{16} = 11101101 \quad 10110110$$

Multiplication and division of large binary numbers follows the basic rules set out in Chapter 2, but can become quite complex when optimized for maximum execution speed. **Appendix B describes some commonly used algorithms.**

Signed Binary Numbers

A microprocessor that could process only positive numbers would not be very useful. **What about negative numbers? Here, for the first time, we get into the question of interpreting binary coded data. A very effective industry convention interprets the high-order bit of a number as a sign bit. If this bit is 1, the number is negative. If this bit is 0, the number is positive:**

Obbbbbbb represents a positive, 7-bit number

1bbbbbbb represents a negative, 7-bit number

Twos Complement Signed Binary Numbers

Table 3-2 gives the most common interpretation for 8-bit signed binary data; negative numbers are coded as the twos complement of their positive counterparts. Here are some examples:

$$+02_{16} = 00000010 \quad -02_{16} = 11111101$$
$$\underline{1}$$
$$11111110$$

$$+6A_{16} = 01101010 \quad -6A_{16} = 10010101$$
$$\underline{1}$$
$$10010110$$

When eight binary digits are being interpreted as a signed number, the range of numbers is from -128_{10} to $+127_{10}$. When sixteen binary digits are interpreted as a signed binary number, numbers must fall in the range $-32,768_{10}$ to $+32,767_{10}$.

Table 3-2. Twos Complement Signed
Binary Numeric Interpretations

Binary	Decimal Equivalent	Hexadecimal
10000000	-128	80
10000001	-127	81
10000010	-126	82
10000011	-125	83
.	.	.
.	.	.
.	.	.
11111110	-2	FE
11111111	-1	FF
00000000	0	0
00000001	$+1$	1
00000010	$+2$	2
00000011	$+3$	3
.	.	.
.	.	.
.	.	.
01111101	$+125$	7D
01111110	$+126$	7E
01111111	$+127$	7F

Sign Magnitude Signed Binary Numbers

You will occasionally see sign magnitude coding used to represent signed binary numbers. Sign magnitude coding represents all numbers in their positive form except that the high-order bit represents the sign: zero for positive and one for negative. An 8-bit word, therefore, will represent numbers in sign magnitude code as follows:

Binary	Decimal Equivalent	Hexadecimal
00000000	0	00
00000001	1	01
.	.	.
.	.	.
.	.	.
01111110	+126	7E
01111111	+127	7F
10000000	0	80
10000001	−1	81
.	.	.
.	.	.
.	.	.
11111110	−126	FE
11111111	−127	FF

Sign magnitude coding is easier for a person to interpret by inspection, but signed binary coding is much easier to compute with. Therefore **signed binary coding has become the universal choice of the computer industry.**

Twos Complement Signed Binary Coding

The beauty of twos complement signed binary coding is that it calls for no special logic when performing arithmetic operations. Providing an arithmetic operation does not generate an answer that is too large to fit in the available space, you can ignore the sign of a number until you wish to interpret an answer; at that time, examining the high-order bit of the answer indicates whether it is positive or negative. If the high-order bit of the answer is 1, then the answer is negative and by taking the twos complement of the answer, the pure binary, positive representation of the answer is created. Here are some examples:

63_{16} ⟶ 01100011
$-3A_{16}$ ⟶ 11000101   Ones complement of $3A_{16}$
                1
$= 29_{16}$ ⟶ 00101001
                2   9   Answer = $+29_{16}$

This 0 indicates a positive result

$3A_{16}$ ⟶ 00111010
-63_{16} ⟶ 10011100   Ones complement of 63_{16}
                1   Answer = $D7_{16}$
$= D7_{16}$ ⟶ 11010111
                D   7

This 1 indicates a negative result

Take the twos complement:
00101000
        1
00101001
2   9   Answer = -29_{16}

3-19

Now consider the above example, rewritten as $(3A_{16}) + (-63_{16}) = (-29_{16})$. (-63_{16}) will be represented by the twos complement of $+63_{16}$.

$$+63_{16} = 01100011$$
$$\text{Ones complement of } +63_{16} = 10011100$$
$$-63_{16} = 10011101$$

Therefore:

$3A_{16}$	00111010
$+(-63_{16})$	10011101
$= (-29_{16})$	11010111

↑ ———————————— This 1 indicates a negative result

00101000
      1   Taking the twos complement of the answer
————   generates the positive representation
00101001
  2   9

Observe that using twos complement notation to represent signed binary numbers, $3A_{16} - 63_{16}$ and $3A_{16} + (-63_{16})$ have identical binary representations, which is only to be expected of a viable scheme for representing negative numbers.

Multiword Signed Binary Numbers

Multiword signed binary numbers generate no special problems so long as you understand that operations must be performed one word at a time. This is illustrated below for the simple case of 16-bit, signed binary data, which generates the same results when handled as single 16-bit words or as two 8-bit words.

One 16-Bit Word

Sign bit ——→ 1011001011000010

8-bit Word 1   8-bit Word 0

Consider the subtraction of two 16-bit, signed binary numbers, where each number is stored in two 8-bit words. As for unsigned multiword addition, signed multiword addition proceeds in two steps, as follows:

	Word 1	Word 0
$1A2C_{16} =$	00011010	00101100
$+(-0810_{16}) =$	11110111	11110000
$121C_{16} =$	00010010	00011100
	1 2	1 C

Sign bit ——— Step 2   Step 1

Observe that -0810_{16} is generated by taking the twos complement of 0810_{16} as follows:

$$0810_{16} = 0000100000010000$$
$$\text{Ones complement} = 1111011111101111$$
$$\text{Twos complement} = 1111011111110000$$

Binary Coded Decimal

It is possible to code decimal numbers using binary digits. Four binary digits can represent values from 0 to F_{16}, or from 0 to 15_{10}. By ignoring binary digit combinations above 9, decimal numbers can be coded two digits per 8-bit memory word, or four digits per 16-bit memory word. Table 3-3 identifies the combinations of four binary digits that may be interpreted as decimal numbers. When four binary digits are thus being used to represent decimal numbers, the result is called Binary Coded Decimal (BCD) data.

Negative BCD Data

Signed binary number rules cannot be applied to BCD data, since BCD demands that binary data be interpreted in 4-bit units:

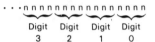

Each 4-bit digit can have one of the bit patterns shown under the BCD column of Table 3-3. An 8-bit word uses the high-order bit for all numbers in excess of 79_{10}. If the high-order bit is needed to represent decimal digits 8 or 9, then it cannot be used to represent a sign.

Table 3-3. Binary Representation of Decimal Digits

Binary	Hexadecimal	BCD
0000	0	0
0001	1	1
0010	2	2
0011	3	3
0100	4	4
0101	5	5
0110	6	6
0111	7	7
1000	8	8
1001	9	9
1010	A	Illegal
1011	B	Illegal
1100	C	Illegal
1101	D	Illegal
1110	E	Illegal
1111	F	Illegal

The sign of signed BCD numbers is therefore represented using a special "control" word that must accompany the multiword BCD number. There are no common rules for control word format, but here are a simple example and a complex example. First the simple example:

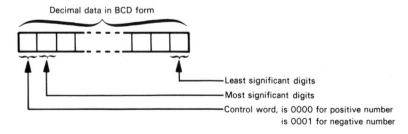

Now the complex example:

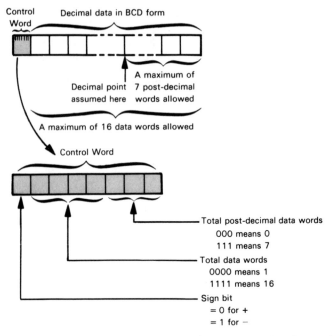

BCD data cannot be added and subtracted using straightforward binary addition and subtraction rules. Here are some examples of the errors that could result:

Decimal		BCD	Decimal		BCD
23	=	00100011	54	=	01010100
+47	=	01000111	−26	=	11011010
70		01101010	28		00101110
		6 Illegal			2 Illegal

Note that 11011010 is the twos complement of the binary representation of 26.

BCD Arithmetic
In order to perform BCD arithmetic, special rules must be applied, and the carry out of each BCD digit must be recorded. Consider the addition:

$$\begin{array}{r} 97 \\ +68 \\ \hline 165 \end{array}$$

It is insufficient to record the fact that there was a carry out of the high-order digit addition. Any intermediate carry out of the low-order digit addition must also be recorded. Here are some examples showing the status of the carry (C) and the intermediate carry (IC):

C IC	C IC	C IC	C IC
↓ ↓	↓ ↓	↓ ↓	↓ ↓
0 0	0 1	1 0	1 1
21	29	91	97
+32	+32	+32	+68
53	61	123	165

Conceptually, BCD addition is performed as follows:

1) Add the two numbers.
2) Serially add six to each invalid digit, starting with the low-order digit. (This "jumps over" the six invalid bit combinations to yield the correct BCD representation.)

For example,

$$25_{10} + 19_{10} \text{ becomes}$$

```
            0010  0101
         +  0001  1001
            ───────────
            0011  1110
 Add 6:     0000  0110
            ───────────
            0100  0100 = 44₁₀
```

$= 44_{10}$

This method is rather clumsy to computerize. The following process, as described for two digits of a BCD number, is more efficient; it adds six to each digit, then based on the carry statuses, subtracts those sixes that were not needed.

1) Using binary addition, add 66_{16} to the first number (the augend).
2) Add the second number (the addend) to the sum generated in step 1. The carry generated in this step reflects the true carry to the next higher digit.
3) Using binary addition, add a factor to the sum from step 2. The factor to be added depends on the carry (C) and the intermediate carry (IC) statuses as follows:

C	IC	Factor
0	0	$9A_{16}$
0	1	$A0_{16}$
1	0	FA_{16}
1	1	00_{16}

Here are some addition examples:

	23	29	92	87
	+32	+34	+32	+79
	55	63	124	166
Augend =	00100011	00101001	10010010	10000111
66_{16}	01100110	01100110	01100110	01100110
Step 1 sum =	10001001	10001111	11111000	11101101
Addend =	00110010	00110100	00110010	01111001
Step 2 sum =	10111011	11000011	00101010	01100110
C/IC =	0 0	0 1	1 0	1 1
Factor =	10011010	10100000	11111010	00000000
Step 2 sum =	10111011	11000011	00101010	01100110
Answer =	01010101	01100011	00100100	01100110
Decimal =	5 5	6 3	2 4	6 6
C (from Step 2) =	0	0	1	1

BCD subtraction is performed for two digits of a BCD number via these two steps:

1) Add the twos complement of the subtrahend (the number being subtracted) to the minuend (the number being subtracted from). The carry generated in this step reflects the true carry to the next higher digit.
   Recall that when multiword numbers are subtracted, only the lowest order word of the subtrahend is twos complemented. Higher order words are ones complemented.

2) Perform step 3 as described for BCD addition.

Here are some subtraction examples:

		75	71	25	21
		-21	-28	-71	-78
		$+54$	$+43$	-46	-57

Subtrahend =	00100001	00101000	01110001	01111000
Twos complement =	11011111	11011000	10001111	10001000
Minuend =	0110101	01110001	00100101	00100001
Step 1 sum =	01010100	01001001	10110100	10101001
C/IC =	1 1	1 0	0 1	0 0
Factor =	00000000	11111010	10100000	10011010
	01010100	01001001	10110100	10101001
Answer =	01010100	01000011	01010100	01000011
=	5 4	4 3	5 4	4 3
C (after AC) =	1	1	0	0

When performing BCD subtraction, a negative result is indicated by a final carry of 0 (as for binary subtraction), but in keeping with the decimal representation of numbers, the numeric value of the negative answer is in tens complement form, not in twos complement form. Thus the answer to $25 - 71$ appears as 54, which is $100 - 46$, and the final carry is 0. Similarly, the answer to $21 - 78$ appears as 43, which is $100 - 57$, and the final carry is 0.

**Floating
Point
Numbers**

**Floating
Point
Significance**

Scientific applications frequently use numbers that vary between great extremes of magnitude without demanding equivalent digit precision. Using decimal notation, for example, astronomers may handle numbers ranging up to 10^{30} or more. Chemical engineers use numbers varying between 1 and 10^{-30} or less. Physicists need numbers across the entire range encountered by astronomers and chemical engineers. Such incredibly large or incredibly small numbers are never computed to the final digit of precision. **Five significant digits, or ten, or some other arbitrary number of significant digits, may suffice.** For example, the decimal number:

2,637,485,968,463,425,463,774,856,308,291

looks impressive, and is very large. But there are few, if any instances when anyone will need so much precision. If this number were to be rounded off to five significant digits, it would be:

2,637,500,000,000,000,000,000,000,000,000

which, in itself, is a clumsy way of writing numbers and is prone to inaccuracy since the reader must count zeros, with a good chance of miscounting. Instead **the number should be represented using floating point format, as**

follows:

Exponent

$$2.6375 \times 10^{30}$$

Mantissa   Base

This is the same as:

Exponent

$$0.26375 \times 10^{31}$$

Mantissa   Base

Mantissa

Base

Exponent

As illustrated above a floating point number consists of a mantissa, a base, and an exponent. Usually the mantissa is written with the decimal point either to the left or right of the leftmost (most significant) digit.

A floating point number can be written using any base. A binary floating number might appear as follows:

Exponent

$$0.110100110 \times 2^{10111}$$

Mantissa   Base

A binary floating point number will be encoded in memory words using some arbitrary format. There is no "natural" encoding format for binary, floating point numbers. Here is an encoding possibility:

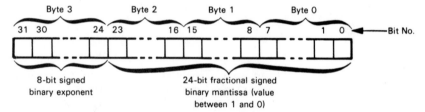

Floating Point Conversion

Converting between binary and decimal floating point numbers is not much of a problem. To convert a binary floating point number to its decimal equivalent, you first convert the mantissa and exponent to their decimal equivalents as described in Chapter 2. Then you multiply the decimal exponent by 0.30103. Consider the binary floating point number:

$$0.11010101 \times 2^{11010001}$$

The mantissa is converted to a decimal fraction as follows:

$$2^{-1} + 2^{-2} + 2^{-4} + 2^{-6} + 2^{-8} = 0.5 + 0.25 + 0.0625 + 0.015625$$
$$+ 0.00390625$$
$$= 0.83203125$$

The exponent, as a decimal number, equals:

$$128 + 64 + 16 + 1 = 209$$

Therefore,

$$0.11010101 \times 2^{11010001} = 0.83203125 \times 2^{209}$$

To convert from base 2 to base 10, look at the equation:

$$2^X = 10^Y$$

Taking logarithms, this becomes:

$$X \ln 2 = Y \ln 10$$

Therefore,

$$Y = X \left(\frac{\ln 2}{\ln 10} \right) = 0.30103 X$$

Therefore,

$$2^{209} = 10^{(209 \times 0.30103)}$$
$$= 10^{(62.915269)}$$

Since we do not want a fractional exponent, rewrite it as:

$$10^{(62 + 0.915269)}$$

which is the same as:

$$(10^{0.915269}) \times 10^{62}$$
$$10^{0.915269} = 8.2275228$$

Therefore,

$$2^{209} = 8.22754 \times 10^{62}$$

Finally we derive the following result:

$$0.11010101 \times 2^{11010001} = 0.83203125 \times 2^{209}$$
$$= 0.83203125 \times 8.2275228 \times 10^{62}$$
$$= 6.845556 \times 10^{62}$$

If we want the decimal point preceding the most significant mantissa digit, we must rewrite this mantissa number as follows:

$$0.6845556 \times 10^{63}$$

Decimal-Binary Floating Point Conversion

We will now illustrate decimal-binary floating point conversion by converting the decimal floating point number above back to its binary equivalent. First we will convert the base to 2. This requires dividing the exponent by 0.30103, the inverse of converting the base from 2 to 10. Therefore,

$$0.6845556 \times 10^{63} = 0.6845556 \times 2^{63/0.30103}$$
$$= 0.6845556 \times 2^{209.28147}$$

Once again we must eliminate the fraction from the exponent by rewriting the number as follows:

$$0.6845556 = 2^{0.28147} \times 2^{209}$$

We now convert the exponent as follows:

```
2)209
 2)104 r 1
  2)52 r 0
   2)26 r 0
    2)13 r 0
     2)6 r 1
      2)3 r 0
        1 r 1
```

The exponent is

$$11010001$$

The mantissa is

$$0.6845556 \times 2^{0.28147}$$
$$2^{0.28147} = 1.2154327$$

Therefore the mantissa is

$$0.8320313$$

Now we convert the mantissa to an 8-bit fraction by successive multiplication, as follows:

```
        0.8320313
              ×2
    1   1.6640626
              ×2
    1   1.3281252
              ×2
    0   0.6562504
              ×2
    1   1.3125008
              ×2
    0   0.6250010
              ×2
    1   1.2500032
              ×2
    0   0.5000064
              ×2
    1   1.0000128
```

The mantissa is

$$11010101$$

Therefore,

$$0.6845556 \times 10^{63} = 11010101 \times 2^{11010001}$$

which is the binary floating point number we began with.

Binary Floating Point Arithmetic

Binary floating point arithmetic is very straightforward. To perform addition or subtraction, you must scale the numbers so that they both have the same exponent. Then you simply add or subtract the two mantissas using signed binary arithmetic.

This may be illustrated as follows:

$$0.1101011 \times 2^{1011} \times 0.1011001 \times 2^{1010}$$
$$= 0.1101011 \times 2^{1011} \times 0.01011001 \times 2^{1011}$$
$$= 1.00101111 \times 2^{1011}$$
$$= 0.100101111 \times 2^{1100}$$

Following addition you may have to increment the exponent if the sum of mantissas is greater than one, as it was in the example above. Following a subtract, you may have to decrement the exponent if there are any leading zeros.

Floating point multiplication and division is particularly simple; to multiply two floating point numbers you multiply the mantissas and add the exponents. To divide two floating point numbers you divide the mantissas and subtract the exponents. Here is an example:

$$0.1101 \times 2^{101} \times 0.1011 \times 2^{1101}$$
$$= (0.1101 \times 0.1011) \times 2^{101+1101}$$
$$= 0.10001111 \times 2^{10010}$$

CHARACTER CODES

A computer would not be very useful if it required data to be entered as a sequence of binary digits, or if answers were output in one of the uncoded or coded binary formats. It must be possible for a computer to handle text and other nonnumeric information.

If we bear in mind that the combination of binary digits within any memory word can be reused in any number of ways, then all the binary codes that have been used to represent numeric data, as described so far, can all be reused to represent letters of the alphabet, digit characters, or any other special printed characters.

So long as a program correctly interprets the binary digits of a memory word, then confusion and ambiguities cannot arise.

For example, if you as the programmer decide to use memory words with addresses $0A20_{16}$ through $0A2A_{16}$ to hold binary-coded decimal data, then it is up to you, the programmer, in your subsequent program logic, to remember that the binary data in these memory words must be interpreted as binary-coded decimal digits — and any other interpretation will cause errors.

Likewise, if memory words $12A4_{16}$ through $12A6_{16}$ are reserved to hold binary data that are to be interpreted as character codes, then the fact that character codes have exactly the same binary digit pattern as binary-coded decimal words is irrelevant. So long as program logic correctly interprets the contents of memory words, errors cannot arise; if program logic does not correctly interpret the contents of memory words, then program logic is in error and must be corrected.

Character Sets

In order to handle English text, a complete and adequate set of necessary characters includes:

- 26 lower case letters
- 26 upper case letters
- approximately 25 special characters (e.g., {+/@!#, etc.)
- 10 numeric digits

The above character set adds up to 87 characters. A six binary digit group allows 64 combinations of 0 and 1 binary digits (2^6), which is insufficient to represent 87 characters. A seven binary digit group allows 128 possible arrangements of 0 and 1 binary digits, which is sufficient for our needs.

The 8-bit byte has been universally accepted as the data unit for representing character codes. The most common character codes are known as the American Standard Code for Information Interchange (ASCII) and Extended Binary Coded Decimal Interchange Code (EBCDIC). ASCII is used by all minicomputer and microcomputer manufacturers and is listed in Appendix A.

Parity

Eight binary digits are used to represent characters where seven binary digits suffice. This being the case, the eighth binary digit is frequently used to test for errors, and is referred to as a parity bit; it is set to 1 or to 0, so that the number of 1 bits in the byte is either always odd or always even.

If odd parity is selected, then the parity bit will be set or reset so that the total number of 1 bits is always odd. Here are some examples:

```
Parity bit ┐
           ▼
          10000000   Number of 1 bits = 1
          00000001   Number of 1 bits = 1
          11001011   Number of 1 bits = 5
          11011111   Number of 1 bits = 7
          01010100   Number of 1 bits = 3
```

If even parity is selected, then the parity bit is set or reset so that the total number of 1 bits will always be even. Here are some examples:

Parity bit ─────────┐

00000000	Number of 1 bits = 0
10000001	Number of 1 bits = 2
01010101	Number of 1 bits = 4
10010101	Number of 1 bits = 4
11111111	Number of 1 bits = 8

The parity bit is used to ensure that between the creation of a character byte and reading it back, no bit was erroneously changed. If, for example, parity is odd, then whenever an even number of 1 bits is detected in a character byte, clearly the byte must be in error. Similarly, if even parity is selected, then whenever an odd number of bits are detected in a character byte, the byte must be in error.

Here is an example of how a message might be stored in sequence of contiguous memory words using ASCII character codes with even parity:

E	n	t	e	r	blank	
11000101	11101110	01110100	01100101	01110010	10100000	• • • etc.

A few comments regarding parity and error codes would be useful at this point.

Clearly, **the high-order bit of a byte can be used as a parity bit only when the byte contents are being interpreted as character codes.** If the contents of the byte are being interpreted as any form of binary data (coded or uncoded), then the high-order bit has already been specified as an integral part of the byte's data contents; therefore, this bit cannot be used as a parity bit, so coded and uncoded binary data cannot have parity checked.

Many elaborate schemes are used, not only to check that sequences of binary digits contain no errors, but further to detect what these errors are and to make appropriate corrections. These error correction codes have nothing in particular to do with microprocessor concepts; therefore, they are not discussed in this book.

Memory Parity Bit

Most mainframe computer memories are built with one or more extra bits attached to each memory word; these extra bits detect (and frequently correct) errors. Occasionally microcomputer memory modules are now built with a ninth bit appended to every memory byte; this ninth bit is used to set and check parity.

A microcomputer whose word size is not eight bits will, nevertheless, use the byte to represent character codes. A 16-bit microcomputer will pack two bytes into each memory word as follows:

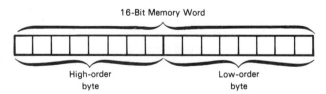

16-Bit Memory Word

High-order byte   Low-order byte

A microcomputer that uses 12-bit words will store the character code in the lower eight of the 12 bits and will waste the higher four bits as follows:

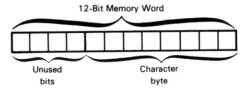

12-Bit Memory Word

Unused bits   Character byte

A 4-bit microcomputer creates a byte out of two contiguous memory words:

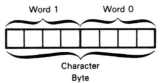

Word 1   Word 0

Character Byte

4-bit microcomputers may actually be better suited to BCD applications such as hand held calculators. These applications treat 4-bit data units as unique entities — one BCD digit per 4-bit data unit; the 8-bit byte is not significant, so the fact that the 4-bit microcomputer always handles data in 4-bit units can greatly simplify programming.

INSTRUCTION CODES

Memory words have so far been interpreted as data of one form or another. The contents of a memory word can also be interpreted as a code, identifying an operation that is required of the microprocessor.

Binary Addition

Consider the simple example of binary addition. Assume that the contents of the memory word with address $0A30_{16}$ are to be added to the contents of the memory word with address $0A31_{16}$, and the sum is to be stored in the memory word with address $0A31_{16}$. Program steps to accomplish this binary addition may proceed as follows:

1) Identify the address of the first memory word to be added.
2) Transfer the contents of this memory word to the microcomputer.
3) Identify the address of the second memory word to be added.
4) Add the contents of this memory word to the memory word that was transferred to the microcomputer in step 2.
5) Identify the address of the memory word where the sum is to be stored.
6) Transfer the sum to this memory word.

Program logic specifies that the memory words with addresses 0A30 and 0A31 are to contain pure binary data:

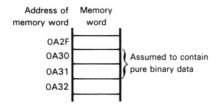

Let us assume that the six program steps are to be stored in memory words with addresses starting at 0400; we will create some instruction codes to implement the six-step binary addition.

The instruction code that identifies memory addresses will occupy three bytes, as follows:

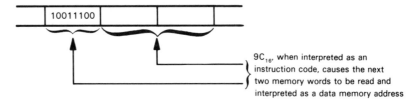

We can now start to create a program as follows:

Address of memory word	Memory word	
		Read the contents of the next two memory words.
0400	9C	Interpret them as a data memory address
0401	0A	0A30 is the data memory address
0402	320	which the CPU will read
0403		
0404		

Step 2 requires the contents of the addressed memory word to be read and interpreted as data. Note that there is no need for the instruction to specify what kind of data the memory word contains. You, the programmer, must remember what kind of data the addressed word contains, and not try to do anything incompatible with the data type. So far as the microcomputer is concerned, data is pure binary data — nothing more, nothing less.

Let us assume that the binary code:

01000000

if interpreted as an instruction, causes the contents of the addressed data memory word to be read and interpreted as data. Our program now becomes:

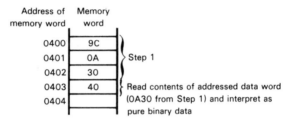

Step 3 is a repeat of step 1, only a different data memory address (0A31$_{16}$) needs to be specified. Our program now becomes:

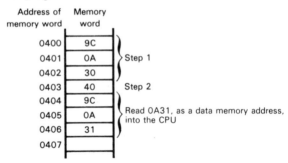

Step 4 is a variation of step 2; however, instead of simply reading the contents of the address data memory word, the data memory word is added, using binary addition, to the data memory word that was previously read; assume that this operation is identified by the instruction code:

10000000

Our program now increases one step as follows:

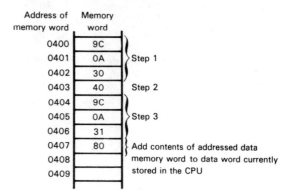

Address of memory word	Memory word	
0400	9C	} Step 1
0401	0A	
0402	30	
0403	40	Step 2
0404	9C	
0405	0A	} Step 3
0406	31	
0407	80	Add contents of addressed data
0408		memory word to data word currently
0409		stored in the CPU

Step 5 is a repeat of step 3; the address of the data memory word where the sum is to be stored, $0A31_{16}$ is the data memory word most recently addressed (in step 3), so the instruction need not be repeated for step 5. Instead we will proceed to step 6, and assume that the binary word:

01100000

when interpreted as an instruction code, causes data to be output to the most recently addressed data memory word. The complete program now looks like this:

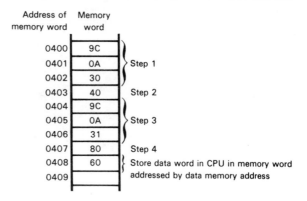

Address of memory word	Memory word	
0400	9C	} Step 1
0401	0A	
0402	30	
0403	40	Step 2
0404	9C	
0405	0A	} Step 3
0406	31	
0407	80	Step 4
0408	60	Store data word in CPU in memory word
0409		addressed by data memory address

Provided the microcomputer can be told in some way that a sequence of instruction codes will be found beginning at memory word 0400_{16}, then the fact that each of these memory words may have a pattern of 1 and 0 binary digits, which is also valid binary data or ASCII characters, is irrelevant.

Notice that the program creates memory addresses that identify memory words which are assumed to contain pure binary data. You, the programmer, must make sure that these memory words do indeed contain binary data. If, by mistake, instructions elsewhere in your program store character codes in these same memory words, then upon being commanded to do so, the microprocessor will add two character codes as though they were binary data. Only the strange results that are created will alert you to the fact that a mistake has been made.

Illustrating the concept of a microcomputer program via this six-step binary addition is, of course, just a beginning.

How does the microcomputer perform the operations required by the instruction code? That question will be answered in Chapter 4.

What does the microcomputer demand of external logic in order to complete the operations specified by an instruction code? That question will be answered in Chapter 5.

How do you write a microcomputer program? We will address that question in Chapter 6.

4

The Central Processing Unit

Whatever else a microprocessor has, or lacks, it must have a Central Processing Unit (CPU).

The logic that constitutes a CPU can differ widely from one microprocessor to the next; underlying these variations there are certain necessities, however. Our purpose in this chapter is to identify these necessities.

Recall from Chapter 3 that the contents of a memory word may be interpreted in one of the following ways:

- As pure binary data
- As coded binary data
- As a character code
- As an instruction code

These four ways of interpreting the contents of a memory word can be broadly separated into two major categories: data and instructions.

Pure binary data, coded binary data, and character codes have one thing in common: they are all data. The contents of data memory words can be operated on or can be used in conjunction with the contents of other data words.

Program **Instruction codes are input to the CPU as a means of identifying the next operation you want the CPU to perform. A sequence of instruction codes, stored in memory, constitutes a program.**

Consider the six-step binary addition program described at the end of Chapter 3. Let us examine in the following paragraphs the logic that the CPU must contain to perform this binary addition.

CPU REGISTERS

Accumulator   **The CPU must have one or more registers in which data that has been fetched from memory can be stored; we will call these registers accumulators. Since the majority of microcomputers still use an 8-bit word size, that is the word size we will adopt — and assume an 8-bit accumulator:**

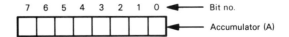

To keep things simple, we will for the moment assume that there is just one accumulator in the CPU.

The data fetched in step 2 of the binary addition program described in Chapter 3 is stored in the accumulator.

The CPU usually operates on the contents of an accumulator rather than accessing memory words directly. Does this make sense? Remember, the accumulator is a register within the logic of the CPU:

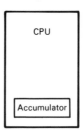

Since data is permanently stored in external memory, you may argue that operating on data in a CPU register forces programs to define a three-step instruction sequence:

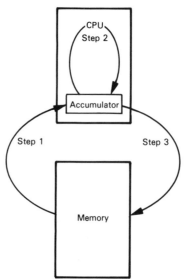

where one step would do:

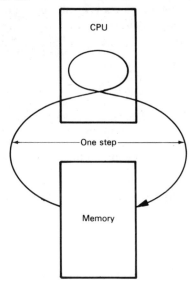

Unfortunately the "one-step" illustrated above does not always work. Some CPU operations require two memory words' contents to be fetched from memory:

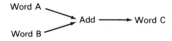

Sometimes the CPU operates on a single word:

Word A ⟶ Ones Complement ⟶ Word C

Or we can look at the one-step operation negatively: must we always spend time fetching data from memory, then returning results to memory? The answer is no. Every memory access takes time and logic. By having a few data storage registers in the CPU, we can get by with one memory access for every five CPU operations (approximately); that is better than two memory accesses for every CPU operation, which the one-step sequence requires. Therefore nearly all microprocessors have accumulators or accumulator-type registers in the CPU.

Data Counter

In order to access a data memory word, either to read its contents or to store data into the memory word, the data memory word address must be identified; this address is held in a register which we will call the data counter. The size of the data counter will depend on the maximum amount of memory that the microprocessor can address. Here is a l6-bit data counter; it can address up to 65,536 words of data memory:

																Accumulator (A)
																Data Counter (DC)

A microprocessor's CPU can have one or more data counters. To keep things simple we will, for the moment, assume that the CPU has only one data counter.

Referring again to the binary addition program described in Chapter 3, the data memory addresses $0A30_{16}$ and $0A31_{16}$ would be held in the Data Counter register.

In order to access a word of data memory, the CPU needs an accumulator to store the contents of the accessed data word, and a data counter to store the address of the data word being accessed.

Similarly, in order to handle instruction codes, the CPU is going to need a register to store instruction codes, and a register to store the address of the memory word from which the instruction code is going to be fetched.

Instruction Register

The instruction code is stored in an Instruction register; the CPU will always interpret the contents of the Instruction register as an instruction code.

Program Counter

The address of the memory word from which the instruction code will be fetched is provided by a register which we will call the program counter.

The program counter is analogous to the data counter, but the data counter is assumed to always address a data memory word, while the program counter is assumed to always address a program memory word. We now have the following four registers:

	Accumulator (A)
	Data Counter (DC)
	Instruction Register (I)
	Program Counter (PC)

There is one important conceptual difference between the data counter and the program counter. **By storing instruction codes in sequential memory words, the problem of creating instruction code addresses in the program counter is resolved.** All that is needed is to find some way of loading an initial address into the program counter. If, after accessing a memory word to fetch an instruction code, the contents of the program counter are incremented by one, then the program counter will be left pointing to the memory word containing the next instruction code.

The data counter, on the other hand, is not likely to have long runs of sequential memory accesses. Only when data is stored in multiword units, or data tables are held in contiguous memory words, will the data counter be required to access sequential memory locations. Even when the data counter is required to access sequential memory locations, it is not clear whether the data counter should start at a low memory address and increment, or start at a high memory address and decrement. Therefore, **CPU logic is going to have to provide the microcomputer user with a greater flexibility when it comes to setting addresses in the data counter.**

How CPU Registers are Used

Instructions   **In order to fully understand how microprocessor CPU registers are used, we will step through the binary addition program of Chapter 3, showing how the contents of the four registers change.** We will, from here on, refer to each step of the program as an Instruction, since in reality, each step, as illustrated, merely identifies an instruction's binary code.

Initially the program counter (PC) contains 0400_{16}, the address of the first instruction word in program memory; the contents of other registers are unknown. We assume, to complete the illustration, that data memory words $0A30_{16}$ and $0A31_{16}$ initially contain $7A_{16}$ and $2F_{16}$, respectively.

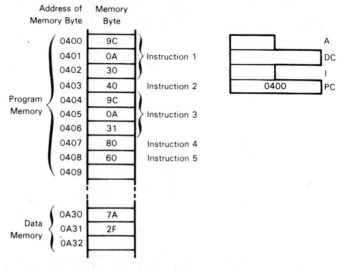

The instruction codes and memory addresses, as illustrated, are realistic but have been selected quite arbitrarily.

The CPU loads the contents of the memory word addressed by PC into the Instruction register (I), thus ensuring that the memory word contents will be interpreted as an instruction code. The CPU then increments the contents of PC:

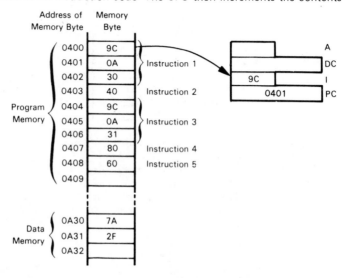

The code 9C, appearing in the Instruction register, causes CPU logic to implement two steps. First, the contents of the memory byte addressed by PC is fetched from memory, but is stored in the high-order byte of the data counter (DC). The CPU then increments the contents of PC:

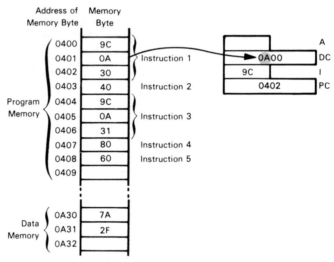

Next, the contents of the memory byte addressed by PC is fetched from memory and stored in the low-order byte of DC. Again the CPU increments the contents of PC:

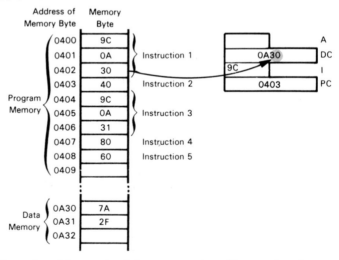

Literal, or Immediate Data

Execution of Instruction 1 is now complete. Observe that the contents of memory bytes 0401_{16} and 0402_{16} have been loaded into the DC register, even though these two memory bytes are in program memory, and are addressed by the program counter (PC). The important concept here is that the instruction code requires data to follow it immediately. This type of data, appearing immediately after instruction codes in program memory, is called Literal, or Immediate, data.

For example, in Instruction 1, memory bytes 0401_{16} and 0402_{16} contain the immediate data $0A30_{16}$. The instruction code $9C_{16}$, fetched from memory word 0400_{16}, identifies the way in which the immediate data $0A30_{16}$ must be interpreted by the CPU.

Let us now continue to Instruction 2. Upon completion of Instruction 1, the CPU fetches the contents of the memory byte addressed by PC, then increments PC. Having been given no other specific instructions, the contents of the fetched byte are stored in the I register, to be interpreted as an instruction code:

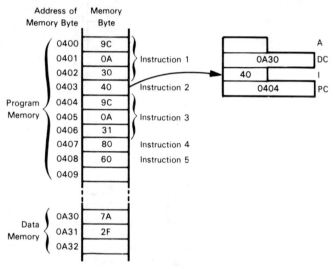

This instruction code causes the CPU to fetch data out of the memory byte addressed by DC and to load this data into the accumulator (A):

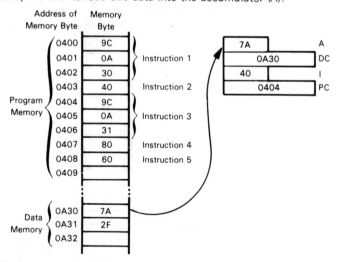

Notice that neither DC contents nor PC contents are incremented. PC contents are not incremented because 7A is not immediate data; it was fetched from data memory. DC contents are not incremented since there is no guarantee that data words will, in the normal course of events, be referenced sequentially.

Instruction 2 has now completed execution, and PC addresses the next program memory word, which contains the instruction code for Instruction 3.

Instruction 3 is a repeat of Instruction 1, except that the literal data 0A30$_{16}$ has been replaced by 0A31$_{16}$. As in Instruction 1, CPU registers undergo changes in three steps when Instruction 3 executes; step 1 fetches the instruction code to the I register:

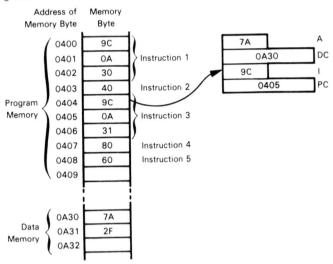

Step 2 fetches 0A$_{16}$ from byte 0405$_{16}$ and stores it in the high-order byte of the DC register; by chance that is what the DC register contained, so the DC register does not appear to change.

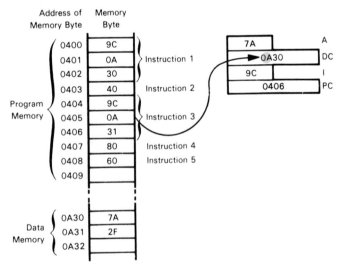

Step 3 changes the low-order byte of DC:

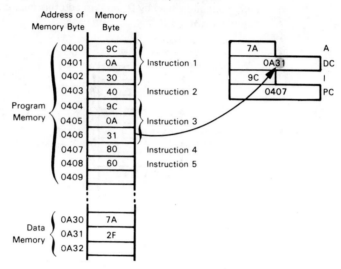

Instruction 3 has now completed execution, and execution of Instruction 4 is ready to begin. As with the previous instructions, the CPU automatically starts by loading the contents of the memory byte addressed by PC into I:

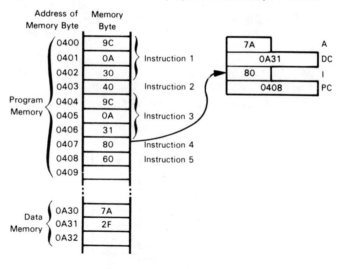

The instruction code 80_{16} requires the CPU to fetch the contents of the data word addressed by DC and to add this data word to the contents of the accumulator (A):

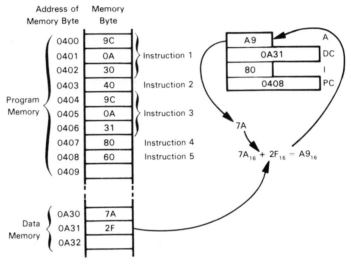

Instruction 4 has now completed execution.

If the sum in A were being returned to any memory byte other than $0A31_{16}$, we would now have to execute another variation of Instruction 1 to load a data memory address into DC. But the accumulator contents are to be stored in memory byte $0A31_{16}$, which is the memory byte currently addressed by DC; so a "load data memory address" instruction is unnecessary. We continue directly to Instruction 5, which stores the contents of the accumulator into data memory byte $0A31_{16}$ via these two steps:

Step 1, fetch the instruction code in the usual way:

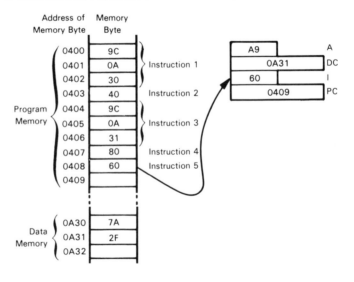

Step 2, store the accumulator contents into the memory byte addressed by DC:

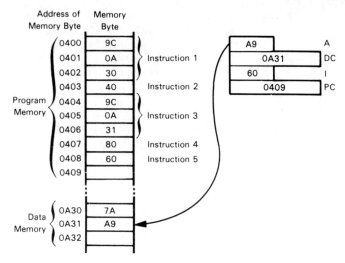

Instruction 5 has completed execution, and the program is done.

THE ARITHMETIC AND LOGIC UNIT

ALU   **Actual data manipulations within the CPU are handled by logic referred to collectively as the Arithmetic and Logic Unit (ALU). An ALU must be capable of operating on binary data in memory word increments; in other words, an 8-bit microprocessor's ALU will operate on 8-binary digit units. The ALU must have logic to perform the following operations:**

- Binary addition
- Boolean operations
- Complement a data word
- Shift a data word one bit to the right, or to the left

Any more complex data manipulation operation required of a central processing unit may be built up from these few logic elements of the ALU.

THE CONTROL UNIT

CU   **It is the control unit (CU) that sequences the logic elements of the ALU in order to implement any required operation.** The control unit, in turn, is driven by the contents of the Instruction register. In other words, the Instruction register contents are decoded by the control unit. In response to the bit pattern of the instruction code, the control unit generates a sequence of enable signals to send the appropriate data through the ALU logic modules at the proper time. **The CPU that results is illustrated in Figure 4-1.**

The "Buffer register" holds data that are transiently in the CPU. For example, when two data bytes are added (as in Instruction 4 of the binary addition example), the data word that is fetched from memory, to be added to the accumulator contents, will be stored in the Buffer register.

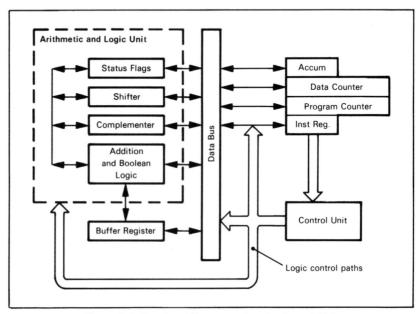

Figure 4-1. Functional Representation of a Control Unit

STATUS FLAGS

A CPU must have a set of single binary digit logic gates that are automatically set or reset to reflect the results of ALU operations. Each binary digit logic gate is called a status flag.

Carry Status

We have already encountered two status flags in Chapter 3: the Carry and Intermediate Carry. In order to perform multibyte arithmetic, any carry out of the high-order bit of two data words must be recorded in the Carry status, so that it may be propagated into higher order memory words:

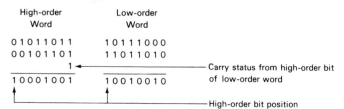

```
        High-order              Low-order
          Word                    Word

      0 1 0 1 1 0 1 1         1 0 1 1 1 0 0 0
      0 0 1 0 1 1 0 1         1 1 0 1 1 0 1 0
      ─────────────── 1 ◄─── ───────────────── ─── Carry status from high-order bit
      1 0 0 0 1 0 0 1         1 0 0 1 0 0 1 0       of low-order word
      ▲                       ▲
      └───────────────────────┴───────────────── High-order bit position
```

The Carry status is also useful when performing multiword shift operations, as described in Chapter 6.

Intermediate Carry Status

In order to perform BCD arithmetic, it is also necessary to record any carry out of the low-order four bits of an 8-bit unit, since as described in Chapter 2, each 4-bit unit of a byte encodes a separate decimal digit.

There are some additional statuses that may also prove useful when performing various types of data manipulation or decision making operations.

Zero Status

A Zero status flag may be set to 1 to indicate that a data manipulation operation generated a zero result; this flag will be reset to 0 otherwise. A word of caution is required at this point. Most microprocessors have a Zero status flag. It is universally accepted that the Zero status flag will be set to 1 if a data manipulation operation generates a zero result, while the status flag is set to 0 for a non-zero result. In other words, the Zero status flag is universally set to the complement of the result condition.

When Statuses are Modified

Another important point should be made concerning the Zero status flag, and most other status flags. **Those instructions that set or reset status flags, and those that do not, are carefully selected by microcomputer designers.**

Consider the very obvious case of multibyte addition, as illustrated above. The low-order bytes of two 2-byte numbers are added, and the Carry status is set or reset to reflect any carry out of the high-order bit of the low-order bytes. The carry must be added to the low-order bits of the two high-order bytes of the two-byte numbers. This means that the Carry status must be preserved while the two high-order bytes are loaded into CPU registers. Clearly it would be disastrous to program logic if, when data was loaded from memory, the Carry status were cleared to reflect the fact that the load operation did not generate a carry.

At this point, it is only important to remember that not every instruction will affect every, or for that matter any, status flags. Moreover, the way in which status flags are set or reset is very important and is one of the most carefully thought out features of any microprocessor CPU design. In other words, status flags do not necessarily represent conditions within the CPU now; they may well represent the results of selected key operations the last time these operations were performed.

Sign Status   **The use of the high-order bit of a memory word as a sign bit, when performing signed binary operations, gives rise to two status flags. First, there is the Sign status, which is simply the contents of the sign bit (or its complement).** The Sign status flag allows tests to be made for positive or negative numbers when memory words are being interpreted as signed binary data.

The sign bit is always the highest order bit of any number, single word or multiword:

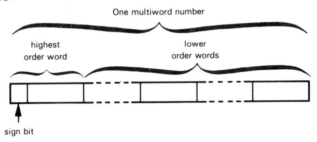

The microprocessor, however, will treat the high-order bit of every byte as a sign bit. Program logic must decide when to ignore the sign status and when to interpret it.

Overflow   **Then there is the Overflow status.** Recall that the microprocessor CPU is
Status   going to treat every binary addition alike — as a pure binary addition. If a carry is generated when adding two lower order words of two multiword numbers, then the carry is valid and simply reflects a carry into the next higher word of the sum. This is illustrated as follows for the addition of two 4-word numbers, with eight bits per word:

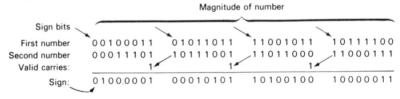

The microprocessor CPU has no way of knowing whether a memory word is a single numeric entity or part of a multiword numeric entity; or if part of a multiword numeric entity, whether it is a middle word, or one of the two end words. This being the case, a carry generated as the result of an addition is, so far as microprocessor logic is concerned, always perfectly valid.

When the high-order bit of a data word is being interpreted as a sign bit, any carry out of the penultimate bit will represent an error overflow, that is, a result that will not fit in the allocated data space. Consider a single, 8-bit data word, being interpreted as signed binary data:

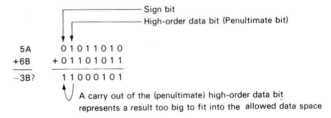

We must devise a strategy for identifying erroneous results of signed binary addition.

Does a carry out of the high-order data bit always signal an error? Indeed not; consider $(-2) + (-2) = (-4)$:

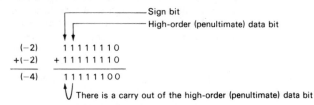

Although there is a carry out of the (penultimate) high-order data bit, the result is -4, which is correct. We will use the symbol C_s to represent a carry out of the sign bit and C_p to represent a carry out of the (penultimate) high-order data bit. What if C_s and C_p are both 0?

```
    2     00000010              (-0C)    11110100
  + 2   + 00000010              + 09   + 00001001
 ─────  ──────────             ──────  ──────────
    4     00000100              (-03)    11111101
```

$$C_s = 0 \longleftarrow \curlyvee C_p = 0 \qquad\qquad C_s = 0 \longleftarrow \curlyvee C_p = 0$$

So long as C_s and C_p are both 0, the answer is always correct. Now consider some examples where C_s and C_p are both 1:

```
  (-75)    10001011.
  + 79    +01111001
 ──────   ──────────
  (+4)     00000100
```

$$C_s = 1 \longleftarrow \curlyvee C_p = 1$$

(Recall that 10001011 is -75_{16} because $+75_{16}$ is 01110101, the twos complement of which is 10001011.)

```
  (-28)    11011000             (-39)    11000111
  + 59    +01011001            + (-1A)  +11100110
 ──────   ──────────           ──────   ──────────
  (+31)    00110001             (-53)    10101101
```

$$C_s = 1 \longleftarrow \curlyvee C_p = 1 \qquad\qquad C_s = 1 \longleftarrow \curlyvee C_p = 1$$

When C_s and C_p are both 1, the answer is always correct. When C_s and C_p differ, the answer is always in error:

```
    45     01000101             (-6E)    10010010
  + 67    +01100111            + (-5C)  +10100100
 ──────   ──────────           ──────   ──────────
  (-54)?    10101100            + 36?     00110110
```

$$C_s = 0 \longleftarrow \curlyvee C_p = 1 \qquad\qquad C_s = 1 \longleftarrow \curlyvee C_p = 0$$

Overflow
Status Set
Strategy

Our strategy for setting and resetting the Overflow status is therefore clear. When carries out of the sign and penultimate bits are the same (C_p and C_s are both 0 or both 1), the Overflow status will be reset to 0. When these two carries differ, the Overflow status will be set to 1, indicating that the answer overflowed the answer space and is therefore wrong.

Stated another way, **the Overflow will be the Exclusive-OR of the carries out of the Sign and penultimate bits:**

$$\text{Overflow} = C_s \oplus C_p$$

Parity
Status

The Parity status is the only other status that is worth mentioning at this time. This flag, if present, is set to 1 each time a data transfer operation detects a data byte with the wrong parity. Clearly this status will be ignored most of the time, since it is only meaningful when the contents of a memory word are being interpreted as a character code.

INSTRUCTION EXECUTION

We have described how a microprocessor CPU may interpret the contents of a memory word as an instruction code. But this leaves a number of unanswered questions. What maximum or minimum number of logical events constitutes an instruction? What occurs within the CPU during the course of an instruction's execution? And what support logic does the CPU demand?

In answering these questions, we introduce a very critical microprocessor concept, and one of the key differences between the minicomputer and the microprocessor.

In the world of minicomputers, the most important feature to look for in an instruction set is the versatility of operations performed by the CPU in response to each instruction code. This is reasonable for minicomputers; minicomputers are frequently called upon to perform varied and varying tasks, and programming may be an ongoing, major expense.

In the world of microprocessors, another question is far more important: what does the CPU demand of external logic?

Complex instructions usually demand complex logic external to the CPU. This is of no concern to the minicomputer user, who buys CPU plus all external logic, packaged in a single box. This is of great concern to the microprocessor user, who must interface his logic, often directly to the microprocessor. If a microprocessor costs somewhere between $1 and $100, the entire economics of using the microprocessor will evaporate unless the interface logic demanded by the microprocessor is also inexpensive.

But this sharp contrast between microprocessors and minicomputers has blurred considerably recently and will become even more confusing over the next few years. This is because microprocessors are being used with increasing frequency as the central processing units of microcomputers in applications where they are indistinguishable from minicomputers. As part of a microcomputer, a microprocessor's instruction set would have to be evaluated in exactly the same way as a minicomputer's instruction set. But when a microprocessor replaces digital logic — and the majority of microprocessors are still used in this fashion — a sharp distinction exists between microprocessors and minicomputers.

Let us therefore examine how an instruction is executed.

INSTRUCTION TIMING

Operations within a microprocessor are controlled by a clock signal whose period may vary from as little as 100 nanoseconds to as much as a microsecond. We will refer to this clock signal using the symbol Φ:

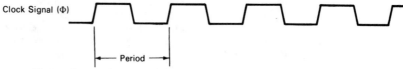

Depending on how the microprocessor has been designed, the clock may be a straightforward single signal, as illustrated above, or it may consist of a more complex interaction of signals. Here is one possible combination of two signals, identified by the symbols Φ_1 and Φ_2:

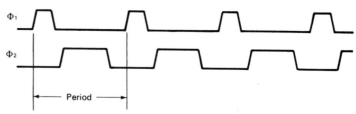

The simple signal provides two edges and two states per period:

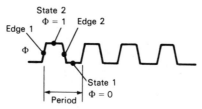

The more complex signals provide four edges and three states per period:

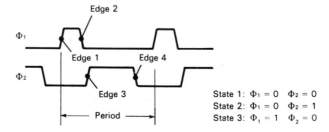

State 1: $\Phi_1 = 0$ $\Phi_2 = 0$
State 2: $\Phi_1 = 0$ $\Phi_2 = 1$
State 3: $\Phi_1 = 1$ $\Phi_2 = 0$

In this book we will use the simple signal Φ.

Synchronous Devices

Asynchronous Devices

Some additional devices surrounding and supporting the microprocessor will also require the microprocessor clock signal as an input; others will not. Support devices that do require the microprocessor clock signal as an input are said to be "synchronous devices." Support devices that do not require the microprocessor clock signal as an input are said to be "asynchronous devices." The recent trend has been towards asynchronous support devices.

Clock
Crystal

The logic that generates a clock signal usually bases the frequency of the clock signal on the resonant frequency of a crystal. Suitable crystals are mass produced and inexpensive.

A resistor and a capacitor (of appropriate value) can substitute for the crystal, providing a less expensive and less precise clock frequency controller.

The discussion at hand does not require that you understand how a clock signal is derived from a crystal or resistor-capacitor circuit.

Clock
Signal
Generator

Early microprocessors did not contain their own clock logic. They required a clock signal generator device as a support circuit. This may be illustrated as follows:

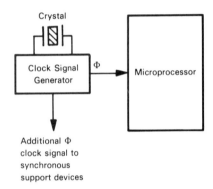

Most microprocessors designed since 1978 have provided their own on-chip clock logic. This may be illustrated as follows:

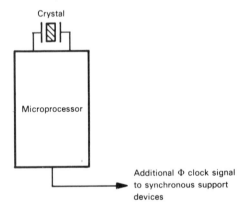

A clock signal generator device and a microprocessor that generates its own clock signal will both output a clock signal to be used by synchronous support devices, as illustrated above.

A microprocessor that generates its own clock signal will usually give you the option of inputting an externally generated clock signal. This is necessary, since two or more microprocessors may be intimately configured in a single logic system. If two or more microprocessors are to coexist, they must be driven by the same clock signal, otherwise they will quickly be running out-of-phase with each other, and that would generate horrendous timing problems. We can illustrate pin connections required by clock logic for a microprocessor that generates its own clock signal as follows:

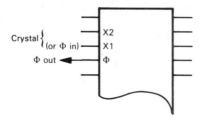

When the microprocessor generates its own clock signal, pins are used as follows:

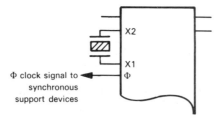

When the microprocessor receives its clock signal as an input, pins are used as follows:

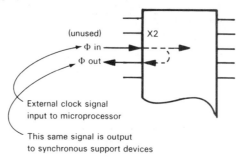

TIMING DIAGRAMS

Clock signal levels and edges trigger other signal level changes in order to effect logic event sequences. Event sequences are illustrated using timing diagrams.

Although timing diagrams have been discussed in Volume 0 **we will** nevertheless **describe them briefly before proceeding to use them in the balance of this book.**

A signal is shown in one of two states, representing digital 0 and digital 1, as follows:

For clarity, signal transitions are usually illustrated as occurring instantaneously:

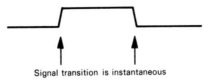

Signal transition is instantaneous

Signal Transition Time

Signal transitions may also be illustrated as occurring over some finite amount of time:

Signal transition time

In fact, **all signals require some finite amount of time to make the transition from low-to-high or from high-to-low.**

Leading Edge

Trailing Edge

High-Going Transition

Low-Going Transition

When a signal makes a low-to-high transition, this is frequently referred to as the signal's "leading edge" or "high-going" transition. A high-to-low transition is referred to as the signal's "trailing edge," or "low-going" transition. This may be illustrated as follows:

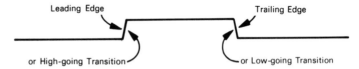

Leading Edge

Trailing Edge

or High-going Transition

or Low-going Transition

Signals are sometimes represented in groups. For example, a byte of data might be represented by eight parallel signals. Rather than drawing eight parallel signal lines, **we use the following notation to represent multiple signal level transitions:**

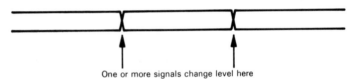

One or more signals change level here

There are occasions when a signal may be either high or low, but there is no way of knowing which. This is represented for single signals and for groups of signals as follows:

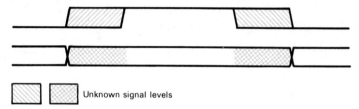

Unknown signal levels

Floating Signal   **It is also possible for a signal to be "off." The signal is then said to be "floating."** A floating signal is, in effect, disconnected. It can neither transmit nor receive. Single and multiple floating signals are illustrated midway between high and low, as follows:

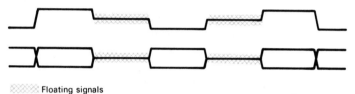

Floating signals

Cause and consequence relationships between signals are illustrated using arrows. A circle at the arrow base identifies the cause. The arrow head identifies the consequence. There can be a single cause and single consequence:

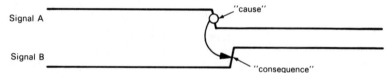

In the illustration above, a high-to-low transition of Signal A causes Signal B to make a low-to-high transition.

Multiple causes may result in a single consequence:

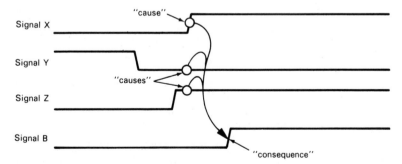

Signal B makes a low-to-high transition whenever Signal X makes a low-to-high transition while Signal Y is low and Signal Z is high.

A single cause may have multiple consequences:

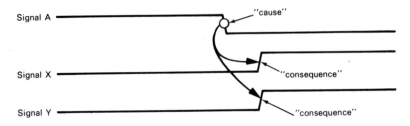

Signals X and Y make low-to-high transitions when Signal A makes a high-to-low transition.

Multiple causes may have multiple consequences:

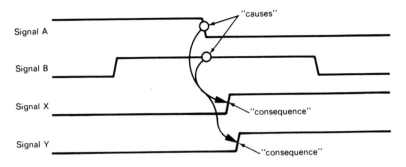

Signals X and Y make low-to-high transitions if Signal A makes a high-to-low transition while Signal B is high.

There are two types of timing diagrams: event sequence timing diagrams and data sheet timing diagrams.

Event Sequence Timing Diagram

An event sequence timing diagram attempts to illustrate event sequences via signal transitions and levels. An event sequence timing diagram does not attempt to correctly represent absolute time delays between one event and another, nor does it attempt to absolutely represent the time required for a signal transition to occur. Event sequence timing diagrams need only be conceptually accurate. All of the timing diagrams in this book are event sequence timing diagrams.

Data Sheet Timing Diagram

Data sheet timing diagrams make no attempt to represent event sequences, but they do accurately represent time intervals and delays. This requires every data sheet timing diagram to have an accompanying table. The following illustrates a data sheet timing diagram and companion table:

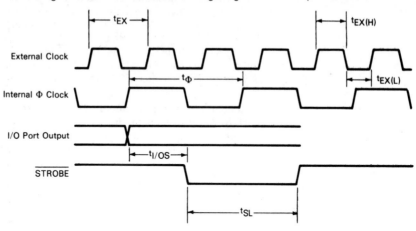

SIGNAL	SYMBOL	PARAMETER	MIN	MAX	UNIT
External Clock	t_{EX} $t_{EX(H)}$ $t_{EX(L)}$	External Clock Period External Clock Pulse Width High External Clock Pulse Width Low	250 90 100	1000 700 700	ns ns ns
Internal Φ Clock	t_Φ	Internal Φ Clock Period	$2t_{EX}$		
$\overline{\text{STROBE}}$	$t_{I/OS}$ t_{SL}	Output valid to $\overline{\text{STROBE}}$ Delay $\overline{\text{STROBE}}$ Low Time	$3t_\Phi$ -1000 $8t_\Phi$ -250	$3t_\Phi$ $+250$ $12t_\Phi$ $+250$	 ns

The illustration above shows four signals: two clock signals, a control signal labeled $\overline{\text{STROBE}}$, and some parallel lines labeled "I/O Port Output." As illustrated, these signals make no attempt to depict event sequences. Rather time intervals and delays are shown. (We will describe the meaning of the bar over $\overline{\text{STROBE}}$ shortly, when describing microprocessor signals in more detail.)

Within the table, the SIGNAL column names the signals whose parameters are described.

The SYMBOL column lists the symbols used to identify time delays in the illustrations.

The PARAMETER column describes, in words, the time interval represented by the symbol.

The MIN and MAX columns provide the smallest and largest allowed times for each time interval. The UNIT column identifies the units for the numbers in the MIN and MAX columns. ns represents nanoseconds.

To illustrate the use of data sheet timing diagrams, consider a couple of examples.

The Internal Φ Clock has a period that must equal exactly twice the External Clock Period. This External Clock Period may vary between 250 and 1000 nanoseconds.

After the many lines that constitute I/O Port Output acquire new permanent levels, signal $\overline{STROBE}$ must make a high-to-low transition after a time delay equal to $t_{I/OS}$. This time delay must be at least three times the Internal Clock Period minus 1000 nanoseconds, but not more than three times the Internal Clock Period plus 250 nanoseconds. The $\overline{STROBE}$ signal must remain low for at least eight Internal Clock Periods minus 250 nanoseconds but for no more than 12 Internal Clock Periods plus 250 nanoseconds; $\overline{STROBE}$ must then make a low-to-high transition.

You need not concern yourself with data sheet timing diagrams until you start to actually design digital logic. At that time data sheet timing diagrams are of extreme importance; you use them to ensure that each event within the sequences you design does indeed have enough time to occur safely.

INSTRUCTION CYCLES

The execution of every instruction, by any microprocessor, may be divided into two parts: the instruction fetch and the instruction execute. This was illustrated earlier in this chapter for the six-step binary addition example. Recall that every instruction starts with the instruction code being loaded into the Instruction register. We refer to this operation as an instruction fetch.

Instruction Fetch

During the instruction fetch, CPU logic outputs the contents of the program counter register, along with appropriate control signals that tell external logic to return the contents of the memory word addressed by the program counter. So far as external logic is concerned, this is simply a memory read operation.

The contents of the memory word, when received by the CPU, are stored in the Instruction register and thus get interpreted as an instruction code.

While external logic is responding to the instruction fetch, the CPU uses its own internal logic to add 1 to the contents of the program counter. The program counter now points to the memory word following the one from which the current instruction code was fetched.

Instruction Execute

Once the instruction code is in the Instruction register, it triggers a sequence of events controlled by the control unit; this sequence of events constitutes the instruction's execution.

There are many ways in which a clock signal can time an instruction's execution. For the discussion at hand we will assume that **two clock periods will be used to execute an instruction. One will time the "instruction fetch," the next will time the "instruction execute."**

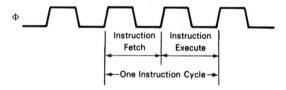

CPU Pins and Signals

What about the signals via which the CPU will communicate with external logic? The 40-pin DIP, being the most popular among today's microprocessor packages is the one we will adopt — which means that 40 signals may be input and/or output, including the clock, power and ground.

The way in which the 40 pins of the DIP are used constitutes one of the most variable design characteristics of microprocessors, but they all begin along these lines:

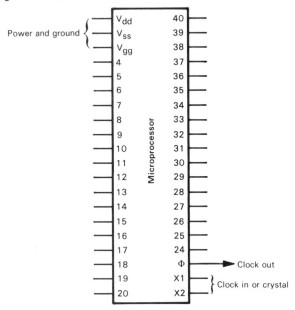

V_{dd} is the current drain connection or power input.
V_{ss} is the current source or ground.
V_{gg} is the gate voltage; it is not required in all LSI devices.

Power Supplies

Power is frequently illustrated using voltage levels as follows:

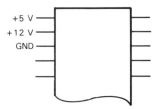

Today most microprocessors require a single, +5 V power supply:

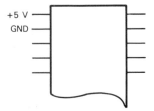

The symbol V_{cc} usually describes a +5 V power supply.

The first step when executing any instruction is the instruction fetch, which in reality is a memory read. It requires a memory address to be output and a data word to be input in response.

If the memory address can range from 0 to 65,535 (FFFF$_{16}$), sixteen address pins will be required, one for each binary digit of the address:

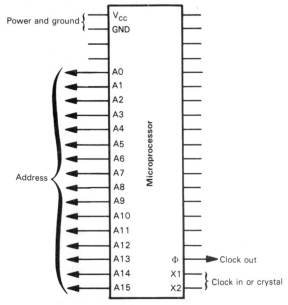

For an 8-bit microprocessor, all data will enter and leave the microprocessor via eight bidirectional data lines. A READ control signal, indicating that data must be input to the CPU, completes the requirements for the instruction fetch:

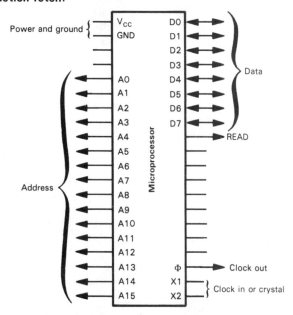

The following timing diagram defines the instruction fetch sequence, as controlled by the CPU:

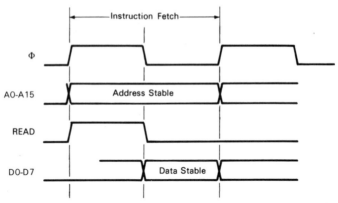

We will now turn our attention to an instruction's execution.

Consider the six-step binary addition program that was described at the end of Chapter 3. There are four separate and distinct types of instructions within the program. They are:

1) Load a memory address into the data counter (Instructions 1 and 3).
2) Fetch the contents of the data word (in this instance a byte) addressed by the data counter and store it in the accumulator (Instruction 2).
3) Fetch the contents of the data byte addressed by the data counter, add it to the contents of the accumulator, and store the result in the accumulator (Instruction 4).
4) Store the contents of the accumulator in the memory byte addressed by the data counter (Instruction 5).

Let us examine how each of these four instruction types are executed, in terms of instruction cycles and control signals output by and input to the microprocessor.

Memory Read Signals and Timing

Instruction 2 is the simplest, so we will begin with it.

Like all instructions, it begins with an instruction fetch.

The control unit decodes the instruction code 40_{16}, and in response causes a data byte to be fetched from memory. In reality, since the data is in an 8-bit memory word on a memory device, all the CPU can really do is generate signals at its pins; logic external to the CPU must respond to these signals if the data fetch is to be accomplished.

As seen by external logic, signals generated by the CPU to fetch data are identical to signals generated for the instruction fetch.

Thus timing for a Memory Read instruction is as follows:

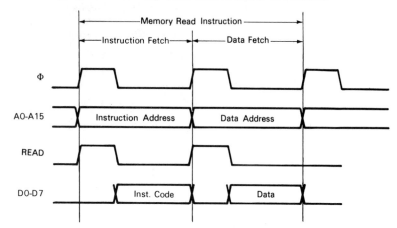

These are the only differences between instruction fetch and data fetch cycles:

1) During the instruction fetch cycle, the address output on A0-A15 is the contents of the PC register; during the data fetch cycle, it is the contents of the data counter.

2) During the instruction fetch cycle, data input is stored in the Instruction register. During the data fetch cycle, it is stored in the accumulator.

External Logic Requirements

This simple scheme demands very little of the external logic. If READ is high, then memory circuits must decode A0-A15. The selected memory module must extract the contents of the addressed memory word and make sure it is at the microprocessor data pins when Φ is low.

What the microprocessor demands of external logic during a read operation is standard, simple logic, that is part of any memory device. But we will defer this discussion to Chapter 5, and continue with CPU signals and timing for the ADD instruction.

Add Operation Signals and Timing

In order to perform an add, the CPU fetches the contents of a memory word, exactly as it did for a Memory Read instruction. However, for the Add instruction, the fetched data are added to contents of the accumulator. In contrast, data fetched during a Memory Read instruction are deposited in the accumulator unchanged.

As seen by external logic, therefore, there is no difference between the signals generated for an Add or a Memory Read instruction.

Memory Write Signals and Timing

Instruction 4 causes the contents of the accumulator to be stored in the memory word (in this case a memory byte) addressed by the data counter; this is called a Memory Write instruction. **As seen by external logic, the only difference between the signal sequences for a Memory Read and a Memory Write is that a WRITE signal must go high, instead of a READ signal. We must therefore add a WRITE signal to our microprocessor.**

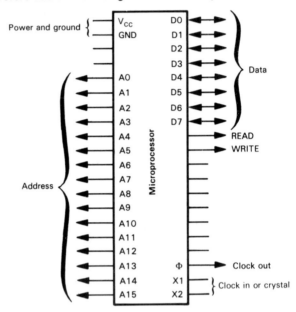

Timing for a Memory Write instruction is as follows:

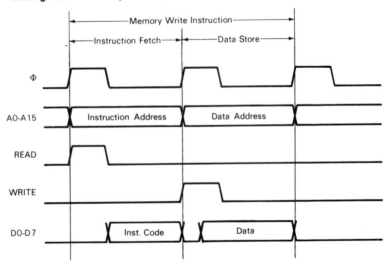

Instruction 1 loads a memory address into the data counter. This instruction occupies three memory bytes, one for the instruction code and two more for the memory address.

Notice that the Load Data Counter instruction is equivalent to two memory reads, with these differences:

1) Both Load Data Counter memory reads are specified by one $9C_{16}$ instruction code. In contrast, the 40_{16} Memory Read instruction code triggers just one memory read.

2) The Load Data Counter instruction fetches data from memory bytes whose addresses come from the program counter. For a Memory Read instruction, the data counter provides the data memory address.

3) Data read from memory by the Load Data Counter instruction is stored in the upper and lower halves of the data counter. For a Memory Read instruction, the fetched data is stored in the accumulator.

The differences between the Load Data Counter and the Memory Read instructions may be contrasted as follows:

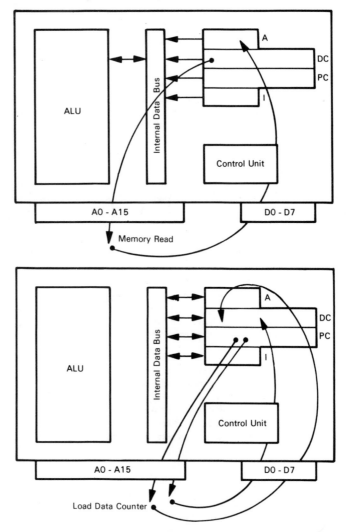

While the logic operations internal to the microprocessor are completely different for the Load Data Counter and the Memory Read instructions, the external timing and signal sequences are remarkably similar.

A smart microprocessor CPU could execute the Load Data Counter instruction in three clock periods, as follows:

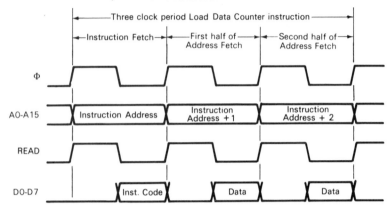

Some microprocessors have simple internal logic that inserts a blank clock period between any two external reference (instruction fetch, read, or write) clock periods. The microprocessor will use this blank clock period to perform various internal logic operations. This simple microprocessor will require six clock periods to execute the load data counter instruction:

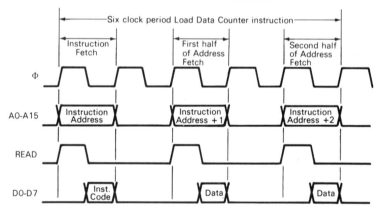

There is, in fact, no "standard" way in which microprocessors time or execute instructions. The two preceding illustrations are realistic, but they do not represent a "norm" or majority design preference.

Having examined some simple read and write timing sequences, let us next look at some of the different ways in which microprocessor address and data lines can be configured.

Microprocessor Addressing Ranges

We have illustrated 16 address lines, capable of addressing 65,536 (FFFF$_{16}$) memory locations. This microprocessor has an addressing range of 65,536. **We use the term "addressing range" to describe the number of memory locations that a microprocessor can address.** 16 is the most common number of address lines found among microprocessors available today. But it is by no means the only available number. A few microprocessors have 15 or 14 address lines, capable of addressing 32,768 or 16,384 memory locations, respectively. There are other low cost microprocessors, packaged in 28-pin DIPs, which have as few as 12 address lines; they are capable of addressing only 4096 memory locations. At the other extreme, the newest, most powerful microprocessors have 20 or more address lines, allowing them to address more than a million memory locations.

It is worth noting that **minicomputers and microprocessors have approximately the same addressing ranges.** Minicomputers typically address 65,536 memory locations. The smallest minicomputers may address as few as 4096 memory locations, and the most powerful recently introduced minicomputers address millions of memory locations — about the same as the most recent microprocessors.

Multiplexed Data and Address Lines

If you look again at the most recent microprocessor pin illustration, you will see very few unassigned pins. As we add new capabilities to our microprocessor, we will have to make new pin assignments. Will we run out of pins? That, of course, depends on the specific logic we add to our microprocessor and on the pin demands that the additional logic may make. **Many microprocessors save pins by having the bidirectional data lines share pins with address lines.** This may be illustrated as follows:

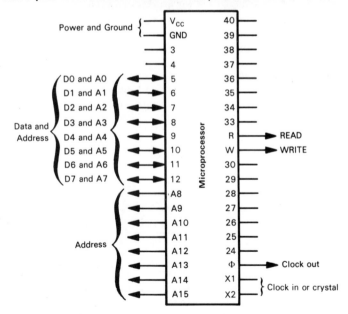

The address and data lines are said to be "multiplexed." Clearly, if pins are multiplexed, one or the other of the signals, but not both, can be active at any time. Thus instruction fetch and memory write timing would change as follows, when data and address pins are multiplexed:

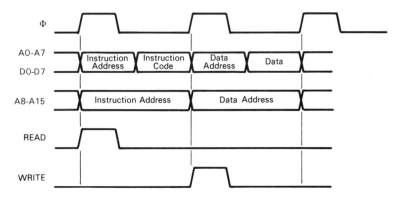

Nearly all 16-bit microprocessors multiplex data and address lines. A 16-bit microprocessor requires 16 data lines, which with 16 or more separate address lines would consume 32 or more of the 40 available pins in a 40-pin DIP. The only 16-bit microprocessors that do not multiplex their data and address lines solve the pin limitation problem by using a 64-pin DIP.

Floating Lines

Recall that we discussed "floating" signals earlier in this chapter. Signals that are turned "off" are said to be "floating."

Three-State Signals

The data and address lines in most microprocessors are turned "off" by logic within the microprocessor when the lines are not in use. Signals that can be "off" are also referred to as "three-state signals." The three states are: high, low, and off. A "high" signal outputs a voltage near +5 V and sources current. A "low" signal is near ground (0 V) and sinks any current from connected lines. An "off" signal neither outputs nor sinks current; it is invisible to external logic.

We can illustrate three-state signals during execution of a write instruction as follows:

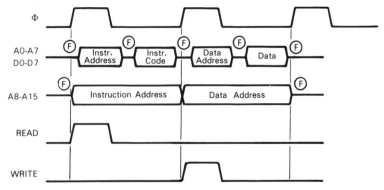

When multiplexed data and address lines share pins, the pin is always floated for a short time in between outputting an address and inputting data. Recall that timing diagrams illustrate floating signals midway between the high and low levels. In the illustration above, Ⓕ identifies floating signals. You will not normally see floating signals so marked; we do so this one time to highlight the floating state.

In Chapter 5, when we look at logic external to the microprocessor, the value of three-state signals will become apparent.

HOW MUCH SHOULD AN INSTRUCTION DO?

Let us now consider ways in which the instructions described in this chapter may be made simpler or more complex.

The Load Data Counter instruction loads the two 8-bit words (bytes) that follow the instruction code into the data counter. This instruction could be broken up into two instructions, one to load the low-order byte of the data counter, the other to load the high-order byte of the data counter. Let us compare the two forms of the Load Data Counter instruction:

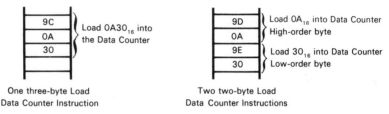

One three-byte Load
Data Counter Instruction

Two two-byte Load
Data Counter Instructions

The 3-byte Load Data Counter instruction's possible signals and timing have been illustrated. The two 2-byte instructions could each execute in two clock periods or in four clock periods. Executing in two clock periods, signals and timing for each instruction would be as follows:

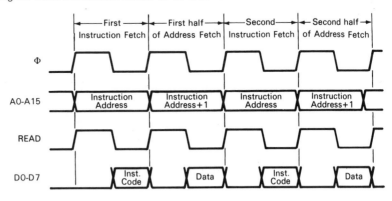

Timing and signals, when executing in four clock periods, would be as follows:

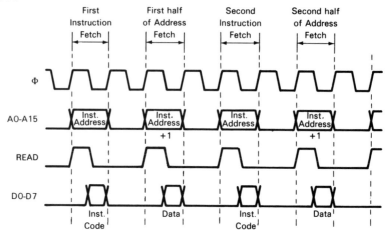

Breaking the 3-byte Load Data Counter instruction into two 2-byte instructions does not simplify the demands placed on external logic by the CPU; but it does make the microprocessor's control unit simpler, as we will demonstrate later in this chapter when describing microprogramming.

Some of the earliest (now obsolete) microprocessors did, in fact, break the 3-byte Load Data Counter instruction into two 2-byte instructions. But no modern microprocessors are so simplistic. On the contrary, the newest microprocessors tend to combine operations in various combinations to generate instructions that grow ever more complex.

Consider, for example, combining the Load Data Counter and Memory Read instructions as follows:

41	Load into the Accumulator the contents of the
0A	memory word addressed by the next two words
30	of the three-byte instruction

As illustrated above, 41_{16} is the instruction code specifying this three-byte Memory Read instruction; $0A30_{16}$ is the address of the memory location whose contents are to be read into the accumulator. Instructions that specify the memory address to be referenced, as this 3-byte Memory Read instruction does, are said to have direct memory addressing.

Signals and timing for the 3-byte Memory Read instructions could take one of many forms. Here is the most compact possibility:

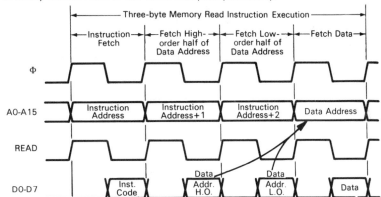

To a minicomputer designer, combining the Load Data Counter instruction with the Memory Read — or with any memory reference instruction — is obvious.

When microprocessors were first being designed, the automatic virtues of direct addressing were not so obvious to microprocessor designers, for the immediately apparent reason that direct addressing instructions would require more complex control unit logic; this will be illustrated later in this chapter when we look at microprogramming — the way in which control units implement the event sequences required by instructions. But today, microprocessor design techniques have advanced to the point where control units are routinely complex enough to handle direct addressing instructions. Microprocessor designers can now emulate the capabilities of minicomputers almost effortlessly.

But there is the less immediately apparent reason why direct addressing is not desirable. Whereas most minicomputer programs are stored and executed out of RAM, many microprocessor programs are stored and executed out of ROM; that means direct addressing can only be used when the data address will not change.

Consider an elementary instruction sequence that receives data input from an external device, then stores the data into a number of consecutive memory locations:

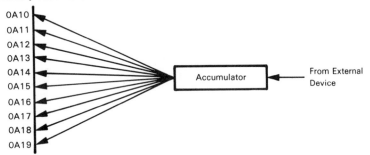

RAM data memory locations in the above illustration constitute a "data table." The beginning address, $0A10_{16}$ has been arbitrarily selected; any other address would do as well. The illustration shows 8-bit (byte) memory locations. In the discussion that follows we will therefore continue referring to memory "bytes," since all memory locations are 8-bits wide. We could just as easily refer to memory words, but that would imply a general case, where memory locations have an undefined bit width.

Ignoring, for the moment, the question of how many data bytes are to be stored in the data table, the following instruction sequence would fill the data table:

Arbitrarily Selected Addresses	Program Memory	
0280	9C	} Load the address $0A10_{16}$ into the Data Counter
0281	0A	
0282	10	
0283	08	Input a byte from an external device to Accumulator
0284	60	Store Accumulator contents in memory
0285	E3	Increment Data Counter
0286	BC	} Reset Program Counter to 0283
0287	83	

A straightforward Load Data Counter instruction, stored in program memory bytes 0280_{16}, 0281_{16} and 0282_{16}, loads the address $0A10_{16}$ into the data counter; this is the address of the first data table byte.

The instruction code 08_{16} in program memory byte 0283_{16} causes a byte of data to be input to the accumulator from an external device.

The instruction code 60_{16} in program memory location 0284_{16} is a simple Store Memory instruction; it causes the contents of the accumulator to be stored in the data memory word addressed by the data counter; initially that is the first word of the data table, with address $0A10_{16}$.

Program Loop **The next two instructions, located in program memory locations 0285_{16}, 0286_{16}, and 0287_{16}, increment the data counter contents** (to address the next word of the data table), **then change the value in the program counter to 0283_{16};** execution now returns to the instruction that brings the next data byte into the accumulator from the external device. We have established a program loop — a group of instructions that continuously get reexecuted. A slightly different task is performed on each reexecution because the data counter contents are incremented on each pass.

Four instructions, occupying five memory bytes, can fill a data table, whatever the length of the data table may be!

Using direct addressing, this program loop could not be executed. We would have:

	Program Memory	
0280	08	Input a byte from an external device to Accumulator
0281	61	} Store Accumulator contents in data memory word addressed by the second and third instruction bytes
0282	0A	
0283	10	
0284		Increment what?
0285		
0286		

The data table is addressed by the second and third bytes of the memory-store-with-direct-addressing instruction. **This address cannot be incremented if it is going to reside in ROM!** Minicomputers have a solution to this problem, of course (we shall see what the solution is in Chapter 6), but the solution adds complexity to microprocessors and this complexity may bring with it more cost than savings.

Two of the new instructions in the program loop need to be described further at this point.

CPU Operate Instructions

The Increment Data Counter instruction simply causes the contents of the data counter to be increased by 1. Following the instructions fetch, logic external to the CPU is idle:

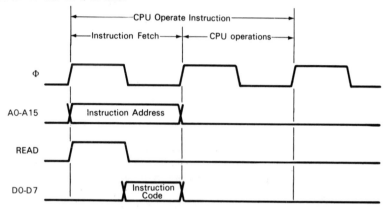

Branch Instruction

Jump Instruction

Absolute Branch

The instruction in program memory locations 0286_{16} and 0287_{16} actually changes the contents of the program counter, and thus changes the sequence in which instructions are executed. This is referred to as a Branch, or Jump instruction.

Branch instructions have many variations. A two-byte version is illustrated in the program loop; the contents of the second instruction byte are loaded into the low-order half of the program counter as follows:

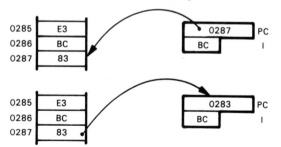

Branching at Page Boundary

The problem with this variation of the Branch instruction is that it will not work if the program counter high-order byte gets incremented. For example, suppose the program loop was stored in memory as follows:

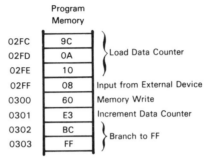

Branch to FF_{16} would branch to $03FF_{16}$, not to $02FF_{16}$, because the high-order byte of the program counter got incremented between the input and memory write instructions.

There are two ways around this problem.

First, we can have a three-byte Branch instruction that changes both halves of the program counter.

Program Relative Branch

Second, we can add the contents of the second Branch instruction byte to the program counter, designing the CPU so that it interprets the second Branch instruction byte as a signed binary number. Referring to the program loop, after the Branch instruction has been executed, the program counter would normally contain 0288_{16}. To change this value to 0283_{16}, 5 must be subtracted. The twos complement of 5 is:

$$1 1 1 1 1 0 1 1$$

Sign Propagation

or FB_{16}. This is the value that must be stored in program memory location 0287_{16}. **Adding an 8-bit value from memory to the 16-bit contents of the program counter using signed binary arithmetic is not a problem; CPU logic simply propagates the sign bit through the high-order half of the value to be added to the program counter.** In this case we have:

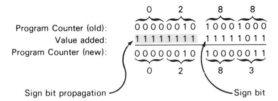

Adding 5 to the program counter contents would proceed as follows:

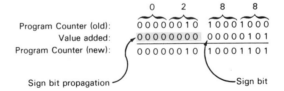

This is referred to as a Program Relative branch.

MICROPROGRAMMING AND THE CONTROL UNIT

Let us now examine how the control unit decodes instruction codes.

A microprocessor CPU may be illustrated functionally, as in Figure 4-1, but in reality, the CPU consists of a number of logic elements, activated by sequences of "enable" signals.

The complementer, for example, is latently able, at any time, to complement the contents of eight data latches within the logic of the complementer circuits. A single enable signal, emanating from the control unit, will activate this logic sequence.

However, complementing eight data latches within the complementer serves no useful purpose. We want to complement the contents of the accumulator, and that means moving the contents of the accumulator to the complementer, then, after enabling complementer logic, returning the results to the accumulator.

Complementing the contents of the accumulator therefore requires these five steps:

1) Move the contents of the accumulator to the data bus:

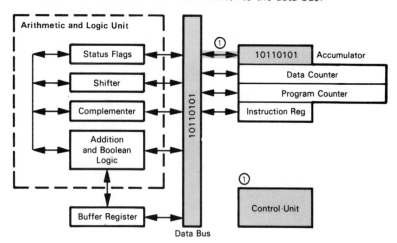

2) Move the contents of the data bus to the complementer:

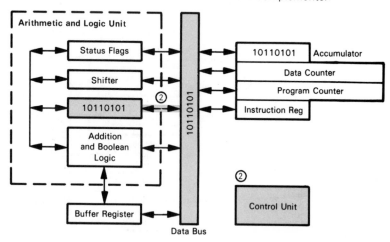

3) Activate complementer logic:

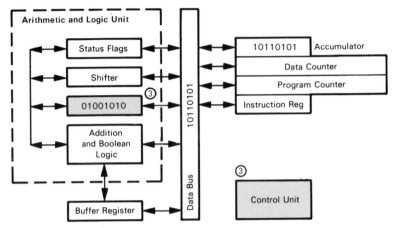

4) Move the contents of the complementer to the data bus:

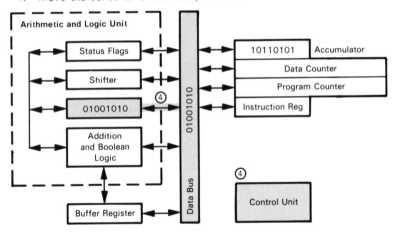

5) Move the contents of the data bus to the accumulator:

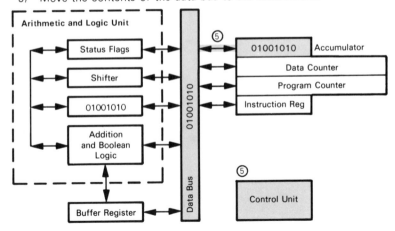

Microinstruction

Macroinstruction

Microprogram

Each of these five steps is referred to as a microinstruction. Each microinstruction is enabled by a signal from the control unit. By outputting the appropriate sequence of control signals, **the control unit can sequence any number of microinstructions, to create a macroinstruction,** which is the accepted response of the CPU to an assembly language instruction code.

In order to complement the accumulator contents, the control unit must contain five binary codes, each of which triggers an appropriate control signal (or signals). This sequence of binary codes within the control unit is referred to as a microprogram. Generating the sequence of binary codes that are stored within the control unit is referred to as microprogramming.

There is a close parallel between microprogramming and assembly language programming.

A microprogram is stored as a sequence of binary digits in the control unit. An assembly language program is stored as a sequence of binary digits, usually in a ROM memory. The assembly language program is referred to as a macroprogram. Each instruction code of the macroprogram initiates execution of an entire microprogram, as stored in the control unit:

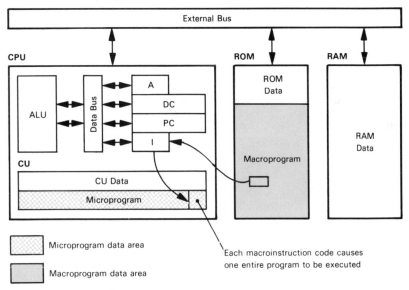

A microprogram stored in the control unit has a data memory, which consists of the CPU registers plus a data area internal to the control unit. A macroprogram also has a data memory, which consists of ROM for constant data, plus RAM for variable data:

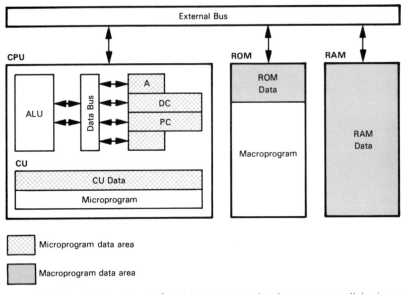

Individual instructions of a microprogram implement a small logic sequence within the logic of the CPU. Individual instructions of a macroprogram cause an entire microprogram to be executed, thus implementing a whole sequence of operations within the CPU.

Macroinstruction Complexity

The complexity of operations associated with any macroinstruction is a direct function of the size of the microprogram whose execution the macroinstruction initiates. There are no logical breakpoints or levels at which a microprogrammer must terminate the microprogram that will be executed in response to any macroinstruction code. Of course, complex microprograms require large control units. A simple microcomputer may have a small control unit and therefore may be forced to execute very simple macroinstructions. Some large computers have no assembly language, but in response to a single macroinstruction code, execute complex sequences of events involving logic throughout the computer system.

Microprogrammable Microprocessor

The control unit of every microprocessor is in reality nothing but a microprogram. If you, the user, are able to create or modify the microprogram within the control unit, then the microprocessor is said to be "microprogammable." If the control unit microprogram is designed by the microprocessor designer, and then becomes an unalterable part of the chip, the microprocessor is not microprogrammable, even though it is microprogrammed.

In this book we are going to describe these two separate and distinct classes of microcomputer product:

1) **The microprocessor that gives you access to a central processing unit but not to the control unit.** You sequence CPU logic using macroinstructions, referred to collectively as an assembly language instruction set. You cannot microprogram this class of microcomputer product; nonetheless, a basic understanding of microprogramming will help you understand the trade-offs that every microprocessor designer must evaluate when putting together an instruction set.

Macrologic

Chip Slice

2) **The "chip slice" or "macrologic"** which presents you with CPU "building blocks;" you must tie these building blocks together with a microprogram.

MICROPROCESSOR CONTROL UNITS

First we will describe microprocessor control units.

Let us identify an arbitrary set of control signals, as illustrated in Figure 4-2. Our microprocessor Control Unit will activate these control signals to implement macroinstructions. Tables 4-1, 4-2, and 4-3 describe these control signals.

Table 4-1. Control Unit Signals

Signal	Function
C_0, C_1	$C_0=0$, $C_1=0$; No data moved onto or off Data Bus or Address Register $C_0=0$, $C_1=0$; Data moved onto Data Bus or Address Register $C_0=0$, $C_1=1$; Data moved off Data Bus or Address Register $C_0=1$, $C_1=1$; Microinstruction will be trapped within the Control Unit (see Table 4-4)
C_2, C_3 C_4, C_5	When $C_0=1$ and $C_1=0$, or $C_0=0$ and $C_1=1$, these four signals are decoded to select specific data flow, as specified in Table 4-2
C_6, C_7, C_8	These three signals are decoded to select ALU operations as specified in Table 4-3
WRITE, READ	Direct connections from the output pins to two CU data bits
Φ	Clock signal input to CU
C, O, S, Z	Four status bits, directly connected to four CU data bits

Table 4-2. Data Flow Select when $C_0=1$ or $C_1=1$

C_5	C_4	C_3	C_2	Function
0	0	0	0	Accumulator ⟶ Data Bus select
1	0	0	0	Data Counter high-order byte ⟶ Data Bus select
0	1	0	0	Data Counter low-order byte ⟶ Data Bus select
1	1	0	0	Program Counter high-order byte ⟶ Data Bus select
0	0	1	0	Program Counter low-order byte ⟶ Data Bus select
1	0	1	0	Instruction Register ⟶ Data Bus select
0	1	1	0	Status Register ⟶ Data Bus select
1	1	1	0	Shifter ⟶ Data Bus select
0	0	0	1	Complementer ⟶ Data Bus select
1	0	0	1	ALU latches ⟶ Data Bus select
0	1	0	1	ALU Buffer ⟶ Data Bus select
1	1	0	1	Data Register ⟶ Data Bus select
0	0	1	1	Data Counter ⟶ Address Register select
1	0	1	1	Program Counter ⟶ Address Register select
0	1	1	1	Data Register ⟶ Buffer Register
1	1	1	1	Not Used

Table 4-3. ALU Select Signals

C_8	C_7	C_6	Function
0	0	0	Select shifter logic
1	0	0	Select complementer logic
0	1	0	Select addition logic*
1	1	0	Select AND logic*
0	0	1	Select OR logic*
1	0	1	Select XOR logic*
0	1	1	Increment ALU latches
1	1	1	No ALU operation

*Operation is performed on contents of ALU latches and Buffer register. Result appears in ALU latches.

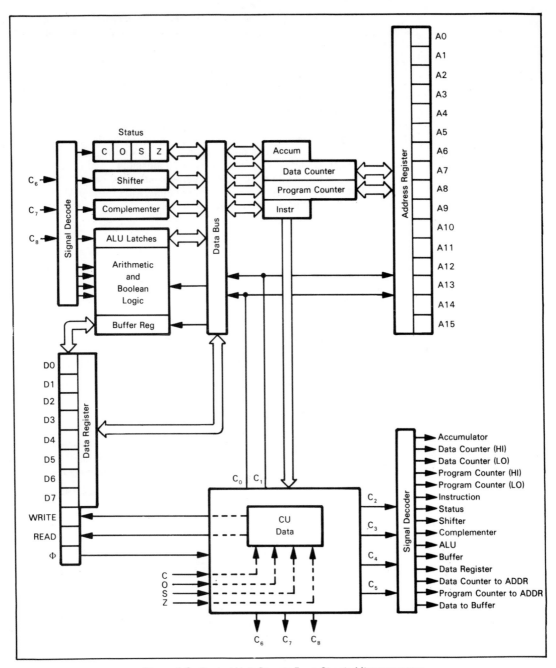

Figure 4-2. Control Unit Signals For a Simple Microprocessor

When compared to the ingenuity of real chip slice microinstruction codes, Tables 4-1, 4-2, and 4-3 represent somewhat simplistic, inflexible CPU logic and organization. Nevertheless, these tables make real chip slice architecture easier to understand by clarifying the goals that the chip slice logic designer strives to attain.

The control signals described in Tables 4-1, 4-2, and 4-3 do not allow the control unit to perform all of the operations that will be needed to support assembly language instructions. For example, nothing is said about how the READ and WRITE control signals will be generated, or how the four status latches C (Carry), O (Overflow), S (Sign), and Z (Zero) will be handled. One primitive scheme for handling these problems is to trap microinstructions that attempt to set both C_0 and C_1 to 1; this is an impossible condition, since it specifies data moving on and off busses simultaneously. **If C_0 and C_1 are both 1, they will be output as 0, and the remaining signals, C_2 through C_8, will be interpreted as specifying the following five different classes of internal control unit operations:**

1) If C_2 through C_8 are all 0, then the status latches Z, S, O, and C, in the ALU, will have their condition recorded in the CU DATA buffer.

2) If C_2 and C_3 are 1 and 0, then C_5, C_6, C_7, and C_8 will be interpreted as corresponding to the Z, S, O, and C statuses, respectively. If C_4 is 0, the status conditions in the ALU are referenced; if C_4 is 1, the status conditions stored in the CU Data buffer are referenced. C_5, C_6, C_7, and C_8 will each be checked for a 1 value. If a 1 is found, then the corresponding status will be checked. If the corresponding status has a value of 1, then the next microinstruction will be skipped. This use of the nine controls C_0 through C_8 may be illustrated as follows:

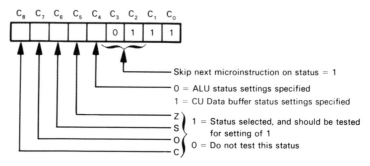

3) If C_2 and C_3 are 0 and 1, then the logic of condition 2 described above will be repeated. However, corresponding status flags will be checked for 0 values as the condition that forces the next microinstruction to be skipped.

4) If C_2, C_3, and C_4 are 1, 1, and 0, respectively, then C_5, C_6, C_7, and C_8 specify the status of four control signals the control unit may output at chip pins. We have only described two control signals thus far: READ and WRITE. We will assume that C_8 specifies the condition of READ and C_7 specifies the condition of WRITE. This use of the nine controls C_0 through C_8 may be illustrated as follows:

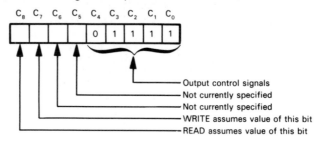

5) When C_2, C_3, and C_4 are all 1, then C_5 through C_8 will be decoded internally to specify one of 16 logical operations internal to the control unit. We will not attempt to define what these operations might be.

We will now create some microprograms. Let us begin simply, by creating an instruction fetch microprogram. Recall that every instruction's execution starts with an instruction fetch; therefore, the instruction fetch microprogram must precede every microprogram that implements an instruction's execution. The instruction fetch microprogram is shown in Table 4-4.

Before analyzing the instruction fetch microprogram, microinstruction-by-microinstruction, a few general comments must be made.

Microinstruction Bit Length

Each microinstruction becomes nine binary digits within the control unit. The 8-bit (or byte) unit is frequently selected as a microprocessor's word size because this word size is useful when representing characters and numeric data, in addition to representing instruction codes. The control unit microprogram does not represent numeric data or instruction codes; therefore, the microinstruction bit length is arbitrarily set as needed — in this case nine bits are selected. Since there are 15 microinstructions in the instruction fetch microprogram, a total of 135 binary digits will be required; they will form a 9×15 binary digit matrix.

Notice that the sequence of 15 microinstructions which are executed during the instruction fetch get executed within one period of clock Φ. Therefore the control unit will split the clock signal internally into 16 subdivisions. For example, if the clock has a period of one microsecond, each microinstruction must execute within 62.5 nanoseconds. Since the average chip consists of densely packed n-MOS or p-MOS logic, this time period is reasonable.

Table 4-4. An Instruction Fetch Microprogram

Instruction Number	Microinstruction Code C_8 C_7 C_6 C_5 C_4 C_3 C_2 C_1 C_0	Function
1	1 1 1 1 0 1 1 0 1	Move Program Counter to Address Register
2	1 0 0 0 0 1 1 1 1	Set READ Control signal true, WRITE false
3	1 1 1 0 0 1 0 0 1	Move Program Counter low-order byte to Data Bus
4	1 1 1 1 0 0 1 1 0	Move Data Bus to ALU latches
5	0 1 1 0 0 0 0 0 0	Increment ALU latches
6	1 1 1 1 0 0 1 0 1	Move ALU latches to Data Bus
7	1 1 1 0 0 1 0 1 0	Move Data Bus to Program Counter low-order byte
8	1 1 1 1 1 0 0 0 1	Move Program Counter high-order byte to Data Bus
9	1 1 1 1 0 0 1 1 0	Move Data Bus to ALU latches
10	1 0 0 0 0 1 0 1 1	Skip next microinstruction if carry status = 0
11	0 1 1 0 0 0 0 0 0	Increment ALU latches
12	1 1 1 1 0 0 1 0 1	Move ALU latches to Data Bus
13	1 1 1 1 1 0 0 1 0	Move Data Bus to Program Counter high-order byte
14	1 1 1 1 1 0 1 0 1	Move Data Register to Data Bus
15	1 1 1 1 0 1 0 1 0	Move Data to Instruction Register

Now consider, in detail, the 15 steps of the instruction fetch microprogram.

The first two bits of the first microinstruction's 9-bit code, representing C_0 and C_1, are set to 1 and 0, respectively. They indicate that data will be moved onto the data bus or into the Address register (see Table 4-1). The next four bits are set to 1 1 0 1. They specify that it is the contents of the program counter that must be moved to the Address register (see Table 4-2). Since no simultaneous ALU operations are to take place, the last three bits are all set to 1 (see Table 4-3). The creation of this microinstruction is illustrated as follows:

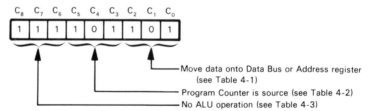

If you have any difficulty understanding the creation of the first microinstruction, you should study some of the other microinstructions in detail, to see how they are also created from the information in Tables 4-1, 4-2, and 4-3.

Microinstruction 1 moves the contents of the program counter to the Address register, thus making the 16-bit contents of the program counter appear at the 16 address pins. Instruction 2 sets the WRITE control signal false and the READ control signal true; this tells external logic that pins A0 through A15 provide the address of an external memory word, the contents of which are to be placed at pins D0 through D7. External logic has 687.5 nanoseconds, the time it takes to execute microinstructions 3 through 13, in which to fetch the requested data.

Microinstructions 3 through 13 increment the contents of the program counter, as is required during every instruction fetch. Since the program counter is 16 bits wide, whereas logic within the CPU is only 8 bits wide, the program counter has to be incremented in two steps. Instructions 3 through 7 increment the low-order half of the program counter. If this increment results in the Carry status being set (in the ALU only), then the high-order half of the program counter must also be incremented. If the Carry status is not set, then the high-order half of the program counter must remain unaltered. Microinstructions 9 through 13 handle the high-order half of the program counter. These microinstructions parallel microinstructions 3 through 7. However, microinstruction 10 specifies that if the Carry status (in the ALU) is 0, then microinstruction 11 is skipped. Microinstruction 11 actually increments the contents of the ALU latches. Thus the high-order half of the program counter is only incremented if the Carry status is set when the low-order half of the program counter gets incremented.

Note that control unit logic must be very specific about when it records statuses in its CU Data buffer and when it does not. You can use the Carry (C) status to control the way in which the program counter gets incremented only if the Carry status is not permanently recorded in the control unit. In other words, the control unit can reference the status latches in the ALU any time. Assembly language instructions reference the statuses stored in the CU Data buffer, never the statuses in the ALU latches. Microinstruction code 00000011 must be executed by the control unit if the statuses in the ALU latches are to be saved in the CU Data buffer.

Now consider the five steps needed to complement the contents of the accumulator. If, during the 15th step of the instruction fetch microprogram, the code loaded into the Instruction register is a Complement Accumulator instruction code, then control unit logic will branch to the microprogram shown in Table 4-5.

Table 4-5. A Complement Accumulator Microprogram

Instruc-tion Number	Microinstruction Code									Function
	C_8	C_7	C_6	C_5	C_4	C_3	C_2	C_1	C_0	
1	1	1	1	0	0	0	0	0	1	Move Accumulator to Data Bus
2	1	1	1	0	0	0	1	1	0	Move Data to Complementer
3	1	0	0	0	0	0	0	0	0	Execute Complementer logic
4	1	1	1	0	0	0	1	0	1	Move Complementer to Data Bus
5	1	1	1	0	0	0	0	1	0	Move Data Bus to Accumulator

In order to complement the accumulator, a 45-bit microprogram must be executed. Even though these five microinstructions can be executed in 312.5 nanoseconds, system synchronization demands that one period of clock Φ be set aside for instruction execution; therefore, the remaining time will be wasted.

Assembly Language Instruction Microprograms

Let us now consider the trade-offs associated with having simple or complex instruction sequences. With reference to the binary addition program described earlier in this chapter, recall that a word of data can be loaded from memory into the accumulator in one of the following ways:

1) Issue two separate instructions, each of which loads half of the data counter with half of the data memory address for the data memory word whose contents must be loaded into the accumulator. Then issue a third instruction to load the contents of the addressed data memory word into the accumulator.

2) Use one instruction to load into the data counter the entire data memory address for the word whose contents are to be read into the accumulator. Then issue a second instruction to move the contents of the addressed data memory word to the accumulator.

3) Have a single direct addressing instruction that loads the data memory word address into the data counter, then loads the contents of the addressed data memory word into the accumulator.

Instruction execution for each of the three cases is shown in Tables 4-6, 4-7, and 4-8.

Table 4-6. Three-Instruction Memory Read

Instruc-tion Number	Microinstruction Code C_8 C_7 C_6 C_5 C_4 C_3 C_2 C_1 C_0	Function
(a) Load Low-Order Half of Data Counter		
1 . . . 14		Repeat microinstructions 1 through 14 of Instruction Fetch (Table 4-4)
15	1 1 1 0 1 0 0 1 0	Move Data Bus to Data Counter, low-order byte
(b) Load High-Order Half of Data Counter		
1 . . . 14		Repeat microinstructions 1 through 14 of Instruction Fetch (Table 4-4)
15	1 1 1 1 0 0 0 1 0	Move Data Bus to Data Counter, high-order byte
(c) Load Addressed Data Memory Word Contents into Accumulator		
1	1 1 1 0 0 1 1 0 1	Move Data Counter to Address Register
2	1 0 0 0 1 0 1 1 1	Set READ Control signal true, WRITE false
3 . . .	1 1 1 0 0 0 0 0 0	Include 12 no operations to give external logic more time to fetch data
14	1 1 1 0 0 0 0 0 0	
15	1 1 1 1 1 0 1 0 1	Move Data Register to Data Bus
16	1 1 1 0 0 0 0 1 0	Move Data Bus to Accumulator

Table 4-7. One Instruction to Load 16-Bit Address into Data Counter

Instruction Number	Microinstruction Code $C_8\ C_7\ C_6\ C_5\ C_4\ C_3\ C_2\ C_1\ C_0$									Function
1 . . . 14										Repeat microinstructions 1 through 14 of Instruction Fetch (Table 4-4)
15 . . .	1	1	1	0	1	0	0	1	0	Move Data Bus to Data Counter, low-order byte
16	1	1	1	0	0	0	0	0	0	Timing filler
17 . . . 30										Repeat microinstructions 1 through 14 of Instruction Fetch (Table 4-4)
31	1	1	1	1	0	0	0	1	0	Move Data Bus to Data Counter, high-order byte

Table 4-6(c) provides the second step for Table 4-7.

Table 4-8. Single Instruction, Direct Addressing, Memory Read

Instruction Number	Microinstruction Code $C_8\ C_7\ C_6\ C_5\ C_4\ C_3\ C_2\ C_1\ C_0$									Function
1 . . . 14										Repeat microinstructions 1 through 14 of Instruction Fetch (Table 4-4)
15 . . .	1	1	1	0	1	0	0	1	0	Move Data Bus to Data Counter, low-order byte
16	1	1	1	0	0	0	0	0	0	Timing filler
17 . . . 30										Repeat microinstructions 1 through 14 of Instruction Fetch (Table 4-4)
31 . . .	1	1	1	1	0	0	0	1	0	Move Data Bus to Data Counter, high-order byte
32	1	1	1	0	0	0	0	0	0	Timing filler
33	1	1	1	0	0	1	1	0	1	Move Data Counter to Address Register
34 . . .	1	0	0	0	1	0	1	1	1	Set READ control signal true, WRITE false
35 . . .	1	1	1	0	0	0	0	0	0	Include 12 no operations to give external logic more time to fetch data
46	1	1	1	0	0	0	0	0	0	
47	1	1	1	1	1	0	1	0	1	Move Data Register to Data Bus
48	1	1	1	0	0	0	1	0	0	Move Data Bus to Accumulator

The briefest glance at Tables 4-6, 4-7, and 4-8 shows that microprograms will have a lot of duplicated microinstruction sequences. The very first thing a microprocessor designer will do is try to eliminate this duplication by re-using frequently needed microinstruction sequences.

Also, a microprocessor designer is going to develop some simple means of giving external logic time to respond to a READ request, rather than creating a time delay by executing 12 no operation microinstructions, using up 108 bits of the control unit storage space.

These are the complications that forced the early microprocessor designers to keep their assembly language instructions simple. There are many ways in which microprogram sequences can be re-used and time delays implemented; we left 16 microinstructions free for just this kind of operation. Precious control unit storage is used up solving these complications, and the more complications there are within a single instruction, the more complex this extra control unit logic gets to be.

CHIP SLICE CONTROL UNITS

Suppose a microprocessor will not meet your needs; frequently this will happen because the microprocessor does not execute programs fast enough. **You are now a candidate for a "chip slice" or "macrologic" based microcomputer,** which lets you design and build your own CPU, with any CPU architecture (within limits), and any, or no, assembly language instruction set.

Before we examine what a chip slice product must consist of, we give a word of caution. This discussion of chip slice products is something of a tangent within the context of products discussed in this book.

Up to this point we have been describing microprocessors — CPU logic that will be implemented on a single chip or maybe part of a single chip. Chapter 5 describes additional logic that supports microprocessor based microcomputers.

Chip Slice
Products vs.
Microprocessors

As compared to microprocessors, chip slice products take a wholly different philosophical direction:

Microprocessors stress logic functions at the expense of performance. Chip slice products stess performance at the expense of logic functions. Microprocessors are designed to minimize the number of parts in a system. Chip slice products are designed as a family of parts, each of which provides one well-defined component, or building block, for a CPU. Chip slice components justify less logic — and therefore more chips — with increased performance.

You could use chip slices to build the equivalent of any microprocessor. You would then have a product with perhaps ten chips, instead of one, but it would execute instructions ten times as fast.

Describing chip slices at the end of Chapter 4 implies that chip slices are essentially CPU building blocks.

That is the frame of reference in which we choose to describe chip slices; however, when you have finished reading Chapter 5, you will realize that chip slices could be used equally well to build the equivalent of any support logic device, excluding ROM or RAM.

If we are to create CPU building blocks, how should CPU logic be divided so that the resulting pieces are very general purpose?

We cannot impose instruction set limitations; the CPU building blocks will not be general purpose if we do. Therefore, we begin by separating control unit logic from the rest of the CPU:

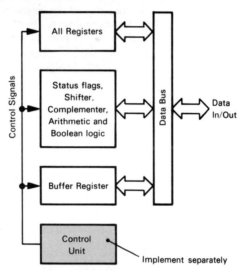

Now if you refer to our discussion of microprogramming, you will see that a control unit, in reality, consists of a microprogram stored in read-only memory:

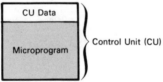

The shaded area marked "microprogram" contains microinstruction sequences just like the sequences illustrated in Tables 4-5 through 4-8.

CU Data represents a small read/write memory work space needed by the control unit.

What we have ignored, so far, is the logic that will allow you to pick your way around the microprogram ROM — concatenating short microinstruction sequences into any macroinstruction's response microprogram:

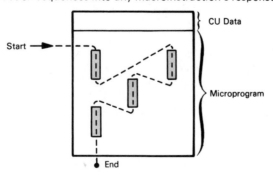

The illustration above arbitrarily shows four separate microinstruction sequences (shaded), which must be executed in order to enable the logical sequence of events required by some undefined macroinstruction. The broken line identifies the order in which macroinstruction sequences must be executed.

Microprogram
Sequencer
Logic

Our control unit must have microprogram sequencer logic that allows it to pick its way around the microprogram ROM, as illustrated above by the broken line. Let us look at some of the functions that our Microprogram Sequencer Logic must be able to perform:

1) It must access a contiguous sequence of microinstructions, beginning with a defined first microinstruction and continuing for a fixed number of microinstructions:

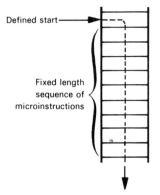

2) It must be able to branch to another contiguous microinstruction sequence:

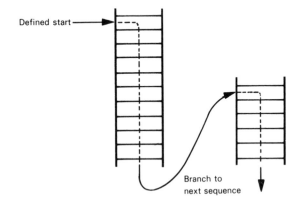

3) It must be able to branch to a frequently used microinstruction sequence, such as a memory access, then return to the point from which it branched.

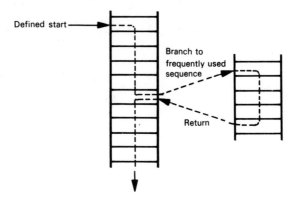

4) It must be able to continuously reexecute a single microinstruction, such as a No Operation, some fixed number of times:

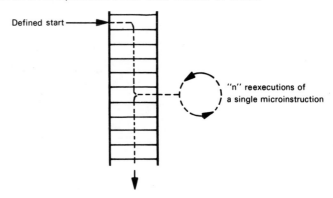

The control unit, in reality, will become a microprogram ROM and associated microinstruction sequencing logic:

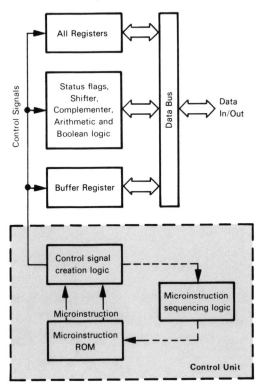

In practice, it is easier to put the logic that creates Control signals into the registers/arithmetic and logic unit:

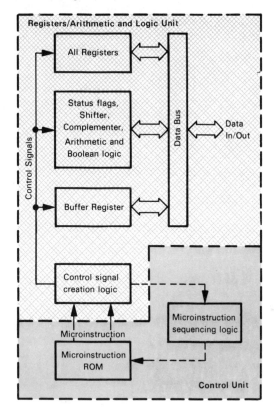

REGISTERS/ARITHMETIC AND LOGIC UNIT CHIP SLICE

We will begin our discussion of chip slice products with the registers/arithmetic and logic unit, which we will slice up into segments.

In dividing up this logic, it is imperative that we place as few restrictions as possible on the number and organization of registers. Also, we cannot limit CPU word size; even though we talk consistently about 8-bit microcomputers, 16-bit microprocessors are also popular, and 32-bit microprocessors will soon be here. **We will therefore slice up our registers/arithmetic and logic unit into identical slices so that slices may be placed side-by-side to form a CPU with any word size:**

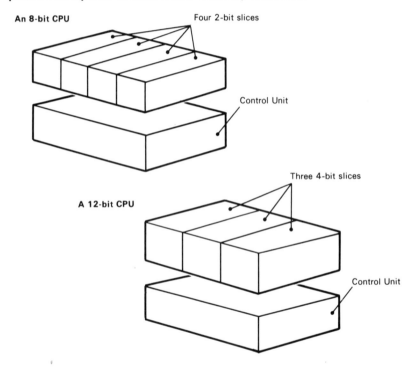

An 8-bit CPU   Four 2-bit slices

Control Unit

Three 4-bit slices

A 12-bit CPU

Control Unit

ALU Slice   We will refer to each slice as an ALU slice.

4-bit ALU slices are common. So long as your word size is a multiple of 4, the 4-bit slice is superior, since it requires fewer chips.

If the combined registers and ALU logic is to be sliced up, each slice must be able to interface with an identical neighbor on either side, in addition to a control unit.

Any simple ALU organization, such as illustrated earlier in Figure 4-1, presents a lot of problems. The many data paths converging on the data bus are going to become even more complex, since the registers, if they are to be general purpose, cannot be predefined or limited in number, as shown. You would have to construct impractical microinstructions to identify the innumerable valid data path combinations. Therefore we will reorganize our registers and ALU with an eye to streamlining the data paths, while maintaining flexibility. Remember, a successful chip slice makes no assumptions regarding the architecture of the end product.

Now there are a very large number of microprocessors on the market, and the number constantly increases. But there are very few chip slice products. Therefore, **we will reorganize the registers and ALU portion of Figure 4-1 to generally conform with the organization of 2900 series 4-bit chip slice products.** This very popular product has become an industry standard. Figure 4-3 illustrates this reorganization.

Figure 4-4 illustrates the concept of a "chip slice;" the figure shows two 4-bit slices creating an 8-bit ALU.

Let us look at Figure 4-3 in overview.

Register Block

Some fixed number of registers must be specified **within the register block. 16 registers are selected,** since a 4-bit select code can address one of the 16 registers.

The register block has two output ports, AA and BB, plus one input port, ZZ. Having three ports, the register block needs three sets of register select logic — one for each port. Select logic identifies the register that is effectively connected to each port at any time. We can get by with two sets of register select logic by combining input ZZ select logic with either output port AA or BB select logic. We will arbitrarily choose to combine ZZ and BB select logic. This means that at any point in time the same register in the register block will be effectively connected to both the ZZ and BB ports.

Thus, **the chip slice DIP needs four A port register select pins and four B port register select pins:**

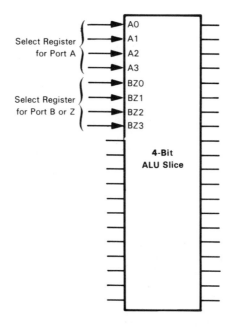

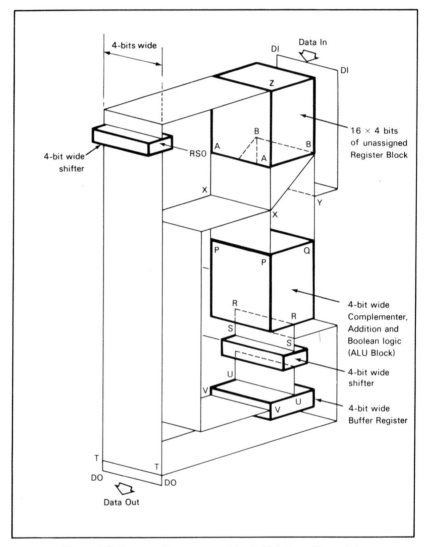

Figure 4-3. Registers/Arithmetic and Logic Unit from Figure 4-1, Reorganized to Meet the Needs of a Chip Slice

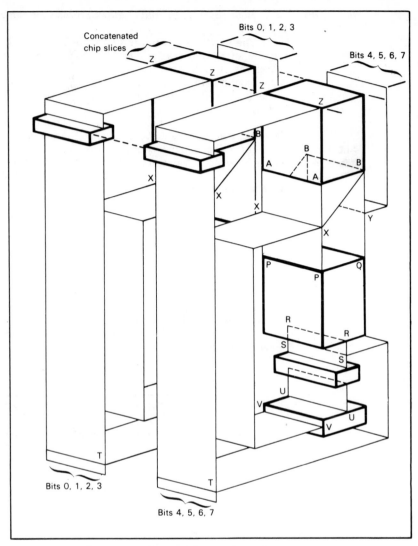

Figure 4-4. Two 4-Bit ALU Slices Concatenated
to Generate an 8-Bit ALU

Data Paths   Now consider the data paths between the register block and the ALU block.

The ALU block requires two input ports, marked PP and QQ, since a number of ALU operations require two inputs to create one output. RR marks the output.

Input port PP can receive register block output AA or BB, or it can receive contents of the Buffer register; XX marks a three-way junction whence input PP is derived.

Input port QQ can receive either register block BB output or external data. YY marks the two-way junction whence the QQ input is derived.

ALU Input   Let us examine the external signals that will be required to support the in-
Identified   terface between the register block and the ALU block. If we assume that an additional option is to input 0 at ports PP or QQ then **the following input combinations are allowed:**

```
QQ:  0  0   0  0 BB BB BB BB DD DD DD DD
PP:  0 AA BB VV 0 AA BB VV  0  AA BB VV
```

BB - 0 is the same as 0 - BB, so ignore it.

Since AA and BB can have the same value, ignore BB - BB, which can be made equivalent to BB - AA, and ignore DD - BB, which can be made equivalent to DD - AA.

0 - 0 is ignored since an ALU operation will never require two 0 inputs.

We will use three input pins to identify the remaining eight possible PP-QQ input combinations. These three input pins will become the low-order three bits of a 9-bit microinstruction code and will be interpreted as shown in Table 4-9.

Table 4-9. ALU Sources as Defined by the Low-Order Three Microinstruction Bits

Microinstruction			ALU Inputs	
I2	I1	I0	QQ	PP
0	0	0	BB	VV
0	0	1	BB	AA
0	1	0	00	VV
0	1	1	00	AA
1	0	0	00	BB
1	0	1	DD	BB
1	1	0	DD	VV
1	1	1	DD	00

The register block-ALU interface also requires four data in pins supporting the data input to YY. Our DIP therefore looks like this:

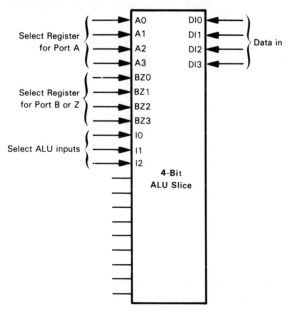

Chip Slice Arithmetic and Logic Unit

Now move on to the arithmetic and logic unit. Notice that the shifter has been moved out of the ALU in Figure 4-3, leaving behind complementer, addition, and Boolean logic. Moving shifter logic out allows the option of shifting data within a short recycle path through the Buffer register (RRSSUUVVXXPP) or we can shift a final ALU operation result on its way back to the Registers block (RRSSTTZZ).

The Buffer register in Figure 4-3 does not serve the same purpose that it did in Figure 4-1. In Figure 4-1 the Buffer register provides the second ALU input whenever an ALU operation requires two inputs. In Figure 4-3 the ALU inputs come from the two register block output ports PP and QQ. In Figure 4-3, the Buffer register has become a holding location for intermediate results of ALU operations.

Chip Slice ALU Operation Identification

We will assign the next three bits of the microinstruction code (I3,I4,I5) to define the ALU operations that are to be performed. There are only five isolated operations: ADD, Complement, AND, OR, and XOR. We could add increment and decrement to the list; instead we generate the equivalent by providing an external carry in:

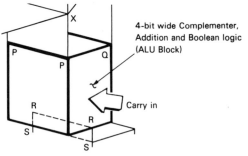

4-bit wide Complementer, Addition and Boolean logic (ALU Block)

Carry in

Output RR results from inputs PP, QQ and Carry in.

Combining the two input options with the carry in and the five ALU operations allows us to generate the ALU operation codes illustrated in Table 4-10.

Our 4-bit ALU slice DIP will need three more microinstruction inputs, plus a carry in:

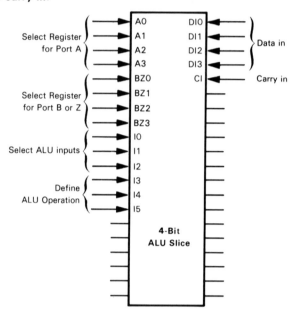

Chip Slice
ALU Destination

Only the ALU destination remains to be specified; we will use three microcode bits for this specification.

These are the three possible destinations for the ALU block output:

1) **The Buffer register, via SS and UU.**
2) **The register block, via SS, TT, and ZZ.**
3) **Data out, via SS and TT.**

Data on its way to the Buffer register or the register block may optionally be shifted left or right. A bewildering variety of output options could be selected, since data can be output to any or all of three destinations, with shifting occurring along two of the destination paths. Until you have used a chip slice product extensively, it will not be clear which of the output path options are useful.

Bear in mind that we really have two types of ALU output — the temporary data that is heading for the Buffer register and permanent answers that are heading back to the register block. Based on this concept, Table 4-11 illustrates one way in which destinations could be specified using three microinstruction bits.

Table 4-10. ALU Operations Specified by Middle Three Microcode Bits

Microcode			Function		
I5	I4	I3	General	Carry In = 0	Carry In = 1
0	0	0	QQ + PP	QQ + PP PP if QQ is 0 QQ if PP is 0	QQ + PP + 1 Increment PP if QQ is 0 Increment QQ if PP is 0
0	0	1	QQ + $\overline{\text{PP}}$ ($\overline{\text{PP}}$ is the ones complement of PP if carry in = 0, or twos complement of PP if Carry in = 1	QQ − PP −1 Ones complement PP if QQ is 0	QQ − PP Twos complement PP if QQ is 0
0	1	0	QQ OR PP	Carry in plays no part in Boolean operations	
0	1	1	QQ AND PP		
1	0	0	QQ XOR PP		
1	0	1	} Currently unassigned		
1	1	0			
1	1	1			

Table 4-11. ALU Destinations Specified by Last Three Microcode Bits

I8	I7	I6	Buffer Register		Register Block		Data Out?
			Shift?	Load Register?	Shift?	Load Register?	
0	0	0	No	Yes	No	No	Yes
0	0	1	Left	Yes	No	No	Yes
0	1	0	Right	Yes	No	No	Yes
0	1	1	No	No	No	No	Yes
1	0	0	No	No	No	Yes	Yes
1	0	1	No	No	Left	Yes	Yes
1	1	0	No	No	Right	Yes	Yes
1	1	1	No	Yes	No	Yes	Yes

Chip Slice Status

The only subject left to discuss is status. The Zero, Overflow, and Sign status flags are easy to generate, so let us look at these three first.

Sign Status

Every chip slice will be built assuming that it can be the high-order slice in the ALU. Every slice will therefore have logic that assumes that the data out lines represent the four high-order bits of the eventual ALU word. The high-order line will therefore represent the sign bit:

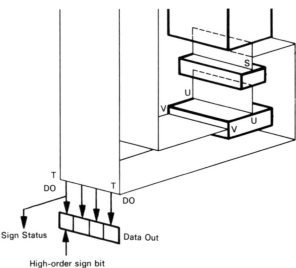

We can generate the sign bit directly from the high-order data out line of every single chip slice. Only the high-order chip slice's Sign bit will be used; other chip slice sign bits will be ignored.

Overflow Status

The Overflow status can be generated from the two high-order lines of every chip slice data out, just as the sign status was generated from the high-order line:

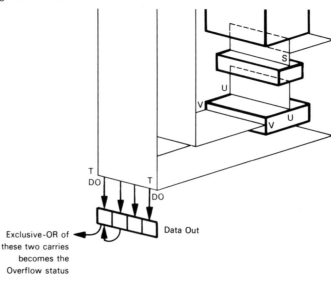

4-68

As described in Chapter 2, the overflow status represents the Exclusive-OR of carries out of the penultimate and ultimate bits of a data word. *Overflow Logic Can Therefore Only Be Generated Within the ALU.*

Zero
Status
Generating a Zero status is also quite straightforward. For every chip slice we will output NOT OR of the four data out lines:

By tying the Zero statuses of all chip slices within the CPU together you can create an overall Zero status:

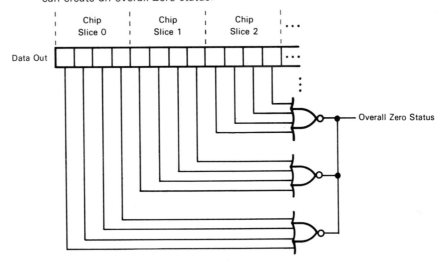

Carry and Shift statuses are not nearly so straightforward. First of all, we need three sets of statuses:

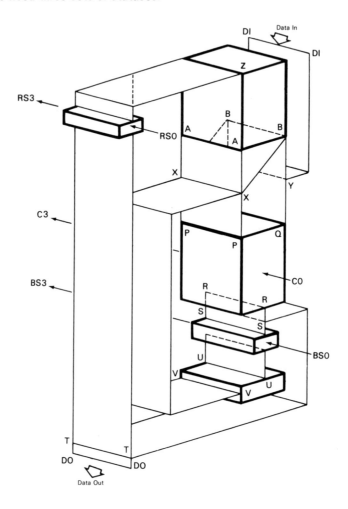

But the statuses illustrated above will not always work efficiently, since chip slices must work in parallel.

First consider a simple, 8-bit shift, created using two chip slices:

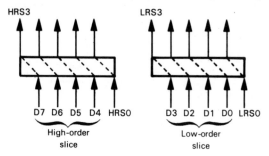

If the shift illustrated above is to occur as a single, parallel step, the low-order slice shift out (LRS3) must become the high-order slice shift in (HRS0).

If LRS3 and HRS0 are both connected to DIP pins, all we have to do is connect these two pins and an 8-bit shift is created:

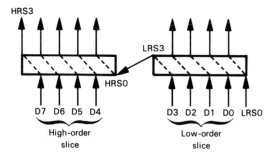

But when it comes to binary addition, the problem is less straightforward. When shifting, LRS3 is created while the shift is in progress. When adding, the carry out is generated at the end of the addition.

Here is a simplified illustration of this timing problem. For a shift, we have no problem:

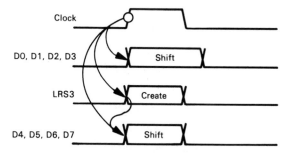

For binary addition, we have a problem:

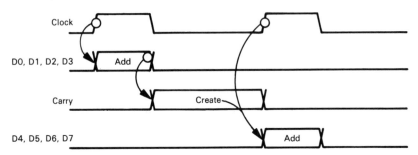

Carry
Status

We could perform the **binary addition in 4-bit increments,** starting with the least significant four bits; and in this case, carry could simply be rippled from one 4-bit slice to the next.

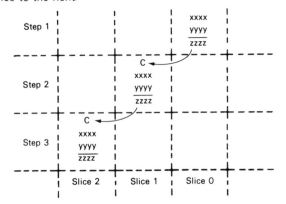

Carry
Look
Ahead

But **rippling binary addition defeats the whole purpose of using chip slice products** — to gain instruction execution speed. We must therefore add logic that allows the ALU to forecast whether a binary addition is going to create a carry or propagate one coming in.

The rules for carry creation and propagation are simple enough.

Carry
Propagation

First consider carry propagation. If there is a carry in to binary addition, then there will be a carry out so long as no two 0 digits are being added; they will break the propagation chain:

```
Two 0 digits ─────────┐
                      ↓        1 ◄──────Carry in
                   1 0 0 1 1
                   0 0 1 0 1
No Carry propagated ──► 0 1 1 1 0 ◄──────Carries propagated
                   ─────────
                   1 0 0 1
```

If P_i and Q_i represent binary digits entering the ALU via ports PP and QQ respectively, we conclude that a carry will propagate if:

$$(P_0 \text{ OR } Q_0) \text{ AND } (P_1 \text{ OR } Q_1) \text{ AND } (P_2 \text{ OR } Q_2) \text{ AND } (P_3 \text{ OR } Q_3) = 1$$

Carry Generation

In order to determine whether a new carry will be generated, we must start at the high-order end of the 4-bit unit and work back to the low-order end. If a carry is generated, then both high-order digits must be 1, or one high-order digit must be 1 while a carry is propagated from the penultimate digits:

```
         1 x x --      1 x x --      1 x x --      1 x x --
         1 x x --      1 x x --      0 x x --      0 x x --
Carry:   1             0             1             0
        ___           ___           ___           ___
         1             0             0             1
    1 ↙            1 ↙           1 ↙           0 ↙
```

If C_3 represents the carry out of bit position 3, then $C_3 = 1$, and a carry is generated if:

$$(P_3 \text{ AND } Q_3) \text{ OR } (C_2 \text{ AND } (P_3 \text{ OR } Q_3)) = 1$$

For C_2 to equal 1, the same relationship applies, with bit positions shifted down:

$$(P_2 \text{ AND } Q_2) \text{ OR } (C_1 \text{ AND } (P_2 \text{ OR } Q_2)) = 1$$

In this fashion the ALU can be provided with logic that predicts a carry generation.

Finally, this is the way pins must be assigned:

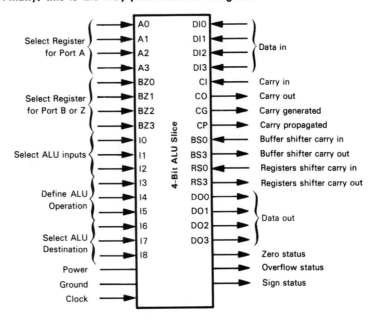

	Left pins	Right pins	
Select Register for Port A	A0, A1, A2, A3	DI0, DI1, DI2, DI3	Data in
Select Register for Port B or Z	BZ0, BZ1, BZ2, BZ3	CI	Carry in
		CO	Carry out
		CG	Carry generated
		CP	Carry propagated
Select ALU inputs	I0, I1, I2, I3	BS0	Buffer shifter carry in
		BS3	Buffer shifter carry out
		RS0	Registers shifter carry in
		RS3	Registers shifter carry out
Define ALU Operation	I4, I5, I6	DO0, DO1, DO2, DO3	Data out
Select ALU Destination	I7, I8		
Power		Zero status	
Ground		Overflow status	
Clock		Sign status	

4-Bit ALU Slice

Carry Generate Device **Carry generate logic will usually be provided on a separate carry gene-rate device.** This device receives Carry Propagate (P) and Carry Generate (G) signals, in the proper sequence, from the 4-bit ALU slices; it generates and returns the correct Carry in (C) to each chip slice:

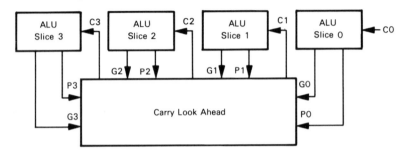

THE CHIP SLICE CONTROL UNIT

The ALU slices, as we have described them, are driven by a 9-bit microinstruction, together with binary data input and various status/control signals.

The control unit must provide the 9-bit microinstruction code; it could also provide the input status/control signals but typically it does not, for reasons we will soon discuss.

We are going to store the microinstruction code in a very fast read-only memory and create addressing logic, which accesses microinstructions in the proper sequence. **The control unit then consists of the microinstructions ROM and its addressing logic, as discussed earlier in this chapter.**

We can gain a lot of insight into desirable control unit addressing logic features by looking back at the microprocessor microinstruction sequences that were developed in Tables 4-5 through 4-8.

Microprogram Counter Under normal circumstances microinstruction codes are accessed sequentially. Therefore, **the control unit addressing logic must have a microprogram counter (MPC), the equivalent of a program counter,** which can be incremented after every microprogram access to reference the next sequential microinstruction.

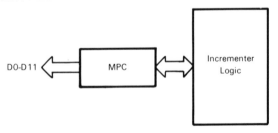

We arbitrarily assume a 12-bit width for the control unit address logic — implying a maximum of 4096_{10} microinstructions in the ROM.

Any microinstruction sequence is going to begin at some initial address; therefore **control unit addressing logic must be able to initialize the microprogram counter.** Consider two possibilities:

1) Every macroinstruction object code is going to be implemented by a microinstruction sequence with its own initial address that must be loaded into the microprogram counter. **We will therefore provide direct data access to the microprogram counter.**

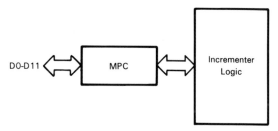

2) It would be highly desirable to have some general purpose microprogram origins to handle special circumstances or alarm conditions that may have nothing to do with execution of an individual instruction. **We will therefore provide a register where some such permanent address may be stored:**

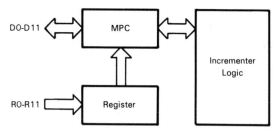

Recall that the control unit addressing logic must be able to reexecute one instruction a number of times. In our example, a "No Operation" instruction was reexecuted simply to keep the control unit synchronized with external timing. **We will therefore add an increment inhibit control to the microprogram counter:**

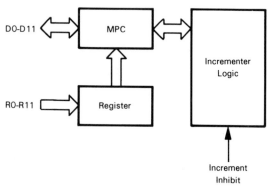

Finally, **recall that there are frequently used microinstruction sequences that perform operations such as memory read and memory write.** We can handle this situation in one of two ways:

First consider having a number of address registers plus a microprogram counter buffer:

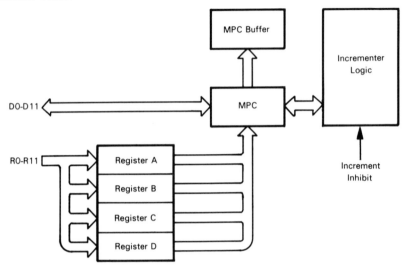

As illustrated above, the addresses of the first microinstruction for four frequently used microinstruction sequences may be stored in Registers A,B, C, and D. The control unit addressing logic can save prior contents of MPC in the buffer, then load the contents of one register:

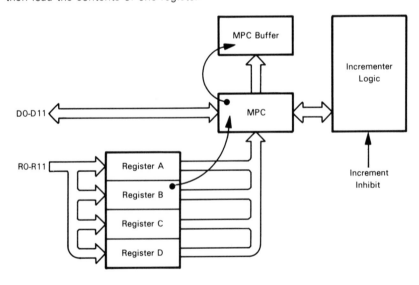

The last microinstruction in the frequently used sequence causes the buffer contents to be returned to the microprogram counter:

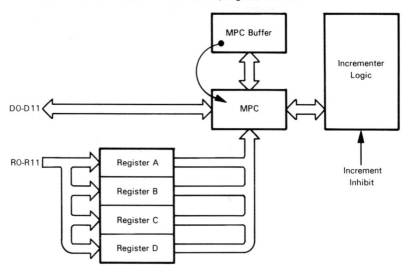

Another approach requires external logic to provide the starting address of each frequently used microinstruction sequence. In this case, **a stack of buffer registers** will back up the microprogram counter:

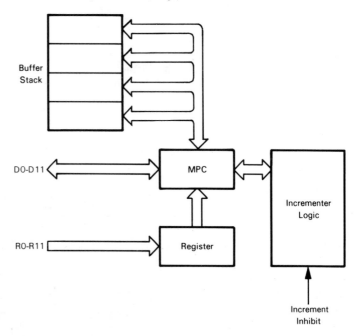

The buffer stack allows one frequently used microinstruction sequence to access another frequently used microinstruction sequence. This is sequence nesting. The stack is a common microprocessor feature and is described in Chapter 6.

This is how the buffer stack would work for microinstruction sequence A accessing microinstruction sequence B, which in turn, accesses microinstruction sequence C:

1) Microinstruction sequence A reaches the point where microinstruction sequence B must be accessed. The current sequence A address is saved on the Stack, then the sequence B address is input:

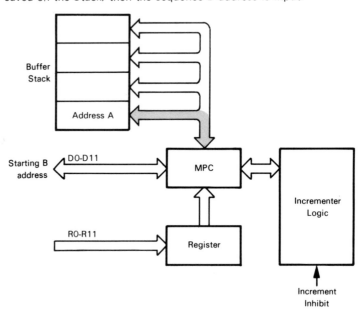

2) Microinstruction sequence B reaches the point where microinstruction sequence C must be accessed. Step 1 is repeated:

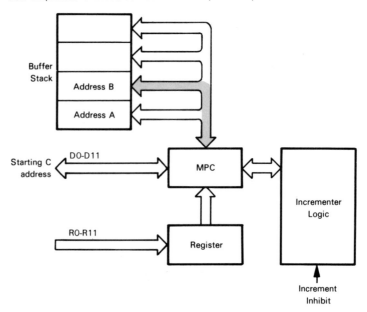

3) Microinstruction sequence C completes execution, so the saved Address B is returned to MPC:

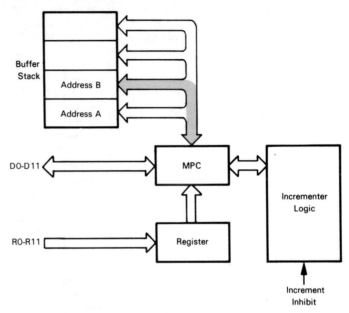

4) Microinstruction sequence B, in turn, completes execution, so the saved Address A is returned to MPC:

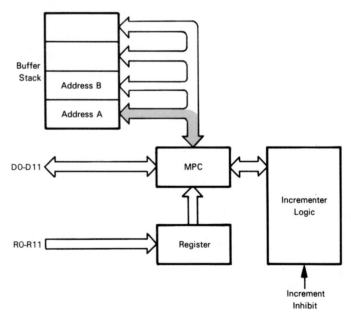

Assuming that our control unit addressing logic has a buffer stack, **two additional control signals will be needed:** one will push the contents of MPC into the stack, as illustrated in Steps 1 and 2; the other will pop the top stack address into MPC, as illustrated in Steps 3 and 4. **Our control unit address logic DIP pin assignments will now be as follows:**

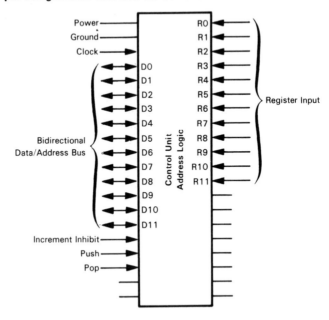

COMBINING ARITHMETIC AND LOGIC UNIT WITH CONTROL UNIT

Conceptually **we are going to build a central processing unit by combining ALU slices with control unit addressing logic and a microprogram in read-only memory** as follows:

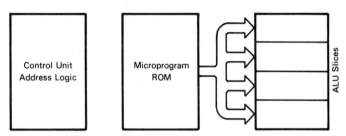

In practice a very considerable amount of additional external logic will be required before the simple configuration illustrated above can perform as a central processing unit. For example, nowhere have we addressed the problem of receiving or transmitting control signals. What about the microprocessor Read and Write control signals?

It would have been possible to add logic to the control unit that automatically senses and creates CPU-type control signals. However, that assumes chip slice products are going to be used as CPU building blocks only. The assumption is unwarranted.

By describing chip slice products in Chapter 4, a chapter devoted to central processing units, we cast chip slice products as CPU building blocks, which makes them conceptually easy to understand only because of the sequence in which information is being presented in this book.

Excluding control signal processing logic from the chip slice control unit means a lot of extra work and extra logic must surround the chip slice and control unit set. But, at the same time, no restrictions are imposed on the way these products are used.

In terms of our current discussion, therefore, we must conclude without illustrating a typical instruction's execution, because the type of information that would have to be covered before necessary external logic could be adequately treated is beyond the scope of this book.

5

Logic Beyond the CPU

In this chapter we are going to identify the additional logic that must accompany a CPU in order to generate a microcomputer system that is comprehensive enough to be useful.

We must separately identify the logical components of a microcomputer system by function (e.g., CPU, RAM memory, etc.) but there is no fundamentally necessary correlation between logical components and individual chips. There are, in fact, wide variations between the type of logic which one semiconductor manufacturer will put on a single chip as compared to another.

INTERFACING PROGRAM AND DATA MEMORY

External memory is the first and most obvious addition needed to support the CPU that was described in Chapter 4. We will therefore describe how ROM and RAM might be connected to a microprocessor; at the same time we will introduce a number of interfacing concepts.

Read-Only Memory (ROM)

Interfacing ROM to a microprocessor is very simple.

As described in Chapter 3, entire words of memory are implemented on a single ROM chip. By contrast, read/write memory (RAM) may require a separate chip for every bit of the memory word.

The signals required by a ROM device are quite elementary. As one would expect, a ROM device will require the following input signals:

1) The address of the memory word being accessed.
2) A read control signal that tells the ROM device when to return the contents of the addressed memory word.
3) Power and ground.

Memory devices are asynchronous; they do not require a clock signal as an input.

The only output signals which the ROM device must have are eight data lines (for an 8-bit word), via which the contents of the addressed memory word are transferred back to the CPU. Figure 5-1 illustrates a hypothetical ROM device. This ROM device is connected to the CPU as illustrated in Figure 5-2.

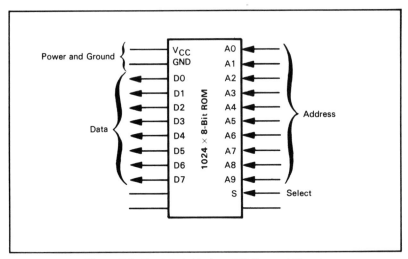

Figure 5-1. Read-Only Memory DIP Pins and Signals

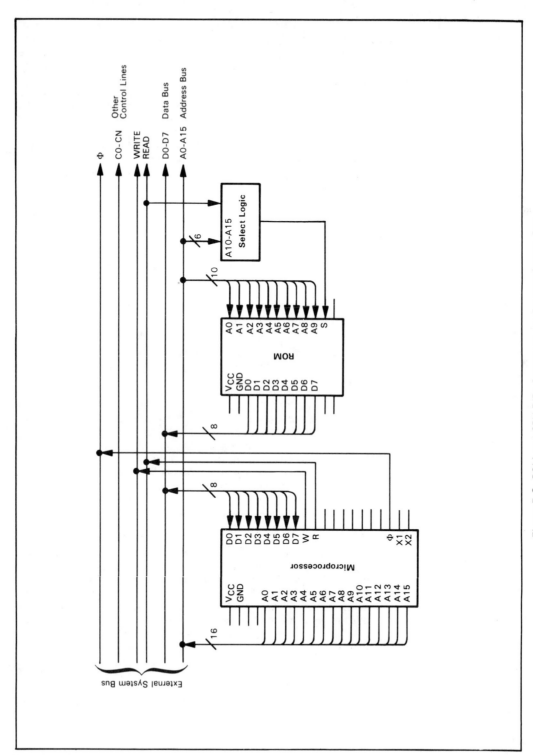

Figure 5-2. ROM and CPU DIPs Connected via External System Bus

**External
System Bus**

**In Figure 5-2 the ROM and microprocessor each connect to a group of
parallel signal lines which are referred to collectively as an external system
bus.** If a microcomputer system were to consist of just two devices — the
microprocessor and the ROM — there would be no need for an external system
bus. The two devices' pins could connect directly. But few microcomputer
systems will be so simple. When numerous devices connect with the
microprocessor — and this is the usual case — all devices, including the
microprocessor, connect with the external system bus, which may be likened to
a signal highway.

**Physically, a system bus consists of a number of parallel conductors.
Today, these conductors are always metal lines etched on a printed circuit
card. Typically there are anywhere from 50 to 100 parallel lines in an external system bus. These lines are arbitrarily assigned to different signals.** A
vast number of different busses have come to exist. Some busses were designed
for a particular microcomputer system, with no pretense at accommodating the
needs of any other application. Some busses were specifically designed as industry standards. Other busses become industry standards by chance.

When different microcomputer systems use the same system bus, their
components are (theoretically) interchangeable. At the present time there is no
"standard" system bus in the microcomputer industry, although there are many
contenders for such a title.

A lot of emotion, prejudice, experience, and ignorance has gone into the
design of different **system** busses. But one thing they all have in common is the
fact that **bus lines can be separated into these four groups:**

**Address
Bus**

1) **Address lines.** There will be one system bus line assigned to every address bit that the microcomputer system might ever accommodate.
Therefore it is possible for the system bus to have more address lines
than current microprocessors that connect to it. For example, current
microprocessors may output 16 address lines, capable of addressing
65,536 different memory locations. However, the system bus designers may anticipate a time in the future when a 20-bit address will be
needed, capable of accessing over one million locations. Their system
bus would then have 20 address lines, even though four address lines
might currently be unused. **The address lines of a system bus are
referred to as an address bus.**

**Data
Bus**

2) **Data lines.** Like the address bus, a system bus line will be assigned to
each data bit of the largest word that will ever be supported. Once
again, the system bus will have enough data lines to accommodate
present and anticipated future word sizes. Most system busses have
16 data lines. This is true even of early microcomputer system busses
that were specified in the days when no microprocessor had more
than eight data bits; the system bus designers correctly anticipated
the advent of 16-bit microprocessors (but not 32-bit microprocessors,
which will likely be available by 1982). **The data lines of a system
bus are referred to as a data bus.**

3) **Control lines.** A separate system bus line must be assigned to every control signal that may be output by, or input to any device that connects to the system bus. We have encountered two such control signals thus far: READ and WRITE. System bus designers will frequently leave a number of unassigned control lines to accommodate unknown future developments. But leaving unassigned lines of any type is a two-edged sword. On the one hand it gives the bus flexibility; you are not permanently locked into using the currently defined control signals, and no others. On the other hand, people independently assign unused system bus lines to meet their specific needs, ignoring assignments that may already exist for these lines; in consequence, a standard system bus that contains unassigned lines quickly degenerates into hundreds of incompatible variations.

4) **Clock, power, and ground.** There will usually be more than one clock signal on a system bus. We show just one, the Φ output from the CPU. Real microcomputer systems will frequently have two or more signals, where secondary signals have frequencies that are some multiple or fraction of the primary clock signal. There will usually be a number of power and ground lines on a system bus to ensure that many devices connecting to power and ground do not overload these lines.

Bus Buffer   Throughout our discussion of microcomputer systems and system busses, we will be examining logical concepts, frequently ignoring design reality. **One system bus design reality** that we will consistently ignore **is the bus buffer.** You cannot simply connect similarly assigned pins of different devices to a system bus line and expect your configuration to work. This is because one device may output a signal that gets input to two or more other devices. Only in the most unusual circumstances will a device output a signal that is strong enough to satisfy all of the inputs. **Usually output signals must be boosted by an appropriate buffer amplifier before connecting the system bus lines.** This may be illustrated as follows:

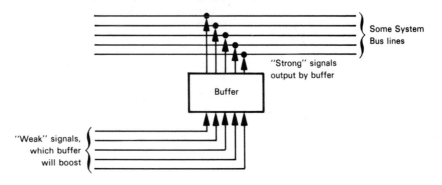

The data sheets that accompany any device you use will specify the exact power input and output requirements for every signal line. One of the most common mistakes made by novice logic designers is to draw more power off a line than they put onto it. This is, in fact, a very elementary concept. If all the showers in your home are connected to a single hot water line, then each time an additional shower is turned on, there will be a marked drop in the pressure of all showers. If you wish to prevent the shower pressure from dropping below some minimum level, you must make sure that the hot water input pressure is high enough at the water heater outlet.

TTL Level Signals	Almost all microprocessors and related devices communicate using signal levels that are said to be TTL level compatible. (TTL stands for transistor-transistor logic.) A standard TTL output signal, when representing 1, must be
TTL Definition	more than 2.4 volts and less than 5 volts; also, it must output at least 400 microamps over this voltage range. A standard TTL output signal, when representing 0, must be between 0 and 0.4 volts and must be capable of sinking at least 16 milliamps of current over this voltage range.
One Standard TTL Load	A standard TTL input will interpret a signal as representing a 1 if the input voltage is between 2.0 and 5 volts; over this range it will not sink more than 40 microamps. A standard TTL input will interpret a signal as representing a 0 if the input voltage is between 0 and 0.8 volts; the input will not source more than 1.6 milliamps over this range. An input that meets these requirements is said to represent one standard TTL load.
TTL Level Compatible	Inputs on most microprocessors and related devices respond properly to TTL voltages but do not source or sink as much current as a standard TTL input. Outputs on most of these devices provide normal TTL voltage levels but only when driving one or two standard TTL loads. A standard TTL output can drive ten standard TTL inputs. Thus these microprocessor inputs and outputs are described as TTL level compatible, even though they are not completely TTL compatible.

You should be aware of the specific voltage and current requirements associated with bus lines, but you can then ignore them for the rest of this book, since they have nothing to do with the concepts discussed.

The eight data pins of the ROM device illustrated in Figure 5-1 will connect to the data bus lines of the external system bus. The microprocessor data pins connect to the same eight data bus lines. Thus **data flows from the ROM device, via the data bus lines of the external system bus, to the microprocessor.**

In Figure 5-2 the microprocessor READ and WRITE control signals are shown connecting to the READ and WRITE lines of the external system bus. **Neither of these control signals is input to the ROM device.** Nevertheless, the microprocessor READ and WRITE control signals are shown connecting to the external system bus on the assumption that other, unillustrated devices will likely exist and will need to receive the WRITE control as an input.

The ROM device has ten address lines, illustrated in Figures 5-1 and 5-2 as A0-A9. The ROM therefore has 1024 addressable locations. Since each location is 8 bits wide, the ROM is an 8192-bit device, with a 1024×8 bit organization.

ROM Device Select

A0-A9 connect to the ten low-order address lines of the external system bus. The remaining six address lines (A10-A15) become inputs to select logic, which outputs the select signal S. S identifies the exact addresses that will select the ROM. We refer to these addresses as the ROM's "address space."

The select signal S must have some predetermined "true" level that causes the read-only memory device to be selected. For example, S may have to be low for the ROM device to be selected, or it may have to be high.

A single select input is sufficient to define an address space for the ROM device; select logic, as described in Chapter 3, may be illustrated for the ROM device in Figure 5-1 as follows:

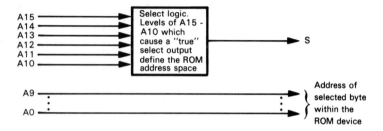

What about the READ control input? Once selected, a "read" is the only operation to which the ROM can respond. Therefore having a separate READ control input is superfluous. Since READ is the only control input that the ROM can expect to receive, ROM logic can assume a read operation has been requested whenever its select input is "true." But the READ control signal will then have to contribute to select logic, to guarantee that the ROM select is "true" only when the READ control signal is also "true." This may be illustrated as follows:

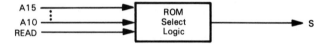

For example, suppose the ROM device is to be assigned memory space 4000_{16} through $43FF_{16}$. If READ and the ROM select are both "true" when high, and "false" when low, the following select logic could be used:

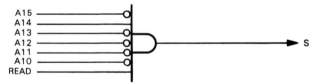

5-7

This select logic uses a 7-input NOR gate to generate the ROM select S, which will be high (true) when all inputs are low. A14 is inverted, since it must be 1 (high) to generate the required address space. READ is also inverted, since it is "true" when high.

The number of address pins required by a ROM device will, of course, vary directly with the amount of memory provided by the device. For example, a 32,768-bit ROM, accessed as a 4096 × 8-bit device, would require 12 address lines. As compared to the read-only memory device illustrated in Figure 5-1, we could accommodate these two extra address lines as follows:

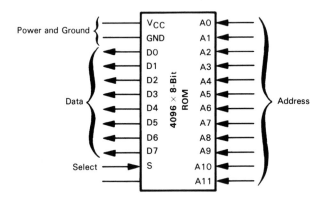

A ROM device (or for that matter any other external circuit) can get by with just one select signal, as illustrated above. But **having two or more select signals can sometimes simplify device select logic.** Suppose a ROM chip with two select inputs, S0 and S1, has four versions, differing only in the levels of S0 and S1 that cause the chip to be selected. This may be illustrated as follows:

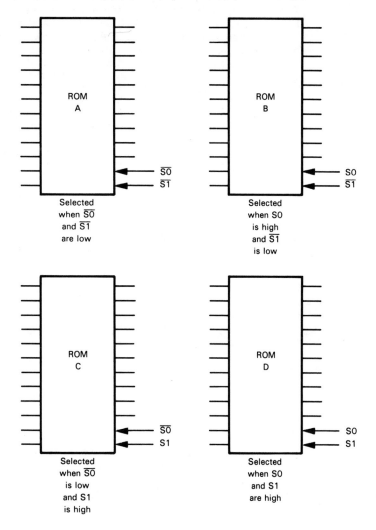

Active Low
Signal
Nomenclature

Signal
Active
Levels

We use a bar over the signal name (e.g., $\overline{SO}$) to identify a signal that is active, or "true," when low. A signal without a bar over the signal name (e.g., SO) is either active, or "true," when high, or it has no inactive state. An address or data line, for example, has no inactive state; a high or a low level are both active and have equal meaning. But a select signal or a control signal (such as READ or WRITE) has a "true" and a "false" state. A bar over the signal name means that the signal is "true" when low. If the signal is "true" when high, then there will be no bar over the signal name.

Reverting to our discussion of select logic, notice that in a very simple configuration you could select two of the four ROM devices illustrated above by connecting READ to one select input (a high one), while a single address line connects to the other select input. This may be illustrated as follows:

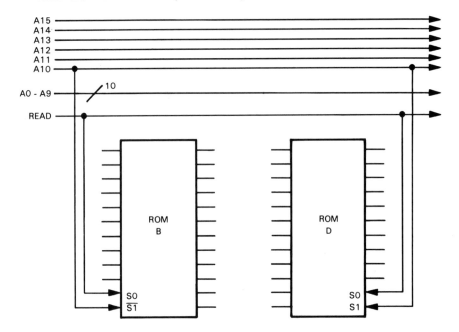

ROM B and ROM D are assumed to be 1024 × 8-bit devices. The ten address line connections to A0-A9 are not shown since they do not contribute to select logic. These **ten address lines have been illustrated above using**

which is easier to read than:

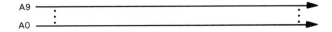

but has the same meaning.

By connecting READ to S0 at ROM B and ROM D we guarantee that these two ROM devices will be selected only while READ is high; and READ will only be high while a read operation is in progress. The second select input ($\overline{S1}$ at ROM B, S1 at ROM D) connects directly to A10. Therefore A10 must be low for ROM B to be selected, while ROM D will be selected only while A10 is high.

The five high-order address lines A15-A11 are ignored. Since ROM B and ROM D respond to all combinations of address lines A0-A12, while A15-A11 are ignored, the select scheme illustrated above will work only in a configuration where no other devices are connected to the address bus. These two ROM devices will, in fact, be selected by a wide variety of addresses; this may be illustrated as follows:

Addresses that select ROM B	Addresses that select ROM D
XXXX X0XX XXXX XXXX	XXXX X1XX XXXX XXXX

X represents a binary digit that may be 0 or 1.

The fact that one device can be selected by more than one block of addresses (address space) is unimportant. What is important is that two devices are never selected by the same address; and in the scheme illustrated above, address line A12 takes care of that problem.

Suppose a variety of other devices are connected to the address bus. We would now like to guarantee that each ROM device is selected by a single block of 1024 addresses. Now every address line must contribute to each ROM device's select logic. Here is a scheme that selects the four ROM devices ROM A through ROM D using two select inputs:

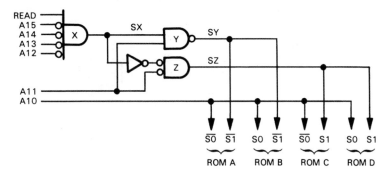

Let us examine how the select logic, as illustrated, actually works. Our intention is to select one ROM device in each of four address spaces as follows:

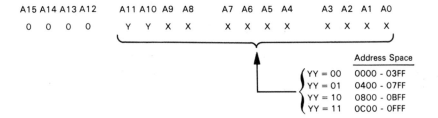

A15 A14 A13 A12	A11 A10 A9 A8	A7 A6 A5 A4	A3 A2 A1 A0
0 0 0 0	Y Y X X	X X X X	X X X X

	Address Space
YY = 00	0000 - 03FF
YY = 01	0400 - 07FF
YY = 10	0800 - 0BFF
YY = 11	0C00 - 0FFF

Address lines A10 and A11 specify the bounds of the four address spaces — providing address lines A12-A15 are all 0 and READ is high (true). In order to implement this required select logic, we use two NOR gates ($\triangleright\!\!\circ$ or $\triangleright\!\!\!D$) and one NAND gate ($\triangleright\!\!\circ$ or $\triangleright\!\!\!D$). We have deliberately selected NOR and NAND gates, rather than OR and AND gates, to reflect the realities of digital logic. **The vast majority of low-cost TTL Boolean logic gates provide you with the complement of Boolean operators.** If you include AND and OR gates, you will find your choice of parts quite restricted, and more expensive.

The select scheme illustrated above uses address line A10 as a direct input to S0 at all four ROM devices. A11 provides the S1 input; however, A11 is conditioned to always provide the "wrong" level of S1 if one or more of address lines A12-A15 are high, or if READ is low (false). If A12-A15 are all low and READ is high, then the X NOR gate will output a high signal. (If NOR logic is not clear to you, see Chapter 2.) Providing the X NOR gate outputs a high signal, something it will do if A12-A15 are all low and READ is high, then A11 is, in effect, inverted but passed on to select one of the four ROM devices. But if the X NOR gate outputs a low level, which will happen if one or more of address lines A12-A15 are high, or if READ is low, then it forces S1 to be "false" at all four ROM devices. This guarantees that the four ROM devices will never be selected outside of their assigned memory spaces. **Signal levels are illustrated in Table 5-1 using a format which we refer to as a "truth table."** From this truth table you will see that ROM devices are selected within the following address spaces:

Address Space	Selected ROM
0000_{16} - $03FF_{16}$	ROM C
0400_{16} - $07FF_{16}$	ROM D
0800_{16} - $0BFF_{16}$	ROM A
$0C00_{16}$ - $0FFF_{16}$	ROM B

Table 5-1. ROM Select Truth Table

A11	A10	SX	SY	SZ	ROM A		ROM B		ROM C		ROM D	
					$\overline{S0}$	$\overline{S1}$	S0	$\overline{S1}$	$\overline{S0}$	S1	S0	S1
0	0	0	1	0	0	1	0	1	0	0	0	0
0	0	1	1	1	0	1	0	1	0	1	0	1
0	1	0	1	0	1	1	1	1	1	0	1	0
0	1	1	1	1	1	1	1	1	1	1	1	1
1	0	0	1	0	0	1	0	1	0	0	0	0
1	0	1	0	0	0	0	0	0	0	0	0	0
1	1	0	1	0	1	1	1	1	1	0	1	0
1	1	1	0	0	1	0	1	0	1	0	1	0

The select logic we have just described makes use of two select inputs at each ROM device. But this select logic has very little going for it. It is not particularly efficient. In fact, the following select logic requires just one select input at each ROM device, and uses fewer discrete components:

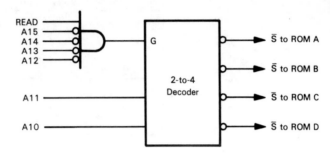

The 2-to-4 decoder generates one low $\bar{S}$ output and three high $\bar{S}$ outputs. The levels input at A10 and A11 determine which $\bar{S}$ output is low. G is a gate input which must be high, otherwise all $\bar{S}$ outputs will be high and the levels input at A10 and A11 will be ignored.

But this simpler scheme does not need two select inputs, which demonstrates that it is not necessarily beneficial for a memory device to have multiple select inputs.

A few special read-only memory devices have been designed with internal device select logic. These devices receive all 16 address lines as inputs, and are selected by internal select logic within a specific addressing range. This may be illustrated as follows:

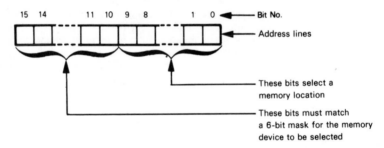

This type of device will have a built-in select code. The 6-bit select code width has been arbitrarily selected in the illustration above. When the high-order address lines match the memory device's select code the device is selected. The select code therefore defines the device's address space. (The Fairchild/Mostek 3851 PSU is an example of a memory device that uses this type of select logic.)

Let us now examine timing associated with the device connections illustrated in Figure 5-2.

Consider a memory read instruction. Timing for this instruction is reproduced below as it appeared in Chapter 4, but with the keying symbols (A) and (B) to link it to Figure 5-2.

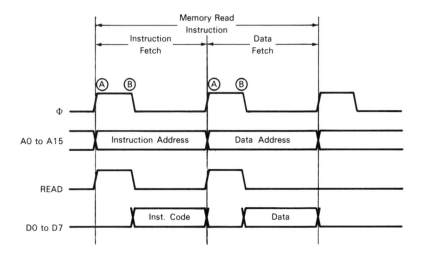

Recall that so far as logic external to the CPU is concerned, **there is no difference between an instruction fetch operation and a data fetch operation.**

Each operation begins with clock Φ rising (at (A)); at this time the CPU outputs an address on the address lines, and at the same time sets READ high. The ROM receives these signals via the external system bus. If the six high-order address lines (A10-A15) cause the ROM select(s) to go true, then ROM logic fetches the contents of the memory word addressed by A0-A9, and places this data at D0-D7.

By the time Φ goes low and READ goes low (at (B)), ROM logic must have placed the requested data on D0-D7; data must stay on these lines until Φ goes high again.

Real microprocessors do not output READ as illustrated above; they **delay the "true" read pulse.** Here is a more accurate timing illustration:

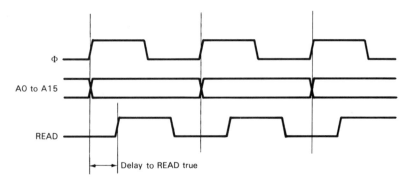

READ true is delayed on behalf of all devices that can respond to a read or a write operation. These devices' select logic decodes the address output via A0-A15; some time is allowed for this select logic to resolve before READ is output "true." The ROM devices we have described do not care when the READ "true" pulse occurs so long as this pulse is long enough, giving the ROM device time to respond.

Read/Write Memory (RAM)

A RAM must be able to take data off the data lines of the external system bus and place this data in an addressed memory word; in addition, a RAM must be able to extract data from an addressed memory word and place this data on the external system bus data lines. Read/write memory is usually implemented using a number of RAM chips, with each chip supplying one bit of the data word.

Using a number of chips to support a single data word is a simple enough concept; it means that each chip will have only one data pin, and this pin will be connected to one of the eight data lines, D0-D7.

As described for ROM, RAM interface logic will partition the address lines A0-A15 into a device select code and a memory address. However, there may be eight RAM chips (for an 8-bit word), each of which has the same device select code, but is connected to a different data line on the external system bus. Figure 5-3 illustrates a single RAM DIP. Figure 5-4 shows one way in which RAM may be added to the ROM-CPU combination illustrated in Figure 5-2.

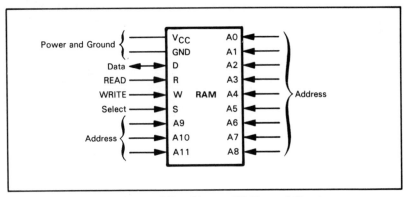

Figure 5-3. Read/Write Memory DIP Pins and Signals

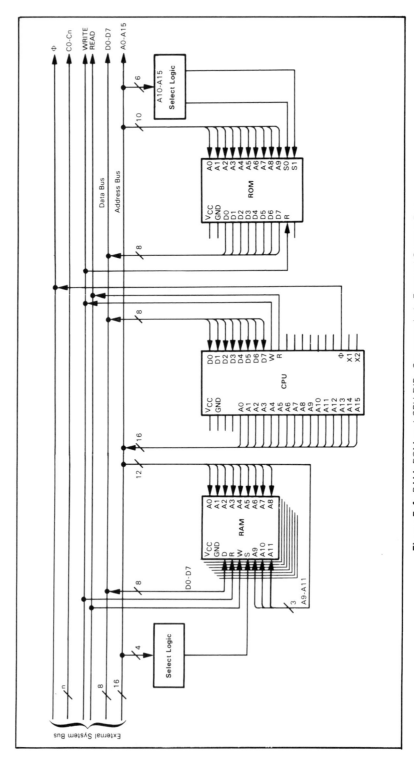

Figure 5-4. RAM, ROM and CPU DIPs Connected via External System Bus

Since a RAM device must respond to a read or a write operation, it will receive READ and WRITE as control inputs.

The RAM device illustrated in Figure 5-3 has 12 address lines and one data line. Therefore it is a 4096 × 1-bit RAM.

Very few large RAMs use a single +5 V power supply (V_{CC}) as illustrated in Figure 5-3, but the recent trend has been towards RAM devices that require a single +5 V power supply. Most RAMs still use two or three power supplies. However, the number and level of power supplies is not important to the discussion at hand, therefore we will note this unrealistic aspect of Figure 5-3, and then ignore it.

If you look at Figure 5-4 you will see that the CPU and ROM, together with their external system bus connections, are identical to Figure 5-2. Only the eight RAM devices are new.

The RAM devices have a single select input (S). S must be decoded "true" for some specified combination of signal levels at address lines A12, A13, A14, and A15. Any of the select schemes illustrated previously for the ROM will, in principle, also work for the single RAM select. This single RAM select connects to all eight RAM devices and determines the exact memory space assigned to the 4096-word RAM memory generated by the eight devices.

The READ and WRITE control inputs are not shown connecting to the R and W RAM pins since this would make Figure 5-4 too confusing to read. The R and W lines terminating above the RAM devices in Figure 5-4 imply that each line connects to the R and W pins at each of the eight RAM devices, analogous to the multiple S pin connections.

TRANSFERRING DATA BEYOND THE MICROCOMPUTER SYSTEM (INPUT/OUTPUT)

The transfer of data between logic that is part of the microcomputer system and logic that is beyond the microcomputer system is generally referred to as Input/Output (I/O).

Microcomputer System Bounds

We will include, within the boundary of a microcomputer system, all logic that has been specifically designed to operate in conjunction with the CPU. We will classify all other logic as external.

External Logic

The interface between the microcomputer system and external logic must be clearly defined; it must contain provisions for transfer of data, plus control signals that identify events as they occur.

There are many ways in which data transfer between the microcomputer system and external logic can be accomplished; but they all fall into the following three categories:

1) **Programmed I/O.** In this case, all data transfers between the microcomputer system and external logic are completely controlled by the microprocessor, or more precisely, by a program which the microprocessor executes.

There will be some well-defined protocol whereby the microcomputer system gives evidence that data being output has been placed in a location where external logic can access it; or, alternatively, the microcomputer system will indicate in some predefined way that it is waiting for external logic to place data in some predefined location from which it can be input to the microcomputer system.

The key characteristic of programmed I/O is that external logic does as it is told by the program which the microprocessor executes.

2) **Interrupt I/O.** Interrupts are a means for external logic to force the microcomputer system to suspend whatever it is currently doing in order to attend to the needs of the external logic.

3) **Direct Memory Access.** This is a form of data transfer which allows data to move between microcomputer memory and external logic without involving the microprocessor in the data transfer.

The physical requirements for each type of I/O will be described in turn.

PROGRAMMED I/O

Data is transferred between a microcomputer system and external logic, in either direction, via an I/O port.

I/O Ports   An I/O port will consist of an I/O Port Buffer connected to the data lines of the external system bus, and to pins which access external logic:

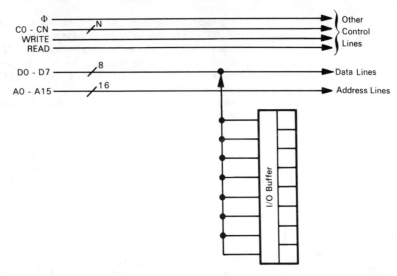

When an external logic device transmits data to the microcomputer system, it does so by presenting the data at I/O port pins, whence the data is passed to the I/O buffer. The binary value 01110100 would be transmitted as follows:

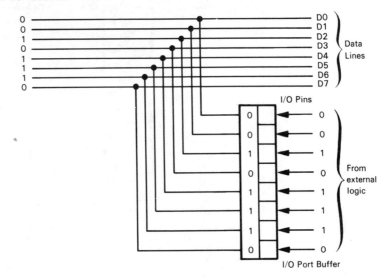

The I/O port buffer cannot be constantly communicating with the data lines of the external system bus, as illustrated above, since the data lines of the external system bus may be carrying data to or from memory. If the I/O port were permanently communicating with the data lines of the external system bus, then every time external logic presented data at the I/O pins, this data would be propagated down the shared data lines, with unpredictable consequences.

The microprocessor will therefore select an I/O port and read the contents of the I/O port buffer in much the same way that data gets read out of memory. This parallel between reading data out of I/O port buffers and reading data out of memory is appropriate, since most microcomputer systems transfer a great deal of data to and from external logic; therefore, they have more than one I/O port.

I/O Ports Addressed Using Memory Address Lines
We can develop an I/O device with one or more I/O ports, where the I/O port buffers have addresses, just as memory words have addresses. A simple scheme would take the high-order address line (A15) and design microcomputer logic such that whenever this line is 0, a memory location is selected, but whenever this line is 1, an I/O port buffer is selected. In other words, memory addresses of $7FFF_{16}$ and below will access memory, whereas memory addresses of 8000_{16} and above will access I/O port buffers. Using the READ and WRITE control lines, Figure 5-5 illustrates an I/O device with one port.

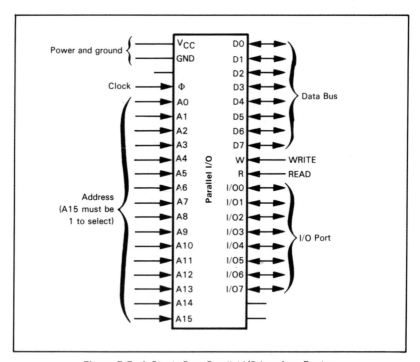

Figure 5-5. A Single Port, Parallel I/O Interface Device

The device in Figure 5-5 is referred to as a parallel I/O device because data is written and read in eight simultaneous parallel binary units.

The parallel I/O interface device illustrated in Figure 5-5 is synchronous, because it inputs the microprocessor's clock signal Φ, using this clock signal to schedule internal logic. In fact, **very few parallel I/O devices are synchronous. Most are asynchronous,** which means that they do not receive the microprocessor's clock signal as an input. Instead, they use the READ and WRITE control signals to time event sequences.

There is no reason why an I/O device should have only one I/O port. The number of I/O ports that a parallel I/O device has is purely a function of the number of pins that are economically available on a dual in-line package. The device illustrated in Figure 5-5 uses its pins as follows:

1) Sixteen pins are connected to the address lines of the external system bus and provide the information needed to determine if this I/O port buffer has been selected. This is a waste of pins. By using external select logic, as we did for ROM and RAM devices, we can eliminate most of these address inputs.

2) Eight pins are connected to the data lines of the external system bus; they are used to transfer information from the external system bus to the I/O port buffer, or from the I/O port buffer to the external system bus.

3) Two control lines, READ and WRITE, determine whether data will flow from the I/O port buffer to the external system bus (read), or from the external system bus to the I/O port buffer (write).

4) Two pins are required for power and ground.

5) One pin is required for the clock signal — for a synchronous parallel I/O device.

29 pins are used by items 1 through 5 above. A 40-pin DIP is thus left with just 11 I/O pins, enough for one 8-bit I/O port. We have not made good use of our 40 pins.

The first and most obvious way of improving our parallel I/O device is to eliminate the 16 address lines, replacing them with a select input, plus whatever few address lines are needed to select individual addressable locations within the parallel I/O device itself.

What addressable locations may exist within a parallel I/O device?

There are, of course, the parallel I/O ports themselves. By making better use of 40 pins we will be able to build **three parallel 8-bit I/O ports** into each parallel I/O device; we must be able to address each individually.

The parallel I/O device will need additional logic, accessed as addressable locations, in order to properly control data transfers as they occur.

Status Register

Consider problems associated with writing data to parallel I/O ports. A microprocessor will write data to an I/O port so that external logic can read this data from the I/O port. The microprocessor should not write new data to the I/O port until the old data has been read by external logic. The parallel I/O device must therefore have some means of telling the microprocessor when data has been read out of I/O ports by external logic. One way of solving this problem is to provide the parallel I/O device with **a Status register.** A Status register will typically be a read-only location whose bits are set and reset by logic internal to the parallel I/O device in order to identify conditions as they exist at the various I/O ports. The Status register must be read as an addressable location, therefore it will have the same bit width as the I/O ports. Since we are dealing with 8-bit I/O ports, we will assume an 8-bit Status register. Assuming that our parallel I/O device has three I/O ports, we will use three Status register bits to identify the status of data written by the CPU to each of the three I/O ports. Here is one way in which the three Status register bits might be interpreted:

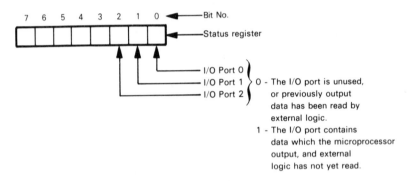

Initially status bits 0, 1, and 2 must be 0. As soon as the microprocessor writes data to an I/O port, the I/O port's status bit will be set to 1 by logic within the parallel I/O device. For example, if the microprocessor writes data to I/O Port 1, Status register bit 1 will immediately be set to 1. When external logic reads data from an I/O port, the I/O port's status bit will be reset to 0 by logic within the parallel I/O device. For example, if external logic reads data from I/O Port 1, Status register bit 1 will immediately be reset to 0.

The microprocessor will write data to an I/O port, then check the Status register; when the microprocessor detects a 0 in the appropriate Status register bit, it knows that external logic has read data from the I/O port. The microprocessor can now write new data to the I/O port. If the microprocessor did not bother to read Status register contents, it would stand a good chance of writing new data to the I/O port before the old data had been read by external logic, in which case the old data would be overwritten, and thus lost.

Output Port

Input Port

When the microprocessor writes data to a parallel I/O port and external logic reads this data, the I/O port must be configured as an output port. A parallel I/O port can also be configured as an input port, in which case external logic transmits data to the parallel I/O port, and the microprocessor reads this data from the I/O port.

A similar status problem exists when a parallel I/O port is configured as an input port. Having read data from an input port, the microprocessor must have some way of knowing that fresh data has been written by external logic to the input port, before attempting to read from the input port again. We can use three more Status register bits to solve this problem as follows:

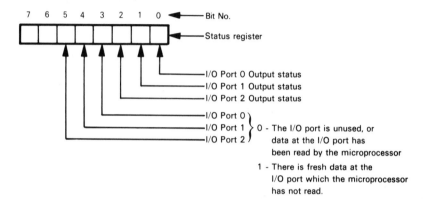

Initially Status register bits 5, 4, and 3 will be 0. When external logic transmits data to an I/O port, the associated Status register bit will be set to 1 by logic within the parallel I/O device. For example, if external logic transmits data to I/O Port 2, Status register bit 5 will immediately be set to 1. When the microprocessor reads this data, the Status register bit (bit 5 for I/O Port 2) is immediately reset to 0 by parallel I/O device logic.

The microprocessor can now check the Status register, seeking a 1 in the appropriate Status register bit as an indicator that fresh data is at an I/O port and should be read. Since the I/O port's input Status register bit will immediately be reset to 0, program logic can ensure that it does not read the same data twice. If the microprocessor does read the contents of an I/O port while its input Status register bit is 0, then it will re-read data which it has previously read. The I/O port input event sequence may be illustrated as follows:

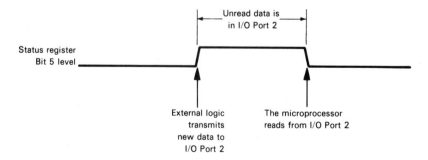

I/O Control Signals

External logic is going to encounter the same problems as the microprocessor — but external logic communicates with the microcomputer system only via I/O ports; external logic cannot read Status register contents, nor can it read the contents of any equivalent register. Instead **we will provide a control signal as a companion to each of the three I/O ports.** Let us construct a possible control signal logic sequence. When the I/O port is configured as an output port, the control signal might go high as soon as the microprocessor writes data to the I/O port; it will go low when external logic reads from the I/O port. This may be illustrated as follows:

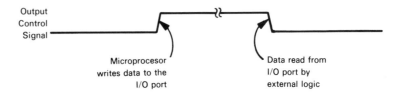

When an I/O port is configured as an input port, the control signal will go high when the microprocessor reads from the I/O port; it will go low when external logic writes to the I/O port. This may be illustrated as follows:

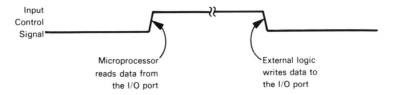

Handshaking

We use the term "handshaking" to describe control information exchanges of the type illustrated by the control signals above.

Error Register

Despite the precautions we have taken, it is possible for error conditions to arise within the parallel I/O device. Through a programming error, or for some other reason, the microprocessor may write fresh data to an output port before external logic got around to reading prior data. External logic, for its part, may write new data to an input port before the microprocessor got around to reading prior data. In order to add an extra level of security, **we will provide our parallel I/O device with an Error register,** which will also have eight bits, and will be read as another addressable location. Error register bits will be assigned as follows, in a manner similar to Status register bits:

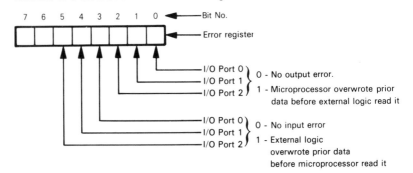

Error Status

Will the microprocessor have to read the Status and Error register contents in between each I/O port access? No. Instead, we will take one of the spare Status register bits and turn it into an Error status as follows:

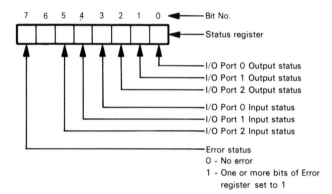

Any time one or more Error register bits are set to 1, the error bit of the Status register will also be set to 1. Now the microprocessor need only read the Status register contents in between I/O port accesses. If the error status bit is 1, then the microprocessor will read the Error register contents in order to determine the nature of the error. If the error status is 0, then the microprocessor knows there is no error and can ignore the Error register.

Control Register

The parallel I/O device will also need a Control register, which the microprocessor will use in order to specify programmable options within the parallel I/O device. We have already encountered one of these options: an I/O port can function as an input port or an output port.

I/O Port Direction Specification

At the present time very few parallel I/O devices have truly bidirectional I/O pins. That is to say, an I/O port pin cannot automatically function as an input pin when it receives data from external logic, and at the same time automatically function as an output pin on receiving data from the microprocessor.

Output Pin

Instead, each I/O port must be preconfigured as an output port or as an input port. If an I/O port is configured as an output port, then pin logic outputs a high signal when receiving a 1 bit from the microprocessor; it outputs a low signal when receiving a 0 bit from the microprocessor. External logic can sense the level of the output pin's signal, but it cannot transmit a signal to the output pin. If it does, the output pin will at best ignore the signal level; at worst, pin logic and external logic will compete with each other, with unpredictable results. We can conceptually illustrate output pin logic as follows:

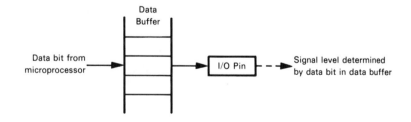

**Input
Pin**
When an I/O port is configured as an input port, each input pin senses the level of a signal which external logic must transmit to the pin. The signal level is translated into a bit level at an I/O port buffer whose contents the microprocessor can read. But I/O port logic will prevent the buffer from receiving data which the microprocessor might attempt to write to the I/O port. Thus we can conceptually illustrate input pin logic as follows:

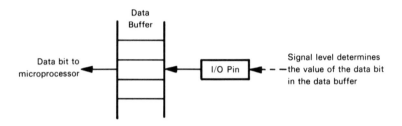

Usually I/O port direction is specified via a Control register. The Control register, like the Status and Error registers, will be an 8-bit addressable location. We will use three Control register bits to specify the direction of I/O ports as follows:

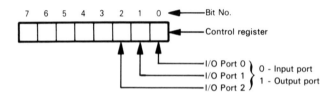

A 0 written to Control register bit 0, 1, or 2 configures the associated I/O port as an input port. A 1 written to the same Control register bit configures the associated I/O port as an output port.

Data Direction Register

Some parallel I/O devices allow you to assign individual pins of an I/O port as input or output pins. Parallel I/O devices of this type will have a Data Direction register associated with each parallel I/O port. You specify each pin individually as an input pin or an output pin by writing an appropriate code to the I/O port's Data Direction register. Here is one possibility:

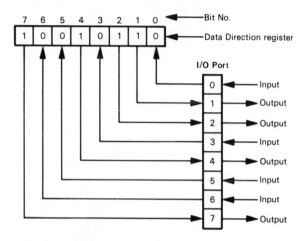

Note carefully that ones and zeros written to a Data Direction register will only determine whether associated I/O pins function as input pins or output pins. Data Direction register contents are never actually output; that is to say, the contents of a Data Direction register bit will never affect the level of a signal output by an output pin, it will only determine whether the pin functions as an output pin or an input pin.

We are not going to use Data Direction registers in our parallel I/O device; the control signal which each I/O port uses to communicate with external logic will base its operation on the entire port being an input port or an output port.

Additional Control register bits will frequently be assigned to reset the entire parallel I/O device, and/or to clear an error condition. We will use Control register bit 3 to reset the device and bit 4 to clear error conditions.

Reset

When a parallel I/O device is reset, all its addressable locations will likely be filled with zeros. We will cause a reset to occur when a 1 is written to Control register bit 3. The reset will also reset the Control register, so that bit 3 is immediately reset to 0.

Error Reset

When an error condition is cleared, the Error register and error bit of the Status register will likely be reset to 0. We will cause error conditions to be cleared when a 1 is written to Control register bit 4. We will cause this bit to be reset to 0 as part of the error clearing process.

Our parallel I/O device now has these six addressable locations:

> I/O Port 0
> I/O Port 1
> I/O Port 2
> Status register
> Error register
> Control register

These six addressable locations will require three address lines. Two address lines will access only four addressable locations, which is insufficient. Three address lines can access eight addressable locations, two more than we need; but we will just have to accept two wasted locations.

Let us now reassign the 40 pins of our reorganized parallel I/O device.

We have three 8-bit I/O ports; each 8-bit I/O port has a companion control signal. The three 8-bit I/O ports, together with their companion control signals, therefore require 27 pins.

We will still need eight bidirectional data pins to connect the parallel I/O device with the data lines of the external system bus. (Remember, these data lines are referred to as the data bus.) Add these eight lines to the 27 I/O port lines and we have allocated 35 lines. Five pins remain to be assigned.

Three address lines and a select line will consume four of the five remaining unassigned pins; this presents a problem, since we still need two pins for power and ground, plus two more pins for READ and WRITE control inputs.

We need 43 pins. What do we do?

Dual In-Line Package with Non-Standard Pin Count

We could repackage our parallel I/O device as a 44-pin DIP, adding two pins to each side of the package. Occasionally, **semiconductor manufacturers have resorted to such non-standard pin counts. But packages with non-standard pin counts are shunned by digital logic designers** because they complicate the design of printed circuit cards. **We will therefore seek a solution which allows our parallel I/O device to remain a 40-pin DIP.**

There is a solution; by playing a few tricks with our addressing logic we can acccess our six addressable locations using two address lines and four addresses. This will free up one additional pin.

The microprocessor must be able to write to each of the three I/O ports; the microprocessor must also be able to read from each of the three I/O ports. But the microprocessor does not need to write to either the Status register or the Error register; it need only read from these two registers. Similarly, the microprocessor need only write to the Control register; it does not need to read from the Control register.

We will therefore **use three addresses to access the three I/O ports. The fourth address will access the Control register on a write. The fourth address will access either the Status register or the Error register on a read;** we will explain how the choice is made shortly.

Let us refer to these four addresses as Addresses 0, 1, 2, and 3. In fact, they will be XXXX, XXXX+1, XXXX+2, and XXXX+3, where XXXX represents the hexadecimal address that causes the parallel I/O device's select logic to go "true."

Address 0 will access I/O Port A on a read or a write.
Address 1 will access I/O Port B on a read or a write.
Address 2 will access I/O Port C on a read or a write.

When writing to Address 3, the microprocessor will access the Control register. The first time the microprocessor reads from Address 3, it will always read the contents of the Status register. If the Status register's (high-order) error bit is 1, the next time the microprocessor reads from Address 3 it will read the contents of the Error register. Whenever the Error register contents get read, the Status register (high-order) error bit will be reset to 0 by parallel I/O device logic. This sequence may be illustrated as follows:

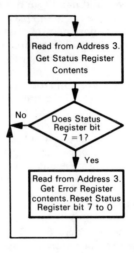

If the Status register's error bit is 1, the microprocessor will have to read the Error register contents before it ever gets to read the Status register contents again.

If the Status register error bit is 0, however, the next time the microprocessor reads from Address 3, it will again read the Status register contents. As long as the Status register's error bit is 0, the microprocessor will never read the Error register's contents.

Semiconductor manufacturers routinely use schemes such as the one illustrated above to reduce the number of address pins required by a support device. **Another common scheme uses a Control register bit in order to determine which of two registers is accessed by a single address.** In our case, if you look again at our Control register bit assignments, you will see that there are three unused Control register bits. **We could assign Control register bit 7 as follows:**

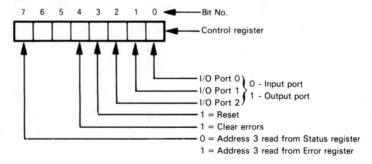

You now determine under program control whether the Status register or the Error register is accessed when you read from Address 3.

We will not use Control register bit 7 to select the Status or Error register on a read; we will instead use the Status register error bit to make this determination. Note that parallel I/O device pin assignments will be the same whichever method we use to discriminate between Status and Error registers on a read.

We still need two more pins to input READ and WRITE controls; and we have no tricks left to play. Therefore the best **we can** do is to **eliminate one of the I/O port control signals, using the freed-up pin to input either the READ or the WRITE control.** We do not need both the READ and WRITE control signals, since logic within the parallel I/O device can assume a read unless the WRITE control is true; or conversely, it can assume a write unless the READ control is true. **We will arbitrarily elect to eliminate the I/O Port A control signal (CA) and we will arbitrarily elect to input the READ control to this freed-up pin.** This means that I/O Port A will be difficult to use as an output port; devious schemes could be devised to create handshaking logic that would allow I/O Port A to function as an output port, but in general this I/O port will be used for input only. Since the parallel I/O device receives a READ control, parallel I/O logic will assume a write operation when it is selected unless it receives a READ control input. Alternatively you can look upon READ as a control signal with two "true" states and no "false" state. READ high specifies a read operation; READ low specifies a write operation.

Figure 5-6 illustrates a realistic set of pin assignments for our parallel I/O device. Figure 5-7 shows how this parallel I/O device might be connected to our external system bus.

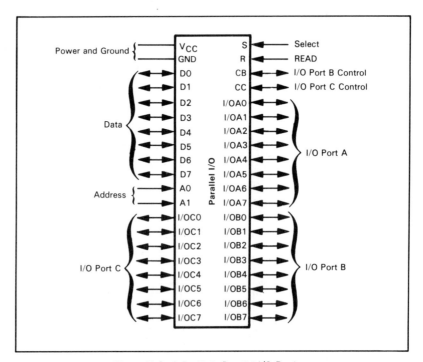

Figure 5-6. A Realistic Parallel I/O Device

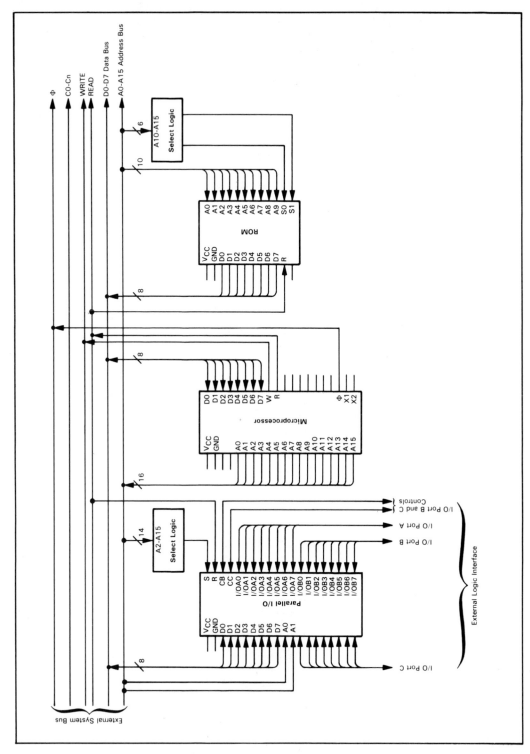

Figure 5-7. Parallel I/O Device Connected to a CPU via an External System Bus

Select logic for the parallel I/O device illustrated in Figure 5-6 **must generate a single enable signal (S) from the 14 high-order address bus lines,** while the two low-order address bus lines connect to the two address pins of the parallel I/O device. This may be illustrated as follows:

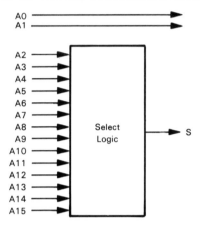

The way in which the 14 high-order address lines generate the select signal S determines the address space for the parallel I/O device. Here is one possibility:

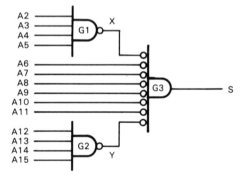

When A2, A3, A4, and A5 are all 1, NAND gate G1 outputs X low. Similarly, when A12, A13, A14, and A15 are all 1, NAND gate G2 outputs Y low. When X, Y, and A6 through A11 are all low, NOR gate G3 outputs S high. Therefore our parallel I/O device will be selected by the four addresses $F03C_{16}$, $F03D_{16}$, $F03E_{16}$, and $F03F_{16}$.

This may be illustrated as follows:

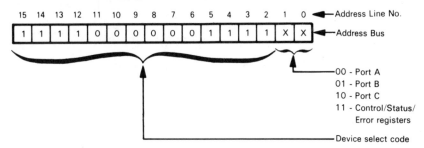

Microprocessors access I/O ports in one of two ways, which has further implications for device select logic. **The configuration illustrated in Figure 5-7 selects an I/O port in exactly the same way as a memory location.** Timing for a memory access or an I/O port access would be identical. In consequence, every parallel I/O device added to the system means four fewer available memory addresses.

I/O Address Space   **Some microprocessors have a separate "I/O space" for I/O ports.** They generate a separate I/O space by having different READ and WRITE control signals for I/O ports, as against memory locations. This may be illustrated as follows:

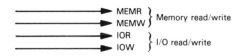

An alternative scheme uses a single control line to identify the access as a memory access or an I/O port access. This may be illustrated as follows:

MEM/$\overline{\text{IO}}$ is high when memory is being accessed; it is low when an I/O port is being accessed. MEM/$\overline{\text{IO}}$ is therefore a signal with two active levels.

The three-signal scheme illustrated above can be used in one of two ways. You can generate four separate signals from the three as follows:

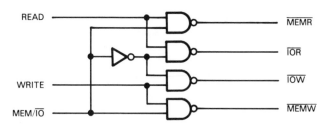

READ and WRITE are active high signals, but $\overline{\text{MEMR}}$, $\overline{\text{IOR}}$, $\overline{\text{MEMW}}$ and $\overline{\text{IOW}}$ are active low signals.

MEM/$\overline{\text{IO}}$ can contribute to memory and I/O device select logic. Here is one of many possible logic schemes:

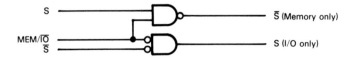

Notice that this logic inverts the "true" level of the final select signal.

INTERRUPT I/O

Most microprocessors have a control signal via which external logic can demand the microprocessor's attention. This signal is referred to as an **interrupt request** because, in effect, the external logic is asking the microprocessor to interrupt whatever it is currently doing in order to service more pressing external logical needs.

**The Concept
of an
Interrupt**

We will begin this discussion of interrupts with an example that is too simple to be realistic, but contains all the key features of a meaningful application.

Suppose a microcomputer system is being used to control the temperature of shower water, as illustrated in Figure 5-8. A thermometer measures the temperature of the mixed hot and cold water issuing from the shower head and transmits this temperature, as a digital signal, to the microcomputer system. The microcomputer system compares this temperature to a set point, which is supplied by an appropriate control. Depending on the difference between the real and desired shower temperature, the microcomputer system outputs data which must be interpreted as a valve control signal, causing a valve to increase or decrease the hot water flow.

There are a number of reasons why this simple sounding application is, in reality, far from simple. As experience will have taught you, there is some delay between the time you adjust a shower tap and the time that the water issuing from the shower head changes temperature. For this reason, **a non-trivial program will have to be executed by the microprocessor to ensure that it does not attempt to make ridiculous adjustments. We will call this program ADJUST, and illustrate it residing in program memory as follows:**

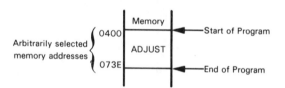

Another program, called RECORD, will input data from the temperature sensor, correctly interpreting the data to represent temperature readings. The only contact between program RECORD and ADJUST are that ADJUST will anticipate finding data in a certain area of data memory and RECORD will place the data, in correct format, in that required area. Our memory now looks like this:

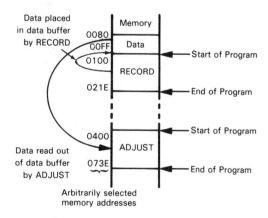

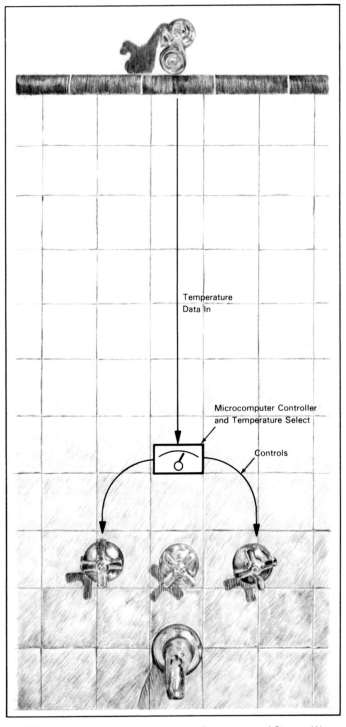

Figure 5-8. A Microcomputer Controlling the Temperature of Shower Water

The way in which shower head temperatures are read and transmitted to the microcomputer system is another feature of this problem which is not as straightforward as it might appear. It will take approximately half a second for an inexpensive temperature sensor to record a temperature. Half a second may not seem like very much time, but a microprocessor can execute approximately a quarter of a million instructions during this period.

How is the microprocessor going to know when the temperature sensor has a new value to transmit? If the temperature sensor simply tries to send data to an I/O port, the microprocessor is very likely not to read the temperature. One temperature reading can easily get lost in a quarter of a million instruction executions. If program logic simply "takes a chance" and inputs data from the I/O port once every quarter of a million instructions, it has very little chance of catching every temperature reading, and reading it just once.

How about using the I/O port's Status register? Yes, program logic could input status from the I/O port's Status register, then input data from the I/O port when status indicates the presence of new data. But if the program has much else to do, using the I/O port's Status register in this fashion could waste a lot of time. In fact, the microprocessor might find it necessary to read the I/O port's Status register hundreds of times in between data inputs to guarantee that no data input gets missed. In this particular example, the important point to note is that I/O data entry requires a tiny fraction of the microprocessor's time; but the I/O data entry is asynchronous. The microprocessor can never predict the time interval separating any two temperature inputs.

**Interrupt
Acknowledge**   Another way of resolving the problem is illustrated in Figure 5-9. **A three-step sequence allows the temperature sensor to attract the microprocessor's attention as follows:**

1) **The temperature sensor transmits an interrupt request signal (IREQ) to the microprocessor via an external system bus control line.**

**Interrupt
Acknowledge**   **2)** **The microprocessor has the choice of accepting or rejecting the interrupt request; it accepts the interrupt request by outputting an interrupt acknowledge signal (IACK) on an external system bus control line.**

3) **The external device uses the interrupt acknowledge signal as an enable, causing it to transmit data to I/O Port A. The external device must remove its interrupt request signal upon receiving an interrupt acknowledge, since once the interrupt request has been serviced, the external device is no longer requesting another interrupt. The microprocessor knows that data is due at a specific I/O port, so program logic needed to process the incoming data is very straightforward.**

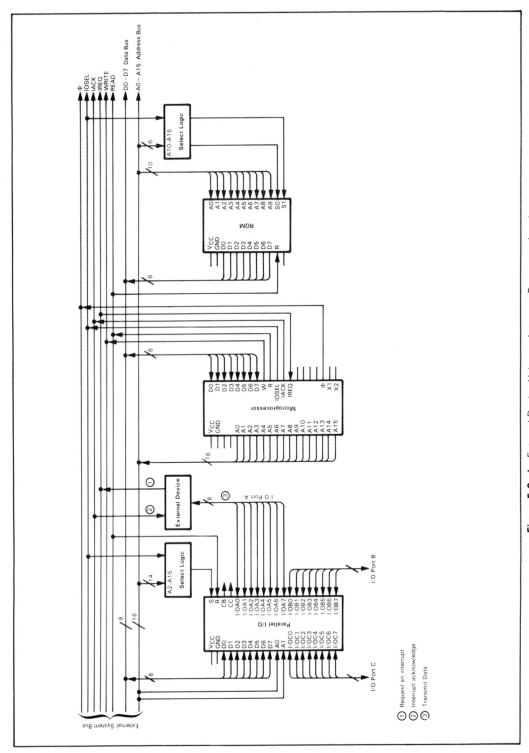

Figure 5-9. An External Device Using an Interrupt Request to Let the Microprocessor Know that Data Is Ready to be Input

5-38

Timing for this three-step sequence may be illustrated as follows:

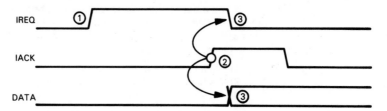

Note that although we have been talking about the external device input-ting data to the microcomputer system, data flow could just as easily be in the opposite direction; in fact, there is no reason why any data flow need follow an interrupt. The program executed following an interrupt could, for example, simply output control signals.

The purpose of any interrupt is to tell the microprocessor that it must, for some pressing reason, suspend whatever it is doing; in this instance the microprocessor must process data being input to an I/O port. With reference to programs RECORD and ADJUST, this is what happens:

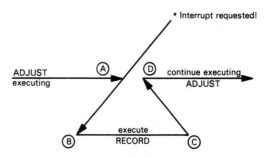

Refer again to Figure 5-9. Steps ① and ② cause the interrupt request to be sensed by the microprocessor at Ⓐ above. The microprocessor responds by suspending execution of ADJUST, and executing RECORD (Ⓑ to Ⓒ). While RECORD is executing, the data transmitted by the temperature sensor (③ in Figure 5-9) is read by the microprocessor, since program RECORD has been written to anticipate arrival of this data.

When RECORD has completed execution at Ⓒ , execution of ADJUST continues at Ⓓ , picking up exactly where it left off at Ⓐ .

The key feature of program RECORD's execution is that it is an unscheduled event. There is no logic within the microcomputer system that can predict when or how often program RECORD will be executed. However, there is logic within the microcomputer system that can suspend any program's execu-tion, later restarting execution from the exact point of suspension.

A MICROPROCESSOR'S RESPONSE TO AN INTERRUPT

At its most elementary level, a microprocessor could respond to an interrupt request by simply loading into the program counter the starting address of the program that external, interrupting logic wants executed. But that begs two questions.

1) What happens to the program that was being executed?
2) Where does the microprocessor get the address of the program which the interrupting logic wants executed?

Consider first what happens to the program that was being executed.

Saving Registers and Status

The old program may have important information in the status flags, the data counter and accumulator; this data is going to be wiped out by the new program, so that when the new program has finished executing, the old program will no longer be able to restart. This problem is resolved by saving the contents of all CPU registers, including the program counter, before starting to execute the new program. When the new program completes its execution, the saved program counter value is the address of the instruction that was about to be executed when the old program was interrupted; so, by merely restoring the saved values into the CPU registers, the old program can pick up where it left off. This concept is illustrated as follows:

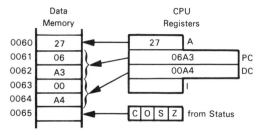

This is the situation when ADJUST is interrupted to execute RECORD (registers' contents and memory addresses have been arbitrarily selected)

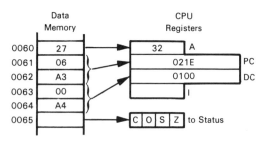

This is the situation when RECORD has finished executing and ADJUST must continue where it left off. (Registers' contents are again arbitrarily selected.)

An interrupt will not be acknowledged until the current instruction has completed executing. This being the case, there is no need to save the contents of the Instruction register, since it contains an instruction code which has been processed. In other words, the interrupt directly precedes the arrival of a new instruction code.

There are two ways in which the old program status flags and registers' contents may be saved, as illustrated above, before the new program starts execution. One way would be for the interrupt request signal to initiate execution of a microprogram (stored in the control unit), which simply writes the contents of CPU registers into a data area of memory which has been set aside for this purpose. A microprocessor designer may be reluctant to use up precious control unit space in this way, and instead may require the programmer to write a short program which will do the same thing. Such a program will be the first part of a larger program called an "interrupt service routine."

Interrupt Service Routine

At the end of the new program's execution, whatever logic was used to save the old program's registers' contents must be executed in reverse, to restore the old program's registers and status. This program sequence will end the "interrupt service routine."

We will consider interrupt service routines in more detail in Chapter 6, after we have discussed programming in more detail.

Interrupt Address Vector

Now consider how the microprocessor gets the address of the program which the interrupting logic wants executed. We will refer to this as the "interrupt address vector."

There are almost as many ways of determining which program must be executed following an interrupt request as there are microprocessors. In the case of our shower temperature control problem, there is an easy solution. The shower head temperature sensor is the only external device that can request an interrupt, and there is only one program it can want executed following the interrupt. This being the case, the microprocessor could be built with internal logic that causes one program, origined at one specific memory address, to be executed following an interrupt.

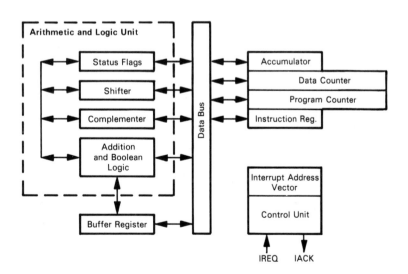

Now every time the control unit receives an interrupt request (IREQ) and it is ready to service the interrupt, it does as follows:

1) Sends out the interrupt acknowledge signal, IACK.
2) Saves the contents of Status flags, the accumulator, the data counter and the program counter, or else allows the programmer some way of doing the same thing.
3) Move the contents of the interrupt address vector to the program counter.

A minicomputer programmer would consider this method of responding to interrupts laughable. Who knows when and how the minicomputer may next have to respond to an interrupt? To specify that all interrupts will be serviced by a program origined at memory address 0400_{16} (for example) would be an intolerable restriction, because it reduces the minicomputer programmer's flexibility.

Having fixed interrupt address vectors makes a certain amount of sense in some microcomputer applications. Remember that microprocessors can be used as logic components instead of being used as general purpose computers. Indeed, most microprocessors are still used in dedicated, non-varying situations, where one or a few specific interrupts will require equally specific responses.

Polling with Interrupt Acknowledge   **Some of the most popular microprocessors do, indeed, have a single interrupt address vector.** These microprocessors always branch to the same program after acknowledging an interrupt, irrespective of the interrupt source. (Remember we call this program an interrupt service routine.) **If more than one external device is capable of requesting an interrupt, then the interrupt service routine will have to execute appropriate program logic in order to determine which external device requested the interrupt. One method of doing this would be to require every external device that is capable of requesting an interrupt to have a Status register which, to the microprocessor, looks like an I/O port.** The external device would then have to set an appropriate bit within its Status register upon accepting an interrupt acknowledge. The microprocessor would read every external device's Status register contents in order to determine which one had accepted the interrupt acknowledge. The interrupt service routine would then cause execution to branch to the particular program required by the identified external device. For the simple case of two external devices, this program logic may be illustrated as follows:

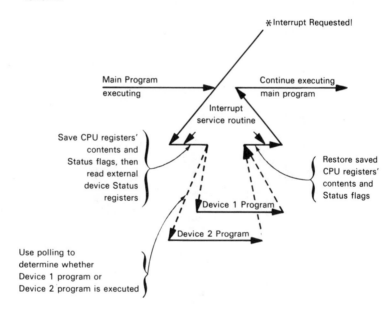

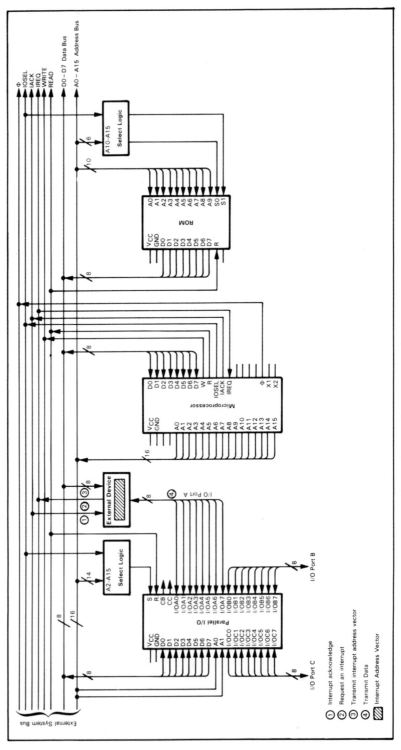

Figure 5-10. An External Device with its Own Interrupt Address Vector

① Interrupt acknowledge
② Request an interrupt
③ Transmit interrupt address vector
④ Transmit Data
▨ Interrupt Address Vector

We use the term "polling" to describe this method of identifying an interrupting device. Polling is slow, but it requires simple microprocessor logic. But simple microprocessor logic is becoming less important as designers learn to cram more logic into the same size silicon chip. **Polling,** as a means of identifying an interrupting external device, **has** therefore **been rendered obsolete.**

The most popular method of identifying an external interrupting device is to have the device identify itself by transmitting an identifying number, or the entire interrupt address vector, following an interrupt acknowledge. If the interrupting device transmits an identifying number, then the microprocessor will use this number in some fashion to compute the interrupt address vector. **The identifying number is called a "device select code."**

Sometimes the external device that requests an interrupt is required to contain the logic which transmits the identifying number or interrupt address vector demanded by the microprocessor. Figure 5-10 represents a modification of Figure 5-9, where the external device is shown with this additional logic added.

Let us examine the event sequence illustrated in Figure 5-10.

The external device will request an interrupt via the IREQ signal at ① . When the microprocessor acknowledges the interrupt request via IACK ② , the external device transmits an interrupt address vector, shown at ③ . (We have arbitrarily elected to have the external device return an interrupt address vector rather than a device select code.) Note that the external device has no device select logic, since the microprocessor is not accessing the external device as an I/O port or memory location.

There are a number of ways in which an external device may be required to return an interrupt address vector or an identifying code. Figure 5-10 shows the external device returning its interrupt address vector as data. Since the interrupt address vector will be 16 bits wide, and the data bus is 8 bits wide, the interrupt address vector will have to be transmitted to the microprocessor in two halves. Had the microprocessor required the external device to transmit a device select code, in all probability this code would be an 8-bit number, which the external device could transmit via the data bus as one data byte.

After transmitting the interrupt address vector to the microprocessor, the external device transmits data to I/O Port A; this is shown in Figure 5-10 at ④ .

The problem with the interrupt scheme illustrated in Figure 5-10 is that it demands that any external device have a certain level of intelligence if it is to be capable of requesting an interrupt. The interrupt-related intelligence demanded of an external device is quite elementary by many minicomputer standards; in fact, most minicomputers demand a great deal more. But in the low-cost world of microprocessors, the constant search is for simplicity.

Consider a simple example. Two minicomputers priced at $3250 and $3640 might be expanded, with various peripherals, into minicomputer systems with prices ranging between $25,000 and $40,000. Options that are not easily compared make it hard to evaluate comparative prices for the two minicomputer systems. But if one minicomputer system requires $10 worth of extra logic at every external device capable of requesting interrupts, this extra expense will have almost no impact on overall economics. Microcomputer systems, on the other hand, will often be configured (without peripherals) in control applications where the entire microcomputer system's cost may range between $50 and $100. If you must add $10 of extra logic to every external device that is capable of requesting an interrupt, this expense will quickly overwhelm any small price differences that may exist between the two minicomputer systems.

In order to reduce external logic expenses, semiconductor manufacturers have built interrupt request/acknowledge logic into support devices such as the parallel I/O device illustrated in Figure 5-10. This allows external logic to use a parallel I/O device's interrupt request capability, rather that having its own.

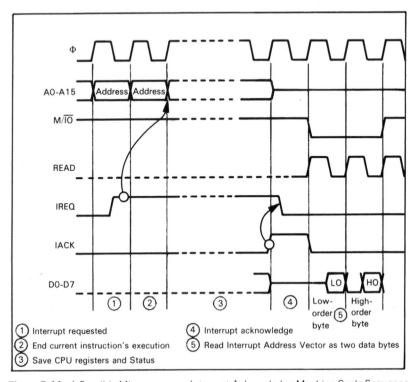

Figure 5-11. A Possible Microprocessor Interrupt Acknowledge Machine Cycle Sequence

Let us examine the logic which we must add to our parallel I/O device in order to let it support external interrupts.

As we stated previously, **a microprocessor may demand that an interrupt address vector** or a device select code **be returned by the device which accepts an interrupt acknowledge.** (We arbitrarily assume that our microprocessor demands an interrupt address vector.) **A typical interrupt request/acknowledge sequence might be accompanied by the machine cycle sequence illustrated in Figure 5-11.**

The interrupt request will be transmitted asynchronously by the parallel I/O device; that is to say, the interrupt request will occur as soon as an interrupt condition arises within the parallel I/O device. The type of machine cycle which the microprocessor might be executing is unimportant. The microprocessor remembers the interrupt request until it has finished executing its current instruction. Figure 5-11 shows the microprocessor executing a few machine cycles that are used to save the contents of the program counter, CPU registers and the Status flags. We do not describe how the microprocessor saves this information; for the moment we are not concerned with such detail. Suffice it to say that this information is saved in a manner that allows it to be retrieved after the pending interrupt has been serviced.

After saving appropriate CPU information, the microprocessor executes a machine cycle whose only function is to transmit an interrupt acknowledge signal (IACK) to the external device which requested an interrupt. The microprocessor requires that the external device transmit an interrupt address vector, as two data bytes, in the two machine cycles that follow the interrupt acknowledge machine cycle. The microprocessor treats these two machine cycles as I/O read machine cycles.

Notice that during the interrupt acknowledge machine cycle both the address and data busses are shown floating. This is because only the interrupt acknowledge signal is meaningful during the interrupt acknowledge machine cycle.

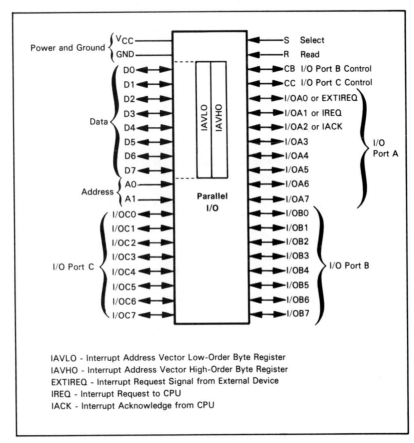

IAVLO - Interrupt Address Vector Low-Order Byte Register
IAVHO - Interrupt Address Vector High-Order Byte Register
EXTIREQ - Interrupt Request Signal from External Device
IREQ - Interrupt Request to CPU
IACK - Interrupt Acknowledge from CPU

Figure 5-12. A Parallel I/O Device with Simple Interrupt Handling Logic

If a microcomputer system includes just one device capable of requesting and acknowledging interrupts, then Figure 5-11 is easy enough to follow. But what if there are two or more devices capable of requesting and acknowledging interrupts? **If more than one device has requested an interrupt, which one will respond to IACK** by returning an interrupt address vector? This decision will have to be made by special interrupt priority arbitration logic — which we will describe later in this chapter.

I/O Device Vector Register

Figure 5-12 illustrates our parallel I/O devices with some simple interrupt logic added. Two 8-bit registers, identified as IAVLO and IAVHO, hold the low-order and high-order bytes of the interrupt address vector. External logic initiates the interrupt request by inputting a high signal at EXTIREQ. The parallel I/O device passes the interrupt request on to the microprocessor via IREQ. The microprocessor returns an interrupt acknowledge via IACK. The parallel I/O device then outputs the low-order interrupt address vector byte from IAVLO and then the high-order interrupt address vector byte from IAVHO.

Multifunction I/O Pins

The first problem we encounter when adding interrupt logic to our parallel I/O device is the fact that we have run out of pins. There is no reasonable way in which we could redesign the parallel I/O device in order to free up three pins. **One of the commonest solutions you will find to this problem is the solution we have adopted in Figure 5-12; some I/O Port A pins are pressed into double service.** I/O Port A lines 0, 1, and 2 are shown alternatively functioning as the external interrupt request input (EXTIREQ), interrupt request output (IREQ), and interrupt acknowledge input (IACK). We choose I/O Port A pins, since this is the I/O port which lost its control signal (CA) in order to free up a pin for the read control input. Since I/O Port A has already lost part of its capability (as compared to the other two I/O ports), we might as well impact this one I/O port further, leaving the other two I/O ports unaffected.

We will use the Control register in order to select I/O Port A pin assignments. If you look again at the most recent Control register illustration, you will see that bits 5, 6, and 7 are still unassigned. We will use Control register bit 5 to select I/O Port A options. If Control register bit 5 is 0, then I/O Port A will function as an 8-bit input or output port. But if Control register bit 5 is 1, then I/O Port A line 0 will become the EXTIREQ input, I/O Port A line 1 will become the IREQ output, and I/O Port A line 2 will become IACK input. I/O Port A lines 3 through 7 will continue to function as a 5-bit I/O port; Control register bit 0 will determine whether it is a 5-bit input port or a 5-bit output port.

But our problems are not all solved. **The two interrupt address vector registers IAVLO and IAVHO need addresses** — and we have none left. We could avoid giving IAVLO and IAVHO addresses by making the interrupt address vector a permanent, unalterable value, built into the parallel I/O device when it is manufactured. That way the microprocessor cannot, and therefore need not write to the interrupt address vector registers. We could also avoid having to read from these two registers by designing parallel I/O device logic to automatically output the contents of these two registers in the two machine cycles that follow IACK being received high, as illustrated in Figure 5-11.

Some early microprocessor support devices had unalterable interrupt address vectors that were built into the device at the time of manufacture. But this design practice has lost favor.

Obviously you cannot use support devices with permanently assigned interrupt address vectors in a microcomputer system that is at all general purpose. Having to set aside specific areas of memory for interrupt service routines could become an intolerable restriction. But even if you can live with this restriction, permanent interrupt address vectors cause annoying complications. Suppose your microcomputer system includes two or more support devices that are identical, apart from their interrupt address vectors; you will, nevertheless, have to treat them as different devices, with different part numbers, because they are not interchangeable. If a part fails, or is out of stock, you cannot substitute an equivalent part, differing only in the interrupt address vector.

Semiconductor manufacturers now design interrupt address vector registers as addressable, read/write locations. This allows program logic to write the interrupt address vector into the interrupt address vector register; and the problems associated with permanent interrupt address vectors disappear.

Our parallel I/O device will have addressable, read/write interrupt address vector registers. And to cope with the fact that we have run out of pins and addresses, we will use Control register bit 6 to address the two interrupt address vector byte registers. Our Control register's bit assignments may now be illustrated as follows:

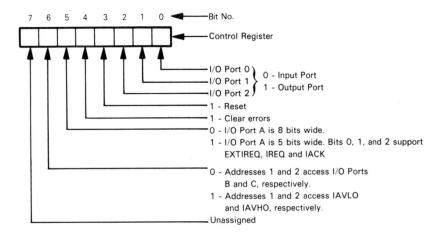

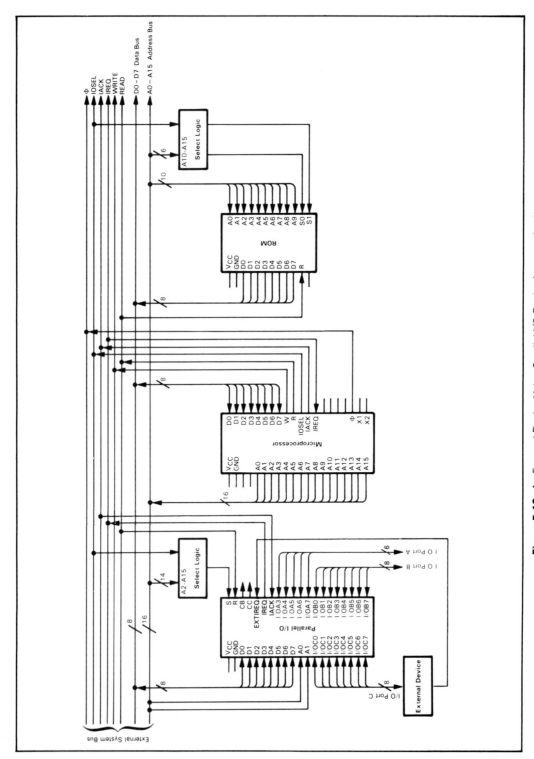

Figure 5-13. An External Device Using Parallel I/O Device Interrupt Logic

Our parallel I/O device's four addresses now access addressable locations as summarized in Table 5-2.

Table 5-2. Addressing Summary for the Parallel I/O
Device Illustrated in Figure 5-12

Address		Control Register Bit 6	Status Register Bit 7	Read (R) or Write (W)	Addressed Location
A1	A0				
0	0	X	X	X	I/O Port A
0	1	0	X	X	I/O Port B
0	1	1	X	X	Interrupt Address Vector Low-Order Byte
1	0	0	X	X	I/O Port C
1	0	1	X	X	Interrupt Address Vector High-Order Byte
1	1	X	0	R	Status Register
1	1	X	1	R	Error Register
1	1	X	X	W	Control Register
X means "don't care"					

Figure 5-13, which is a variation of Figure 5-10, shows external logic connected to the parallel I/O device illustrated in Figure 5-12. Notice that we have moved external logic so that it connects with I/O Port C instead of I/O Port A. External logic had to move from I/O Port A since three I/O Port A lines now support interrupt logic. If external logic is to input or output 8-bit data, then it must connect to I/O Port B or I/O Port C, but not I/O Port A. We have arbitrarily selected I/O Port C.

Let us now look at some simple variations of parallel I/O device interrupt handling logic.

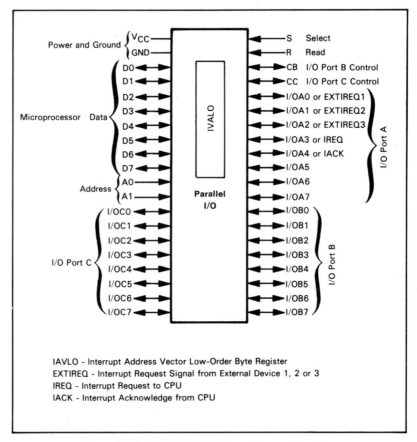

IAVLO - Interrupt Address Vector Low-Order Byte Register
EXTIREQ - Interrupt Request Signal from External Device 1, 2 or 3
IREQ - Interrupt Request to CPU
IACK - Interrupt Acknowledge from CPU

Figure 5-14. A Parallel I/O Device with more Complex
Interrupt Handling Logic

Many microprocessors require only the low-order interrupt address vector byte to be returned following an interrupt acknowledge. These microprocessors have their own internal register into which a program will write the high-order interrupt address vector byte. In consequence, all external interrupts will generate interrupt address vectors with the same high-order byte — provided by the microprocessor — and a low-order byte provided by the external device. This may be illustrated as follows:

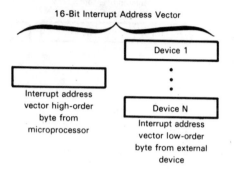

If external interrupts use a parallel I/O device's interrupt logic, then one external interrupt can be serviced by one parallel I/O device. But with just a small increase in interrupt logic complexity we can allow three separate and distinct external interrupts to be serviced by one parallel I/O device's interrupt logic. Figure 5-14 illustrates an appropriate parallel I/O device.** What we have done is allow three external interrupt requests to be input at I/O Port A pins 0, 1, and 2. I/O Port A pin 4 receives a common interrupt acknowledge. When Control register bit 5 is set to 1, these five interrupt signals are enabled at I/O Port A pins 0 through 4. I/O Port A now shrinks to a 3-bit input or output port (at pins 5, 6, and 7).

The parallel I/O device distinguishes between the three external interrupt requests via the interrupt address vector. We could provide the parallel I/O device with three different interrupt address vector registers, but that would add complexity to the parallel I/O device without gaining any significant advantage. Instead, we will take two bits of IAVLO, the interrupt address vector low-order byte register, and have parallel I/O device interrupt logic select these two bits as follows:

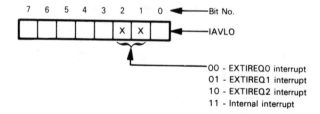

If the parallel I/O device's interrupt logic modifies the two low-order bits of IAVLO, it will generate four interrupt address vectors that are one byte apart. By modifying bits 1 and 2, interrupt address vectors are two bytes apart. This allows a two-byte branch instruction to be inserted at each of the four addresses:

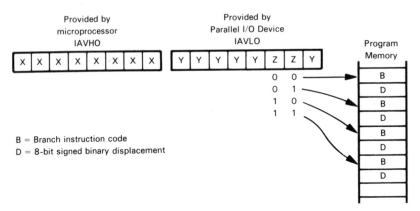

B = Branch instruction code
D = 8-bit signed binary displacement

You will frequently find interrupt logic that modifies bits 2 and 3 of the interrupt address vector so that addresses are four bytes apart. This allows three-byte branch instructions to be inserted in the four bytes as follows:

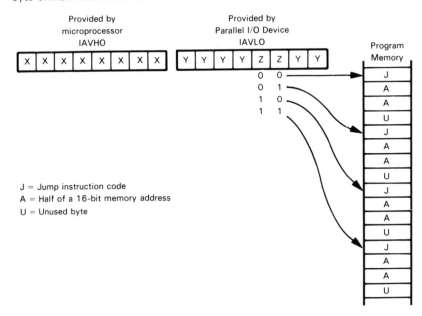

J = Jump instruction code
A = Half of a 16-bit memory address
U = Unused byte

Internal Interrupts

Notice that we have saved one of the four interrupt address vectors for an internal interrupt. You will commonly find such internal interrupt capability in parallel I/O devices, and other microprocessor support devices. **This internal interrupt can be generated in a variety of ways. Here are some examples:**

1) An error condition might cause an internal interrupt request.
2) An internal interrupt request might be generated by a low-to-high or high-to-low transition of I/O Port B or C control signals (CB or CC).

Whenever a microprocessor support device has an internal interrupt, it will usually assign Control register bits to enable or disable this interrupt, and to specify the source of the internal interrupt if there is more than one possibility.

If external device interrupt requests arrive at the parallel I/O device, rather than the microprocessor, then for every parallel I/O device in the system three different external devices can have their own interrupt service routines, each identified by an interrupt address vector which you can modify at any time. This concept may be illustrated as follows:

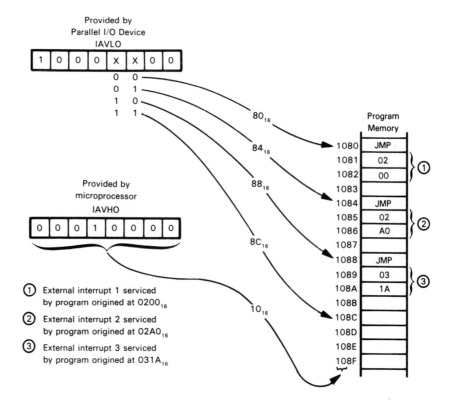

In the above illustration, interrupt request signals arriving at a single parallel I/O device will always specify execution of programs with execution addresses 0200_{16}, $02A0_{16}$, and $031A_{16}$. Each interrupt request arrives at a separate and distinct EXTIREQ signal which the parallel I/O device passes on to the microprocessor via the single IREQ signal. When the microprocessor acknowledges with IACK, the parallel I/O device transmits its interrupt address vector with bits 2 and 3 identifying one external interrupt.

But a new problem arises when more than one device capable of generating an interrupt is included in a microcomputer system. What happens when more than one device simultaneously requests an interrupt? Which device is going to be acknowledged, and how does the external device know that it has been acknowledged? How so we prevent other external devices from assuming that they too were acknowledged?

These problems can be resolved if we use appropriate interrupt priority arbitration logic. Let us now examine what such logic will consist of.

INTERRUPT PRIORITIES

What happens when more than one external device requests an interrupt at the same time? This problem can be resolved in two ways. First, logic within the microprocessor can have a number of interrupt request lines with ascending priorities, as follows:

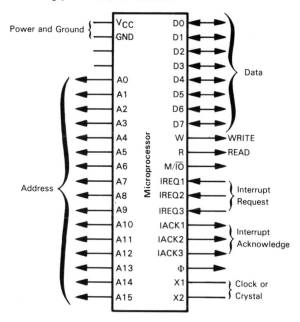

The illustration above shows six microprocessor pins supporting three external interrupts. An external interrupt request input via IREQ1 will be acknowledged via IACK1. External interrupt requests input via IREQ2 and IREQ3, likewise, will be acknowledged via IACK2 and IACK3, respectively. By providing each external interrupt request input with its own companion interrupt acknowledge we are able to identify the external device whose interrupt is being acknowledged.

Were we to run short of pins, we could save one interrupt acknowledge pin by outputting a pair of interrupt acknowledge signals, which would have to be decoded by a 2-to-4 decoder, as follows:

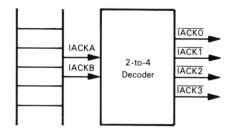

The 2-to-4 decoder outputs one signal low, and three high. The way in which a low signal is selected, based on the levels of the two inputs, is described by the following truth table:

Inputs		Outputs			
IACKB	IACKA	IACK0	IACK1	IACK2	IACK3
0	0	0	1	1	1
0	1	1	0	1	1
1	0	1	1	0	1
1	1	1	1	1	0

The parallel I/O device illustrated in Figure 5-14 could be provided with three interrupt acknowledge outputs at I/O Port A pins 5, 6, and 7, to act as companions for the three external interrupt request inputs at I/O Port A pins 0, 1, and 2. This would provide the parallel I/O device with the same device specific interrupt acknowledge logic that we have illustrated for the microprocessor. **But note that the parallel I/O device does not need to provide device specific interrupt acknowledges, just because it receives device specific external interrupt requests. If three external devices input their interrupt requests via parallel I/O device signals EXTIREQ1, EX-TIREQ2, and EXTIREQ3, it does not necessarily follow that three interrupt acknowledge signals (e.g. EXTIACK1, EXTIACK2 and EXTIACK 3) must be output by the parallel I/O device to the external devices. The microprocessor, or any other device, could provide external devices with their interrupt acknowledge signals, so long as some method exists for associating individual interrupt request inputs with individual interrupt acknowledge outputs.**

Moreover, interrupt logic need not necessarily be part of the microprocessor, the parallel I/O device, or any similar support device. Special interrupt priority devices are available.

Interrupt
Priorities
and What
They Mean
Before discussing how an interrupt priority device works, we will define what is meant by interrupt priorities.

Suppose more than one external device may request an interrupt. If two or more external devices request interrupts SIMULTANEOUSLY, sending IREQ signals that overlap in time, then WHICH external device gets the interrupt acknowledge (IACK)? This will be determined by interrupt priority logic as follows:

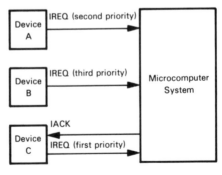

In the above illustration, external devices A, B, and C all request interrupts by simultaneously transmitting IREQ signals to the microcomputer system. By whatever priority arbitration technique the microcomputer system is using, it is determined that Device C has the highest priority. Device A has the second priority and Device B has the lowest priority. The acknowledge signal IACK must therefore be sent to Device C.

The fact that Devices A and B did not have their interrupt requests acknowledged does not imply that they must remove their IREQ interrupt request signals. They can do so if they wish. If they do not, they will be acknowledged, in turn, when the microcomputer CPU is subsequently ready to acknowledge interrupts again.

Refer again to the illustration of Devices A, B, and C, all simultaneously requesting interrupt service. There are three interrupt service programs residing in memory, one for each device. These programs may be executed as follows:

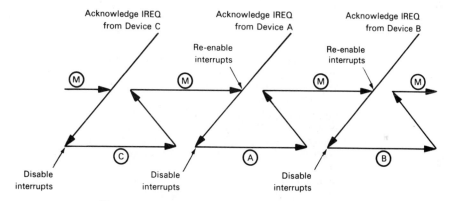

(M) represents the main program which is executing, and which gets interrupted. First Device C's interrupt service routine gets executed at (C) . Subsequently Devices A and B's interrupt service routines get executed at (A) and (B) , respectively.

If interrupt service routines (C) , (A) , and (B) are to be executed sequentially, as illustrated above, then while (C) is executing, the microcomputer system's interrupt handling logic must be disabled, so interrupt requests (IREQ) from Devices A and B are ignored. At some point, after (C) completes execution and (M) has resumed executing, the microcomputer system interrupt logic is re-enabled; now IREQ from Device A is acknowledged. While (A) is executing, the microcomputer system's interrupt handling logic is again disabled until some time when (M) has resumed execution. Since Device B is still requesting an interrupt, (B) now gets executed.

Special instructions are used to enable and disable interrupt logic in microcomputer systems. These instructions, and how they should be used, are described in Chapter 7.

Suppose the microcomputer system did not disable its interrupt logic while executing interrupt service routines such as Ⓐ , Ⓑ and Ⓒ . This is how the interrupts would be serviced:

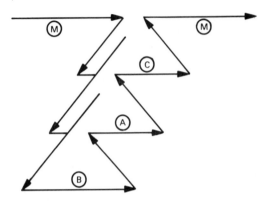

The important concept to understand is that interrupt priorities determine which device receives the interrupt acknowledge IACK when more than one device is simultaneously requesting an interrupt via IREQ.

Interrupt priorities have nothing to do with whether Ⓒ can be interrupted by Device A once Ⓒ has started executing. Device A has lower interrupt priority than Device C; however, once Device C's interrupt request has been acknowledged, Device C removes its interrupt request. Device A's interrupt request is still present and is the highest priority interrupt request. The instant program Ⓒ enables interrupt logic, it will immediately be interrupted, and program Ⓐ will execute. If you do not want program Ⓒ to be interrupted, then when you write program Ⓒ you must make sure it keeps interrupt logic disabled. Instruction steps to do this are described in Chapter 7.

28-Pin DIP

Let us now look at two variations of interrupt priority devices, illustrated in Figures 5-15A and 5-15B. Both devices are packaged as 28-pin DIPs, another very popular pin count that semiconductor manufacturers have adopted.

Interrupt Priority and Multiple Request Lines

The device illustrated in Figure 5-15A has eight separate and distinct lines via which external devices can transmit interrupt request signals to the interrupt priority device. Signals terminate at pins EXTIREQ1 through EXTIREQ8. EXTIREQ1 has highest priority, while EXTIREQ8 has lowest priority.

When one or more interrupt requests arrive at pins EXTIREQ1 - EXTIREQ8, logic within the interrupt priority device sets IREQ high.

At some future time the CPU responds by setting IACK high.

When the interrupt priority device illustrated in Figure 5-15A receives IACK high, it sets IREQ low again; then it identifies the external device whose interrupt has been acknowledged by outputting the device number on the three low ordered data bus lines D0-D2. For example, if an interrupt request arrives at EXTIREQ5, 101 is output via D2-D0 when IACK is sensed high. If two interrupt request signals arrive simultaneously at pins EXTIREQ2 and EXTIREQ5, 010 is output at pins D2-D0 when IACK is sensed high.

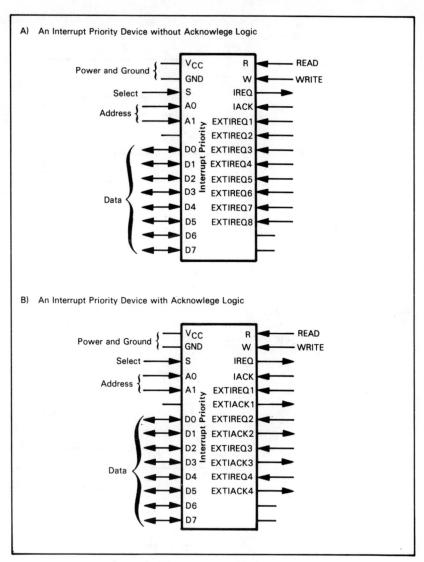

Figure 5-15. Two Interrupt Priority Devices

Timing for the interrupt priority device illustrated in Figure 5-15A is as follows:

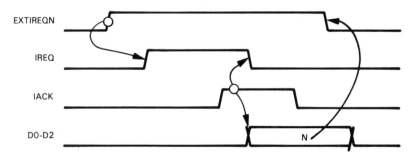

The interrupt priority device illustrated in Figure 5-15B provides discrete interrupt acknowledge signals. However, in order to keep the same device pin count, just four external interrupts are allowed, at EXTIREQ1 through EXTIREQ4. Each external interrupt request has its own dedicated interrupt acknowledge, illustrated in Figure 5-15B as EXTIACK1 through EXTIACK4. If we again assume that EXTIREQ1 has highest priority, and EXTIREQ4 has lowest priority, then two or more interrupt requests occurring simultaneously would result in just one interrupt acknowledge — for the highest priority interrupt request. For example, suppose interrupt requests occur simultaneously at EXTIREQ1 and EXTIREQ3. Only EXTIACK1 would be returned high. Timing may be illustrated as follows:

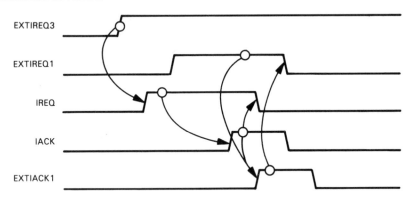

Note that a simple 3-to-8 decoder, enabled by IACK, would allow the interrupt priority device illustrated in Figure 5-15A to generate eight discrete interrupt acknowledge signals for the eight discrete interrupt request inputs. This may be illustrated as follows:

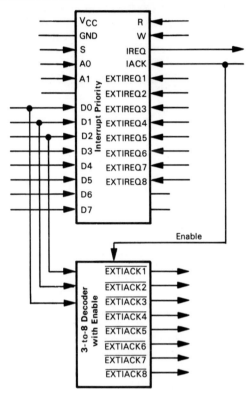

We previously illustrated a 2-to-4 decoder and explained how it works using a truth table. The 3-to-8 decoder illustrated above is a simple extension of the 2-to-4 decoder. The 3-to-8 decoder will output one low signal and seven high signals. The low signal is selected by the combination of the three input signal levels. The 3-to-8 decoder must have a special enable signal, otherwise it would randomly select interrupt acknowledge outputs based on whatever data happened to be flowing across the three low-order lines of the data bus. That could cause problems. The enable signal, in this case the interrupt acknowledge, ensures that the 3-to-8 decoder outputs no high signals unless IACK is high. Timing may be illustrated as follows for EXTIACK3:

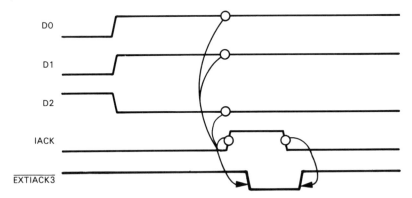

Logic illustrated above generates EXTIACK1 through EXTIACK8. This raises many questions which we will alert you to, but ignore, since they are not relevant to the current discussion of interrupt request/acknowledge concepts.

How long should the high interrupt acknowledge pulse last? Will external logic be satisfied with this interrupt acknowledge signal's timing?

In any actual design project you would have to pay careful attention to questions such as these, and be absolutely certain that the questions had been answered satisfactorily. You would find necessary information in the data sheets accompanying whatever devices you used within the microcomputer system itself, and within the external logic.

Once the interrupt has been acknowledged, the Data, I/O, READ and WRITE signals are used to transmit data to and from external logic. The data lines interface the interrupt priority device to the external system bus, while the I/O pins interface the parallel I/O device with external logic, as illustrated in Figure 5-16.

External logic can use an interrupt priority device to initially request an interrupt, but once the interrupt has been acknowledged, the external logic can transfer data to or from the microcomputer system via a parallel I/O device, or the data lines of the external system bus.

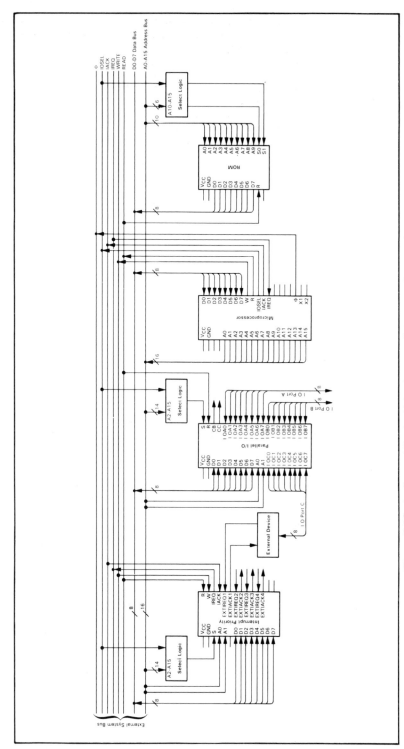

Figure 5-16. An External Device Using Interrupt Priority and Parallel I/O Devices to Interrupt a Microprocessor and Communicate with it

The important point to note is that any programs executed by the microprocessor after an interrupt has been acknowledged will use the same logic as programs executed before the interrupt was acknowledged. Interrupt logic applies only to the process of requesting and acknowledging an interrupt. If external devices connect to the microcomputer system via I/O ports before the interrupt, they will do likewise after the interrupt has been acknowledged. If external devices connect to the microcomputer system via the data lines of the external system bus, they will do so before and after an interrupt is acknowledged.

Interrupt Priority and Daisy Chaining

If a microprocessor has only one interrupt request line, or if more than one external device connects to a single, prioritized interrupt request, then a method called "daisy chaining" can be used to determine interrupt priorities.

A number of devices in a daisy chain will all connect to a single interrupt request line, illustrated below as IREQ. However, the interrupt acknowledge line, illustrated below as IACK, will terminate at one external device. This device must have internal logic which passes on the interrupt acknowledge if no interrupt is being requested, but traps IACK otherwise. Each external device in the daisy chain contains this same logic, except for the last device, which has nowhere to pass the acknowledge on to. Daisy chaining may be illustrated as follows:

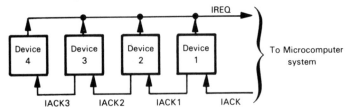

For example, suppose Device 2 has requested an interrupt; IREQ is output high. Some time later the microprocessor acknowledges the interrupt by returning IACK high. Device 1 receives IACK. Device 1 is not requesting an interrupt, therefore it outputs IACK1 high. Device 2 receives IACK1; it is requesting an interrupt, therefore it outputs IACK2 low. Any downstream device receiving a low ("off") acknowledge input will automatically propagate this "off" acknowledge, thereby preventing any downstream device from receiving an interrupt acknowledge.

There are strengths and weaknesses associated with having separate priority lines, as compared to daisy chains, in microcomputer systems.

There are situations where separate Interrupt Priority makes sense, because the microprocessor must attend to one external condition at the expense of all others.

For example, most microcomputers have a "highest priority" interrupt which is activated by a power failure. While this may not at first make a lot of sense, consider what happens when power does go down.

Power Fail Interrupt

Microcomputers typically use +5 V DC power supply which is generated from the normal AC power line. Power failure might be detected when AC power falls below 80 percent of normal. But it may be a few thousandths of a second before power drops so low that +5 volts cannot be maintained for the microcomputer. In these few milliseconds, a hundred or more instructions may be executed to prepare for power failure in an orderly fashion; now when power comes up again, a power fail interrupted program can restart without loss of data.

The limits of daisy chaining may also make separate interrupt acknowledge signals desirable.
Daisy chaining will handle a number of devices, all of which require interrupt service, so long as the number does not become too large. Consider how little service the 100th shower would get if the microcomputer system must first respond to the needs of the 99 showers that came before it in the daisy chain. It is quite conceivable that the microcomputer system will be so busy attending to devices situated at the beginning of the daisy chain that the tail-end devices would get little or no attention. The occupant of Room 100 will get scalded — or freeze.

Another problem with daisy chaining is that it demands intelligence of any external device in the daisy chain. Once again, we are dealing with microcomputer economics. External devices in a daisy chain must identify themselves, otherwise the microcomputer system has no way of knowing how far down the daisy chain the interrupt acknowledge signal IACK went before it got trapped. So we are back to demanding that external devices in the daisy chain contain sufficient logic to trap the acknowledge signal when an interrupt is being requested, then to transmit a device identification code to the microcomputer system. Certainly this logic could be implemented for a few dollars, but remember a microcomputer does not cost too many dollars either.

DIRECT MEMORY ACCESS

The shower temperature controlling microcomputer system will spend a lot of its time simply receiving data from temperature sensors and storing the data in a RAM buffer. Program RECORD is executed at this time.

We have described how interrupts may be used to execute program RECORD whenever the temperature sensor is ready to transmit data. Let us take another, more careful look at this scheme.

Remember the temperature sensor can transmit approximately two temperature readings per second. To a microprocessor this is equivalent to receiving a temperature reading once every quarter of a million instruction executions — approximately.

Asynchronous Events
A cheap temperature sensor is not going to transmit exactly two temperature readings per second. In fact, there could be considerable time period variations between temperature transmittals. As a result, we cannot predict, with any degree of accuracy, the time delay between consecutive data transmittals from the temperature sensor to the microcomputer system. Therefore, data transmittals from the temperature sensor to the microcomputer system constitute asynchronous events:

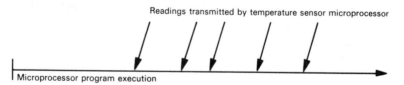

Readings transmitted by temperature sensor microprocessor

Microprocessor program execution

Because data transmittals from the temperature sensor to the microcomputer system are somewhat unpredictable (or asynchronous), program RECORD must be executed every time the temperature sensor transmits a data item. Program RECORD contains the instruction sequence which will move data from an I/O port to a RAM memory byte; this instruction sequence cannot be part of program ADJUST, since the logic of program ADJUST cannot detect the arrival of data from a temperature sensor. **Any scheme that executes program RECORD at fixed time intervals is bound to miss a large number of the data transmittals from the temperature sensor.** Here is an example:

Readings transmited by temperature sensor microprocessor

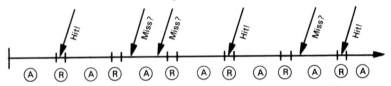

Ⓐ represents normal execution of program ADJUST. Ⓡ represents fixed, periodic execution of the instruction sequence which records data transmitted by the temperature sensor to the microcomputer system. If.transmitted data does not reach the microcomputer system during Ⓡ it may be missed.

In our discussion of interrupts we explained that the only safe way of catching all data transmitted by the temperature sensor is to have the temperature sensor request an interrupt when it is ready to transmit a data item. In response to the temperature sensor's interrupt request, the microcomputer system will execute the data sensing instruction sequence, characterized in the illustration above by Ⓡ . The illustration must now be modified as follows:

Readings transmited by temperature sensor microprocessor

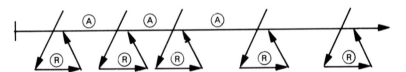

Each time the temperature sensor is ready to transmit data to the microcomputer system, it notifies the microprocessor by requesting an interrupt. In response to the interrupt request, program logic suspends execution of program ADJUST (Ⓐ) while executing program RECORD (Ⓡ). Program RECORD reads the data input by the temperature sensor, then program ADJUST continues execution from the point of suspension.

Even this method of recording data transmitted by the temperature sensor is not very efficient. **This is what happens when the CPU accepts an interrupt and executes RECORD:**

1) The CPU is executing program ADJUST ((A)) in the illustration above. When the CPU senses an interrupt request, it executes an instruction sequence ich saves the contents of CPU registers and status; then it executes an instruction to acknowledge the interrupt.

2) Program RECORD ((R) in the illustration above) is executed. This program contains instructions which load a memory address into the data counter, read data from an I/O port into the accumulator, then output the data from the accumulator to the memory word addressed by the data counter.

3) Step 1 is reversed. Saved contents of registers and status are restored and program ADJUST continues execution.

Out of all the instructions that get executed to implement the above three steps, the only change, each time the temperature sensor transmits a reading and (R) is reexecuted, is the contents of the data counter in Step 2. The contents of the data counter will be one more than it was last time, and one less than it will be the next time. Fifty microseconds, or more, may be needed to repetitively process an otherwise trivial sequence of events. Before we can decide whether this is a serious or an inconsequential problem, we must ask two questions:

1) **Are operations like this fairly common, or is this an isolated and special situation?**
The answer is that it is one of the most common operations performed by a microprocessor. In fact, not only will a microprocessor spend a great deal of time reading data from an external device, it will spend almost as much time routinely transmitting data from RAM buffers to external devices.

2) **If the microprocessor did not spend 50 microseconds every time it input data from an external device (or output to an external device), what else would it do with the time?**
In many simple applications the answer is nothing, in which case the wasted time is irrelevant. But clearly, as a microcomputer application starts to get more complex, the waste of time starts to become more serious. If it takes 50 microseconds to read a data item from an external device, and another 50 microseconds to transmit a data item to the same external device, then one microcomputer system could perform one hundred data transfers per second — but there would be no time left to do anything else.

We must therefore conclude that there will be a significant number of applications in which the time wasted processing interrupts will be intolerable.

CYCLE STEALING DIRECT MEMORY ACCESS

Direct memory access (DMA) provides a much faster way of moving data between I/O ports and memory. We will create a new device for our microcomputer system, and on this device we will place a small amount of CPU-type logic, dedicated to the sole task of moving data across the external system bus.

DMA Controller Device

We will call this new device a direct memory access (DMA) Controller.

The DMA Controller device will suppress CPU logic, take control of the external system bus, then generate appropriate signals to effect the desired data transfer. **The DMA Controller** thus **disables, then mimics the microprocessor.**

Given the microcomputer system architecture that has been described in this chapter, the task of designing a DMA Controller device is quite straightforward.

There are two ways in which a DMA Controller device can suppress CPU logic within the microprocessor: it can manipulate the microprocessor clock signal, or it can force the microprocessor to mark time and float its signal connections.

Stretched Clock Signal

Since every CPU is driven by an external clock signal, if we stop or "stretch" the clock signals, we will stop the CPU.

A "stretched" clock signal may be illustrated as follows:

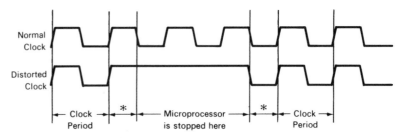

* Two halves of one clock period

The microprocessor can have **a control input that causes it to float all external system bus pin connections** while suspending internal operations. This **may be illustrated as follows:**

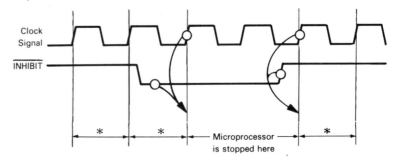

*Normal clock periods

Both of the microprocessor disabling techniques have been used by different semiconductor manufacturers to handle direct memory access.

A microprocessor that is inhibited using the "clock stretching" technique must also have its external system bus pin connections floated before the DMA Controller device can gain control of the external system bus. Were the microprocessor's external system bus pin connections not floated, then contentions would arise when the DMA Controller device attempted to gain control of the external system bus, since the microprocessor would still be competing for bus control, albeit with constant bus signal levels. **Some microprocessors that are inhibited by clock stretching do automatically float their external system bus pin connections as soon as they are inhibited; other microprocessors do not.** It is then necessary to interpose a 3-state buffer between the microprocessor and the external system bus. This may be illustrated as follows:

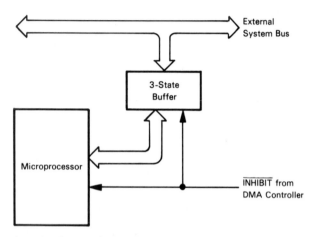

The important point to note is that two separate and unrelated problems must be resolved by a DMA Controller before it can gain control of the external system bus. The DMA Controller must disconnect the microprocessor from the external system bus; but it must also force the microprocessor to "mark time," doing nothing for as long as it is disconnected. In the illustration above the 3-state Buffer disconnects the microprocessor from the external system bus, while the microprocessor's INHIBIT input causes it to mark time.

Figure 5-17 illustrates a simple DMA Controller device. Figure 5-18 illustrates the DMA Controller device integrated into a microcomputer system.

DMA Device Registers

Consider Figure 5-17. The DMA device, as illustrated, contains these four registers:

1) **An Address register** which contains the address of the next memory location to be accessed, either for a read or a write operation.
2) **A Counter register** which contains the number of contiguous memory locations remaining to be filled during a write sequence, or out of which data is to be read for the balance of a read sequence.
3) **A Control register** which identifies the direction of data flow, and is used to start, stop, or otherwise control DMA operations.
4) **A Status register** which is used to identify the status of any DMA operation that may be in progress.

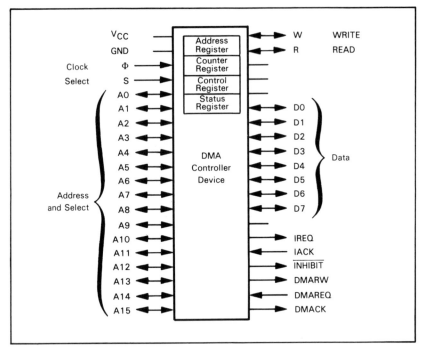

Figure 5-17. A Direct Memory Access Controller Device

We discussed Control and Status registers earlier in this chapter when describing the parallel I/O device. In the discussion which follows we will, therefore, refer to these registers only where it is pertinent to DMA concepts being described. The various addressable locations within our DMA Controller device can be accessed using any number of addresses. **None of the problems that surround parallel I/O device register addressings apply to the DMA Controller.** This is because the DMA Controller must receive all 16 address lines in order to transmit a 16-bit address while executing a DMA data transfer (as we will describe shortly).

Initially the microprocessor will execute instructions to set beginning values in the Address, Counter, and Control registers. Here is an example:

0080	Address Register
007F	Counter Register
03	Control Register

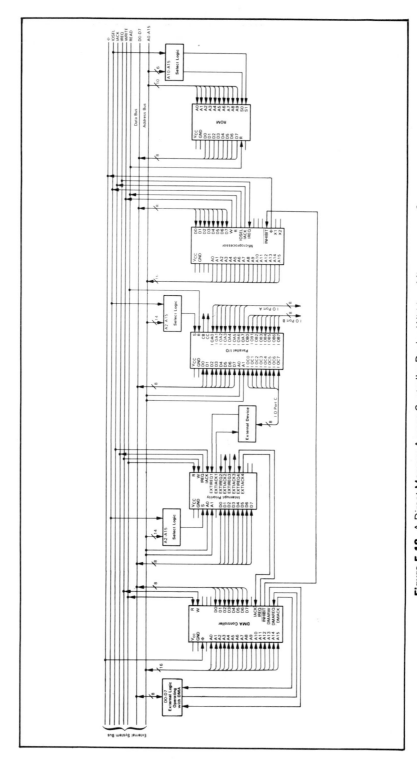

Figure 5-18. A Direct Memory Access Controller Device Within a Microcomputer System

This simple example specifies that a data buffer $7F_{16}$ bytes long and origined at memory location 0080_{16} is to be filled with data from an external device, using direct memory access.

The Control register is, for the moment, limited to these simple bit assignments:

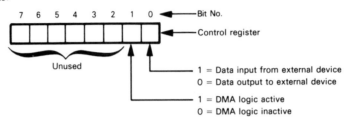

By setting a value of 03_{16} in the Control register, data input from an external device is specified, and DMA logic is activated.

DMA
Initialization
A program must be executed by the CPU to initialize a DMA operation. The program will have to load data appropriately into DMA device registers. There is no other way for data to get into the DMA device Address, Counter, and Control registers.

In order to initialize a DMA operation, a program would be executed by the microprocessor to perform these steps:

1) Transmit a starting memory address to the DMA Controller's Address register.
2) Transmit a memory word count to the DMA Controller's Counter register.
3) Transmit a control code (03_{16}, as illustrated above) to the Control register of the DMA device. The control code must identify the direction of the data transfer and must turn the DMA device on.

Notice that the DMA Controller device READ and WRITE control signals, and its address lines, are bidirectional.

When no DMA operation is in progress, the microprocessor has control of the external system bus; the DMA Controller functions as any other microprocessor support device. At this time the READ and WRITE controls and the address lines function as inputs to the DMA Controller device. The microprocessor uses these control and address inputs to read from, or write to any of the DMA Controller device registers.

Once a DMA operation begins, the microprocessor is disabled; the DMA Controller device takes control of the external system bus. At this time the READ and WRITE controls and the address lines function as outputs. The DMA Controller device outputs READ and WRITE controls and addresses, mimicking the disabled microprocessor. The address which is output by the DMA Controller will always be taken from the Address register.

Bus Master
The microprocessor is usually the "bus master" in a microcomputer system. As bus master, the microprocessor controls activity on the external system bus, and thence, throughout the microcomputer system. For example, as bus master, the microprocessor selects other devices connected to the external system bus in order to activate these devices at the proper time. But the DMA Controller device becomes bus master during a DMA operation, while the microprocessor is disabled.

The DMA Controller device needs a select input, even though the DMA Controller receives the entire address bus as an input. The microprocessor will use this select input to address the DMA Controller device's programmable registers. In the absence of a select input, the DMA Controller would need internal select logic that decoded the incoming 16-bit address. But each DMA Controller would then need a unique internal select code. You will recall from our earlier discussion of ROM select logic that internal select codes are restrictive, and currently unfashionable among semiconductor manufacturers.

However, note carefully that the DMA Controller device's select logic will be active only while the microprocessor is bus master, accessing the DMA Controller as it would any other support device. Specifically, select logic will be inactive while a DMA operation is actually in progress. At that time the DMA Controller device will be bus master and the microprocessor will be disabled: the DMA Controller will be doing the selecting; it will not be selected.

DMA Caught on the Fly

The microprocessor can, and probably will read the contents of DMA Controller registers in order to check on the status of any DMA event sequence. Typically the microprocessor will read the DMA Controller's Status register contents to check for error conditions. The microprocessor may also read the contents of the Address and/or Counter registers in order to determine how far the DMA event sequence has progressed. A program can then adjust its logic sequence based on how far the DMA operation has proceeded. **This is referred to as catching DMA on the fly.**

DMA Being Turned Off

Of course, **the microprocessor can turn a DMA operation off at any time** by simply writing new data to the DMA device's Control register. As described above, resetting bit 1 of the Control register to 0 will immediately stop any DMA operation that was in progress.

Because of the way in which DMA operations occur, any program executed by the microprocessor does not even realize a DMA operation is occurring — except for the fact that program execution will be slowed slightly. Conceptually this may be illustrated as follows:

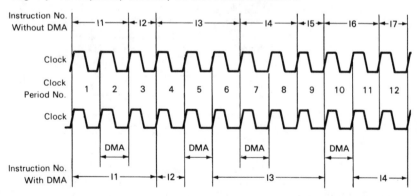

Program logic must, of course, initialize any DMA operation by writing appropriate information to DMA Controller registers. Subsequently, when conditions arise that require a DMA data transfer to occur, the microprocessor simply skips a clock period. As illustrated above, this clock period may, by chance, occur between execution of two instructions, or it may occur in the middle of an instruction's execution.

All operations within the microprocessor freeze — going into a state of suspended animation — for the DMA clock cycles; therefore the occurrence of the DMA transfer is, to the microprocessor, the same as inserting a dummy clock period during which nothing happens.

The important DMA concept to understand is that the occurrence of a DMA transfer has no impact whatsoever on program logic or microprocessor operations — except for the fact that operations are slowed down by the number of clock periods which DMA logic steals. In particular, your program logic need not allow for the fact that DMA transfer may be occurring simultaneously with the program's execution. The only exception to this occurs in those few instances when program logic computes time based on how long it takes a particular instruction to execute (we discuss this programming technique in Chapter 6). Such logic ceases to work if simultaneous DMA operations occur, since DMA logic steals clock cycles unpredictably, and in consequence increases an instruction's apparent execution time by one or more clock cycles.

Let us now examine exactly how a DMA READ or WRITE operation occurs.

What starts a DMA operation?

DMA Transfer Initiation

In Figure 5-18 notice that external devices connect directly to the data lines of the external system bus. In addition, three signals connect external devices with the DMA Controller. An external device outputs the DMA request signal DMAREQ to the DMA Controller when it is ready for the next DMA transfer. The DMA Controller acknowledges the DMA request by returning DMACK to the external device. At the same time the DMA Controller outputs DMARW to the external device, telling it whether the next DMA operation will be a read or write. We arbitrarily specify that DMARW will be high for a "read" from memory to external logic. DMARW will be low for a "write" from external logic to memory. **If data is being read from the external device and written into memory, the following signal sequence will occur:**

DMA Write Operation

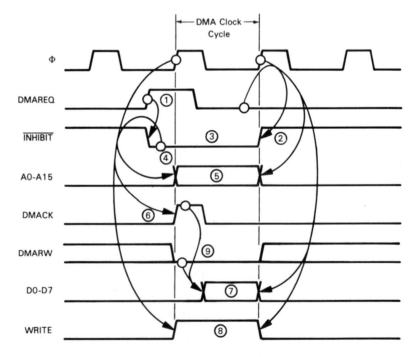

For this DMA WRITE operation, events occur as follows:

1) When external logic is ready for a DMA transfer, it outputs a high DMAREQ pulse.

2) As soon as the DMA Controller senses a high pulse at the DMAREQ input, it immediately lowers the INHIBIT control output (① above). The INHIBIT control is kept low until the second rising edge of clock Φ (at ② above).

3) The microprocessor will suspend all operations for one clock period, while it is receiving a low INHIBIT input (③ above). The microprocessor will also float its external system bus connections at this time.

4) The DMA Controller acknowledges the external device's DMA requests by outputting DMACK high (⑥ above).

5) The DMA Controller now mimics everything the microprocessor would have done during a write operation. It outputs an address (⑤ above) and a high WRITE control pulse (⑧ above). The address is output directly from the Address register of the DMA Controller. (Prior to the DMA operation the microprocessor will have written a beginning address to the DMA Controller Address register in the process of initializing the DMA operation.)

6) The DMA Controller outputs the DMARW signal low to external logic (⑨ above) in order to identify the DMA operation as a write. Note that external logic must provide the data during a write operation, and receive the data during a read operation.

   We have arbitrarily assigned bit 0 of the DMA Control register to determine whether the DMARW control line will be high or low. As illustrated above, it is low, indicating to external logic that it must transmit data to the data lines of the external system bus. The combination of DMACK high and DMARW low causes the external device to place its data on the data lines of the external system bus (⑦ above).

7) All RAM interface devices will decode the address on the address lines. One RAM device will find itself selected. On sensing the WRITE control high, the selected RAM device will take whatever data is on the data lines of the external system bus and will write this data into the addressed memory word. RAM interface logic neither knows nor cares where data, address, and control signals originated. It simply responds to any situation which activates its internal logic.

8) The DMA Controller will decrement the contents of its Counter register. It will also increment or decrement the Address register contents. Incrementing or decrementing the Address register prepares the address for the next sequential DMA operation. Some DMA Controller devices increment the address; others decrement it. Still others allow you the option of incrementing or decrementing the address using a Control register bit to determine whether the address is to be incremented or decremented. Invariably the Counter register, when it decrements to 0, triggers a DMA termination in some fashion. We discuss common termination options later.

9) The second rising edge of Φ terminates the DMA write operation.

**DMA Read
Timing**

Here is the signal sequence for a DMA read operation:

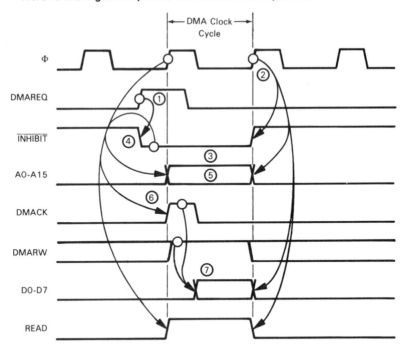

The DMA read operation differs from the DMA write operation only in that the DMA device sets the READ control signal high when it places the contents of its Address register on the address lines of the external system bus. This causes the memory module which is selected by the memory address to place the contents of the addressed memory word on the data lines of the external system bus. DMARW, set high by the DMA Controller, causes the external device to read the contents of the data bus.

Once again the DMA device will decrement its Counter register and increment (or decrement) its Address register, so that it is ready for the next DMA operation.

One, or both of the following may happen when the Counter register decrements to zero:

DMA End

1) **The DMA device may signal the fact that the DMA operation is over by sending an interrupt request to the CPU.** This interrupt would be handled according to whatever interrupt processing logic the CPU is using.

2) **The DMA Controller may simply restart the DMA sequence just concluded** by saving the original value of the Counter register and Address register; the DMA Controller can reload these original values and allow operations to proceed endlessly, or until stopped by the CPU.

The two options available when the DMA device counts down to zero are illustrated as follows: First the "end of DMA interrupt":

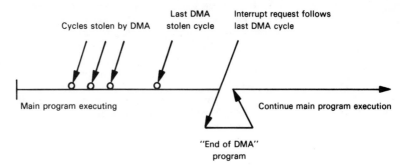

Next consider a DMA device with additional storage registers for the initial address and buffer length count:

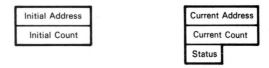

When "Current Count" goes to 0, "Initial Count" is loaded into "Current Count," and "Initial Address" is loaded into "Current Address"; Control register contents remain unchanged (unless modified by the CPU), and the just-ended DMA operation starts over.

DMA WITH MULTIPLE EXTERNAL DEVICES

One DMA Controller device can control DMA operations for many external devices. Since a DMA Controller does not actually transfer any data, it does not need any data pins. External devices connect directly to the data lines of the external system bus. This arrangement is very convenient, since it allows the DMA Controller to manage DMA accesses for a number of external devices without needing an excessive number of pins.

Many schemes could be devised which allow one DMA Controller to manage DMA access for more than one external device; Figure 5-19 illustrates just one possibility.

The DMA Controller illustrated in Figure 5-19 controls DMA access for five external devices. Each external device has its own DMA request line (DMAREQ1 through DMAREQ5). Common DMA acknowledge (DMACK) and DMA read/write control (DMARW) lines are used by all devices.

There are five sets of registers within the DMA Controller, one set for each external device. Each external device, when it is ready to transmit or receive data, indicates this fact by setting its own DMA request line high. DMA Controller logic accesses the correct four registers based on the DMA request received. For example, DMAREQ3 high identifies Address 3, Counter 3, Control 3, and Status 3 as the registers containing the information to be used this time.

When the DMA Controller illustrated in Figure 5-19 steals a cycle and transfers a data word via DMA, the signal sequence is identical to that which we have already described for a single external device. However, external devices in Figure 5-19 must contain their own select logic. In other words, a device which raises its DMA request line must be the only device to respond to DMACK, DMARW and the external system bus; no other external device may respond to these lines. It is the responsibility of external logic, not the DMA Controller, to ensure that only one external device considers itself selected at any time.

If only one external device considers itself selected for DMA at any time, then there is no possibility of confusion in DMA data transfers. Memory modules merely respond to address and control signals output by the DMA Controller. Memory modules neither know nor care where this information had its origin. Only the selected external device is active at the other end of the external system bus, so the two ends of the data transfer are clearly defined.

Let us consider an example in detail.

External device 2 is ready for another access, so it raises DMAREQ2 high:

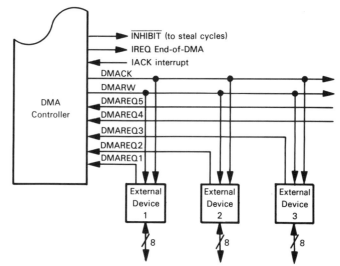

To Data Lines of External System Bus

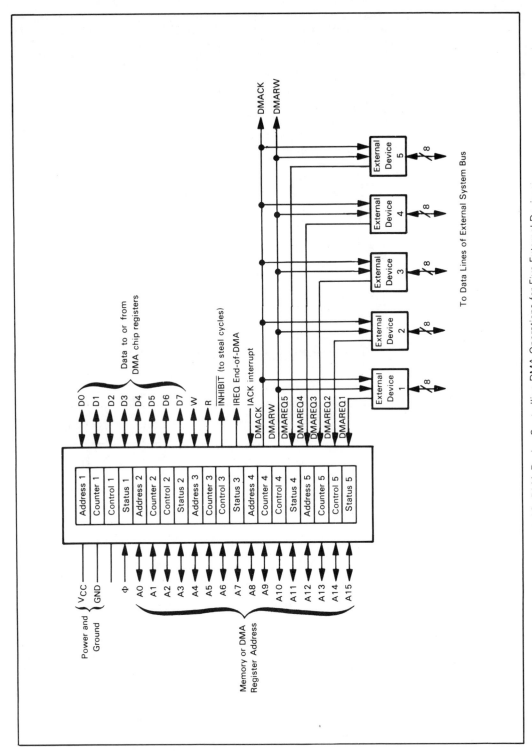

Figure 5-19. DMA Device Controlling DMA Operations for Five External Devices

The first thing DMA Controller logic will do is check the control register associated with DMAREQ2, in this case, register Control 2. If the enable bit (bit 0) is 0, DMA Controller logic will ignore the DMA request. If the enable bit is 1, DMA Controller logic will acknowledge the DMA request via DMACK and steal a CPU cycle by lowering INHIBIT.

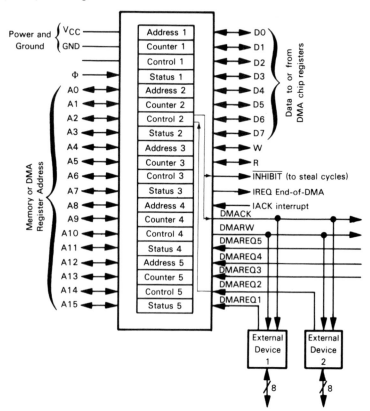

To Data Lines of External System Bus

For the upcoming DMA operation, only external device 2 can participate at the external end of the data transfer.

DMAREQ2 causes the contents of Address register 2 to be output at the DMA Controller's address pins:

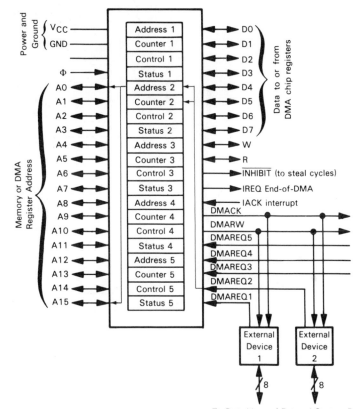

To Data Lines of External System Bus

DMA Controller logic will decrement the contents of Counter 2 and increment the contents of Address 2.

Since DMAREQ2 identifies Address 2 as the DMA Controller register containing the required memory address, no confusion can result from the fact that four other addresses, in four other Address registers, are present.

DMAREQ2 also identifies Control 2 as the Control register controlling current operations. The W, R, and DMARW control lines are set based on the contents of Control 2:

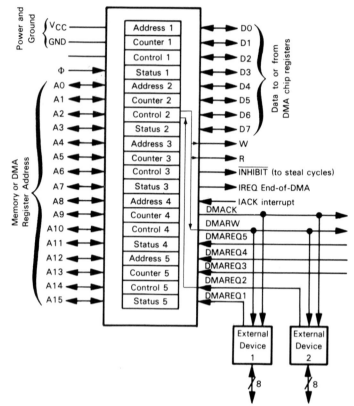

To Data Lines of External System Bus

A data transfer now occurs between the memory word addressed by Address 2 and external device 2. Signal sequences associated with the data transfer are exactly as described for the single external device DMA chip.

DMA Acknowledge Priorities

External devices could daisy chain the DMA acknowledge signal DMACK in order to establish priorities among themselves. We have already described daisy-chaining logic in conjunction with our discussion of interrupt priority controllers. In this instance, daisy-chaining logic might be illustrated as follows:

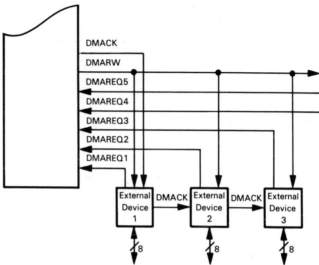

To Data Lines of External System Bus

Daisy Chaining

External device 1 receives DMACK directly from the DMA Controller. If external device 1 has an active DMA request, then it will trap DMACK, passing on a low signal to external device 2, which in turn will propagate this low signal to all lower priority devices. But if external device 1 is not requesting DMA access, then it will pass on a high DMACK to external device 2, which will handle its DMACK input and output in the same fashion as external device 1.

Daisy-chaining will frequently be unacceptable as a means of establishing priorities among a number of external devices connected to a single DMA Controller. This is because by its very nature, direct memory access operations come in bursts and demand immediate service. A burst of activity at a high priority external device would deny access in any reasonable amount of time to a low priority device. **Some DMA Controllers resolve this problem by providing external devices with individual DMA acknowledge signals,** just as our Interrupt Controller (in one of its optional variations) was shown providing external logic with individual interrupt acknowledge signals.

The 40-pin package illustrated in Figure 5-17 would restrict us to three DMA requests and companion DMA acknowledge signals. DMA Controller devices that provide individual DMA acknowledge signals usually give you a bewildering profusion of programmable options whereby you can determine DMA acknowledge priorities via appropriate Control register bit settings.

Data Paths During Direct Memory Access Operations

During the direct memory access read and write operations we have described thus far, the DMA Controller device sits outside of the data path, mimicking the CPU during the DMA clock period, by providing appropriate addresses and control signals. This may be illustrated as follows:

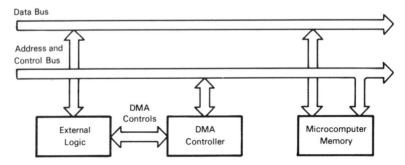

Most DMA Controller devices did indeed operate as illustrated above. But **recently a number of DMA Controller devices have been designed to actually receive and retransmit data.** This may illustrated as follows:

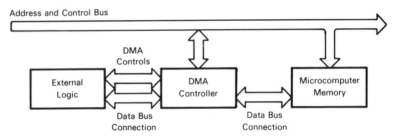

The DMA Controller device that receives and retransmits data gains something and loses something. It gains the ability to interpret or process a stream of data being transferred via direct memory access. It loses the ability to perform a DMA operation in a single machine cycle.

DMA Data in Transit Operations

Being able to operate on data being transferred via direct memory access is more valuable than might at first appear. For example, a DMA data stream frequently consists of bytes representing ASCII characters, interspaced with control codes. The ASCII characters are to be handled as data. The control codes modify program logic. For example, control codes might be interpreted by a program as identifying the first or last ASCII character of a message; or a control code may identify the type of message.

If your DMA Controller device does not receive and retransmit data, then the microprocessor must execute a special program, once the DMA transfer has been completed, in order to detect and interpret control codes that might be imbedded in the data stream. But a DMA Controller that receives and retransmits data will usually perform this task as part of the DMA operation.

Each DMA transfer will be slower if the DMA Controller has to receive and retransmit data. This is because each piece of information transferred using DMA will now require two clock periods, one to receive the data, the next to retransmit it. This may be illustrated as follows:

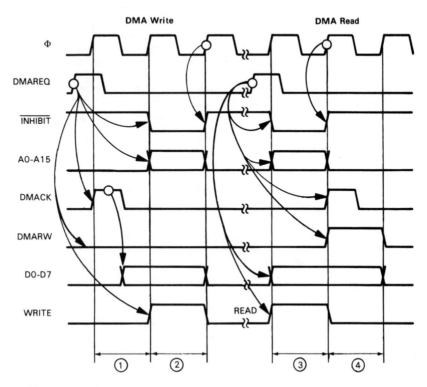

① Data from External Logic to DMA Controller
② Data from DMA Controller to Memory
③ Data from Memory to DMA Controller
④ Data from DMA Controller to External Logic

Our DMA timing diagrams show a read or write occurring within a single clock period, rather than within a single machine cycle (that may have two or more clock periods). Different microprocessors will time a DMA transfer in a clock period or a machine cycle. There is nothing significant in our use of single clock period transfers; **we select them simply because they make illustrations easier to follow.**

The timing diagrams above are minor variations of the DMA write and DMA read single-cycle transfers which we described previously. In the variations illustrated above, data is shown transferring between external logic and the DMA Controller in one clock period, while it moves between the DMA Controller and memory in an adjacent clock period. External logic is not addressed in the manner of memory or I/O ports, since external logic will be selected by control signals generated by the DMA Controller. When we were dealing with a DMA transfer that occurred in a single clock period, it was mandatory that external logic be identified without a memory or I/O port address, since the entire DMA transfer occurred within a single clock period, during which just one address could be output. This address identified a memory location or I/O port within the microcomputer system. But a two clock period DMA transfer can output two addresses, one in each clock period. This allows DMA logic to handle data transfers occurring entirely within the microcomputer system; for example, data may now be transferred, using DMA logic, from memory to memory, from I/O port to I/O port, or between memory and an I/O port. Adjacent read and write clock periods, with the DMA Controller providing the addresses and control signals, implement this two-address DMA transfer.

Data
Transfer
Types

The various types of DMA operation which you might encounter may therefore be summarized as follows:

1) A data transfer occurring in a single clock period (or machine cycle), transferring data between external logic that is identified without an address, and a memory location or I/O port within the microcomputer system that is identified via an appropriate address. During this type of DMA transfer, data bypasses the DMA Controller itself; therefore the DMA Controller cannot operate on the data in any way.

2) A two clock period (or machine cycle) data transfer. Data is transferred between external logic which is identified without a memory address, and a memory location or I/O port within the microcomputer system that is identified via an appropriate addess. The data can now be transferred via the DMA Controller itself, in which case the DMA Controller can operate on the in-transit data. It is possible for the DMA transfer to require more than two clock periods, with additional clock periods being used by the DMA Controller to perform required operations on in-transit data.

3) DMA transfers as described above for 2, but occurring entirely within the microcomputer system, between memory and memory, I/O port and I/O port, or between memory and an I/O port. An appropriate address will identify the source and the destination.

Multiple Bus Microcomputer Configurations

A microcomputer system that makes extensive use of cycle stealing direct access will soon start to have an impact on the microprocessor's program execution speed. In the majority of microprocessor applications this never becomes a problem, since the microprocessor is capable of executing the program much faster than the application demands. But in those applications where program execution speed does have a problem, there is a solution: we can create a second external system bus and use it to handle direct memory access operations, which can occur in parallel with microprocessor program execution. Figure 5-20 conceptually illustrates such a configuration.

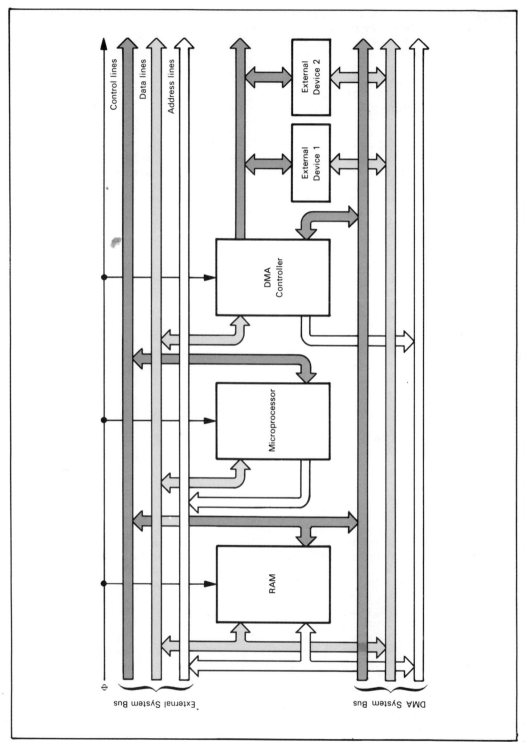

Figure 5-20. Data, Address, and Control Paths Used in Simultaneous DMA.

Figure 5-20 shows a microcomputer system with an external system bus and a DMA system bus. The microprocessor connects to memory devices via the external system bus; it also accesses the DMA Controller as a support part — much as it would a parallel I/O device or an Interrupt Controller. Thus the microprocessor can transmit control and address information, as data, to the DMA Controller, in order to initiate any DMA operation.

The DMA Controller may be likened to a CPU which is capable of executing just two instructions:

1) Transfer data from an external device to memory.
2) Transfer data from memory to an external device.

On the DMA system bus shown in Figure 5-20, the DMA Controller will function as bus master, controlling DMA system bus activity. Thus the DMA Controller will connect with the address, data and the control lines of the DMA system bus. In addition, external devices and RAM connect with the DMA system bus. This allows DMA data to be transferred between RAM and external devices, via the DMA system bus, under DMA Controller management, while the microprocessor simultaneously executes programs that use the external system bus.

There is a major problem inherent in the configuration illustrated in Figure 5-20; RAM access contentions are going to arise. If the microprocessor and the DMA Controller are to access the same read/write memory, then this **read/write memory must have a 3-state buffer, functioning as a T-junction, connecting it to the external and DMA system busses.** This may be illustrated as follows:

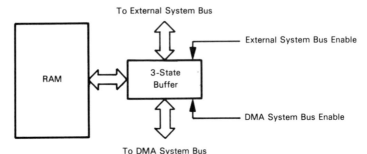

This T-junction connection negates much of the second DMA system bus' value, since memory cannot connect to both busses at the same time. Therefore, if the microprocessor and DMA Controller both wish to access the same read/write memory device at the same time, one or the other will have to wait. This is not as bad a contention problem as cycle stealing, where every DMA access takes machine cycles from the microprocessor, whether or not there is the possibility of a memory access contention; but it is, nevertheless, a problem.

Logic surrounding the T-junction which connects memory to two busses is also far from trivial. Not only must we worry about the microprocessor and DMA Controller simultaneously trying to access the same memory device, we must also worry about access delays on one bus affecting instruction execution timing or DMA transfer. These are all problems that can be solved, the solution depending on specific characteristics of the microprocessor and/or the DMA Controller. But **the most recent microprocessors have avoided memory access contention problems by moving the T-junction to the microprocessor and the DMA Controller, where it can be handled within program logic.**

Figure 5-21 illustrates a simple two-bus configuration where the microprocessor and the DMA Controller both connect to two busses. Separate memory and support devices connect to one bus, or the other, but no memory or support device connects to both busses. In this configuration, the microprocessor will spend most of its time accessing memory and support devices on the external system bus while the DMA Controller spends most of its time accessing external devices and memory via the DMA system bus. Occasionally the microprocessor will access external devices, or memory connected to the DMA system bus, while the DMA Controller will occasionally access memory and support devices connected to the microprocessor's system bus. These occasional accesses will occur only when information processed by the DMA Controller must be accessed by the microprocessor, or vice versa.

I/O Processor

Taking this concept a step further, Figure 5-22 illustrates a configuration where the microprocessor and DMA Controller each connect to a shared system bus, while also connecting to their own unshared local bus. In such configurations the DMA Controller will often acquire a new character; it will gain a CPU and its own set of executable instructions. Its ability to execute instructions will expand considerably beyond simple data transfer. **Such a device is referred to as an I/O Processor.** An I/O Processor may be visualized as a cross between a DMA Controller and a microprocessor. It can perform DMA data transfers, but in addition it will be able to execute programs. Currently I/O Processors execute programs using instruction sets that are quite restricted, compared to a microprocessor; but in the future that may well change. There is no reason why future microprocessors might not all have DMA capability, while DMA Controllers all include microprocessor logic.

The configuration illustrated in Figure 5-22 is, essentially, two subsystems: the microprocessor system and the I/O Processor system. The two subsystems will use the shared system bus to pass data between themselves. Most of the time the microprocessor will access memory and support devices on its local system bus; the I/O Processor, likewise, will generally access memory and support devices on its local system bus. When the microprocessor wishes to communicate with the I/O Processor, or vice versa, they will deposit information in memory connected to the shared system bus, and then alert the other processor, via an appropriate control signal.

Let us consider an example.

Assume that the I/O Processor receives a stream of data from external devices. This data is stored in memory connected to the I/O Processor's local system bus. The I/O Processor performs certain operations on this data, putting it into a form needed by the microprocessor. After these operations have been performed, the I/O Processor moves the data from its local system bus memory to shared system bus memory. The I/O Processor then transmits an interrupt request to the microprocessor. The microprocessor, meanwhile, has been executing its own program, accessing its own local system bus. Upon detecting the I/O Processor's interrupt request, the microprocessor can execute an interrupt service routine that reads data from the shared system bus memory to memory on the microprocessor's local bus. The microprocessor can then operate on this data while the I/O Processor returns to performing its tasks.

This is the key difference between the configurations illustrated in Figures 5-21 and 5-22: there will be far fewer bus contentions in the configuration illustrated in Figure 5-22; and given the same components, you will generate a microcomputer system that is more powerful and more flexible.

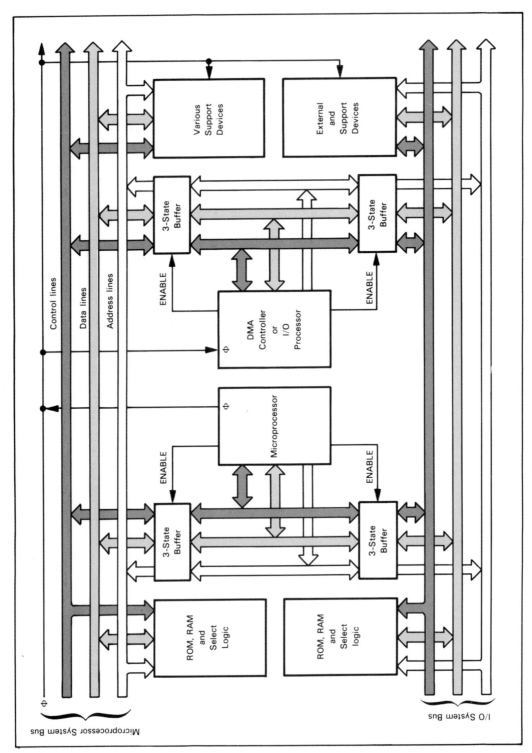

Figure 5-21. A Microcomputer System with Two Shared Busses

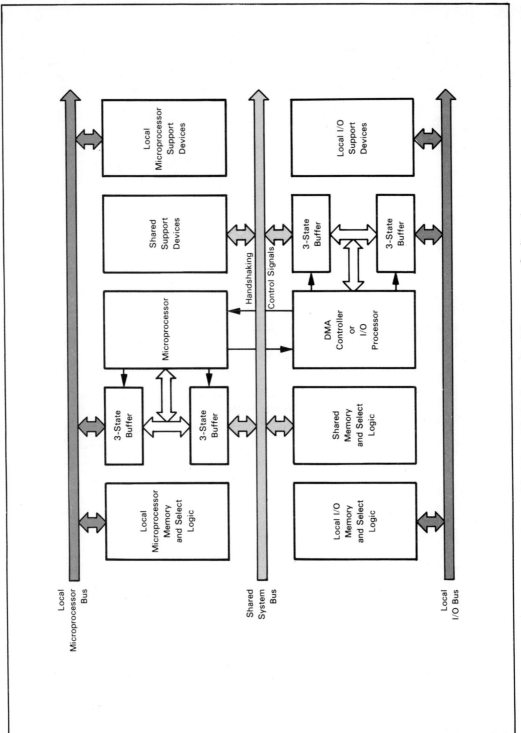

Figure 5-22. A Shared/Local System Bus Microcomputer Configuration

SERIAL INPUT/OUTPUT

Data is transferred over telephone lines serially. There are also some slow I/O devices, such as the common teletypewriter and magnetic tape cassettes, which transmit and receive data serially. If a microprocessor is to transmit or receive serial data, then it must have interface logic capable of converting serial data to parallel data, or parallel data to serial data:

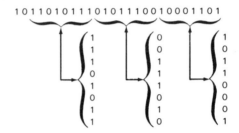

These are the setups via which data is transferred between a telephone line and a microcomputer system:

Modem   A modem is a device which can translate telephone line signals into digital logic levels, or digital logic levels into telephone line signals. Some semiconductor manufacturers build modems as single logic devices, but we do not consider the modem to be part of the microcomputer system; therefore modems are not described in this book.

A magnetic tape cassette unit, a teletypewriter, or any other serial device can connect directly to the serial interface:

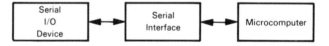

Identifying Serial Data Bits

The unique property of a serial data stream is that the data is transmitted and received as a single signal, via a single device pin:

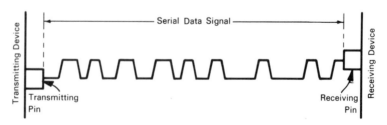

How is the receiving device to interpret a serial signal? Like any other digital signal, the data signal can have a "high" level (near +5 V), or a "low" level (near 0 V).

There are two ways in which a serial data signal can be interpreted.
The first and most obvious way treats a low level signal as a 0 bit and a high level
signal as a 1 bit; the binary digit sequence 011100100 would then be decoded
from a serial data signal as follows:

NRZ
Serial Data

The serial data interpretation illustrated above is called NRZ (non-return to zero) serial data.

NRZI
Serial Data

NRZI (non-return to zero inverted) represents the other common interpretation for serial data. **NRZI interprets signal level changes rather than the signal levels themselves.** A signal level change represents a 1 bit:

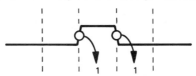

A 0 bit is represented by no signal level change:

Thus the binary data sequence 011100100 would be encoded as follows
by an NRZI serial signal:

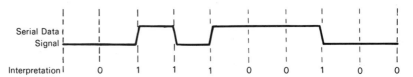

We will use the NRZ convention throughout this chapter.

Clock
Signal

Whereas it is easy for you to look at a serial data signal and interpret it
within the vertical broken lines, the receiving device will require more tangible
evidence of data bit boundaries. **We will use a clock signal to identify the instant at which the receiving device must interpret the data signal:**

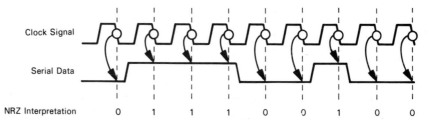

As illustrated above, the falling edge of the clock signal identifies the instant at which the serial data signal must be sampled. We could just as easily sample on the rising edge of the clock signal:

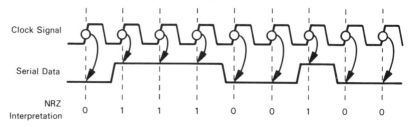

A serial data signal must be created by the transmitting device before it can be interpreted by the receiving device. Let us look into the implications of this simple necessity.

If the receiving device uses a clock to interpret the serial data signal, then the transmitting device must use a clock with the same frequency to create the serial data signal:

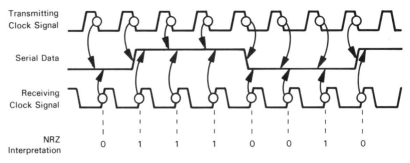

The transmitting and receiving clock signals cannot be identical; this is because, in reality, it takes a finite time for a signal to change state.

Now it makes figures easy to follow if signal transitions are drawn as clean square waves:

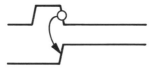

Signal Settling Time
But in reality, as discussed in Chapter 4, every signal that changes state requires a finite settling time:

If you use the same signal transition to transmit and receive serial data, then the signal settling time will result in the receiving logic sampling the serial data signal before a transmitted level change has had time to occur. This may be illustrated as follows:

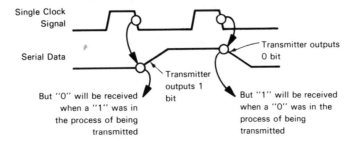

Single Clock Signal

Serial Data

Transmitter outputs 0 bit

Transmitter outputs 1 bit

But "0" will be received when a "1" was in the process of being transmitted

But "1" will be received when a "0" was in the process of being transmitted

Serial Data Transmitting Clock Signal

We conclude that **the transmitting and receiving clock signals,** while they have a great deal in common, **cannot be a single signal subject to identical interpretation.**

The transmitting clock signal will identify the duration of one binary digit:

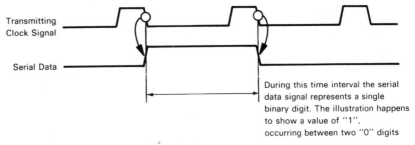

Transmitting Clock Signal

Serial Data

During this time interval the serial data signal represents a single binary digit. The illustration happens to show a value of "1", occurring between two "0" digits

Serial Data Receiving Clock Signal

At some point within the single-digit time interval a **receive clock signal will identify the serial data signal level:**

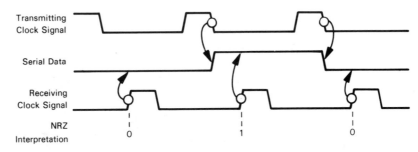

Transmitting Clock Signal

Serial Data

Receiving Clock Signal

NRZ Interpretation

0   1   0

The illustration above shows the transmitting clock signal active on its trailing edge, whereas the receiving clock signal is active on its leading edge; there is nothing significant in this use of signal edges.

**Signal
Settling
Delay**

The receiving device must wait for the Serial Data signal to settle, presuming it has changed state, before trying to read the signal level. At the transmitting end, a signal's settling delay is a characteristic of the transmitting device; the length of this delay is given in the manufacturer's device data sheet. Here is an illustration of settling delay:

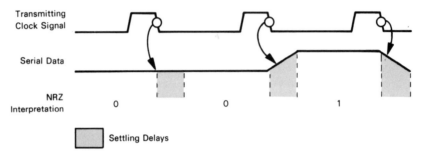

Settling Delays

We can use a single clock signal to transmit and receive serial data, providing we transmit on the trailing edge of a clock pulse, and receive on the leading edge of the next clock pulse:

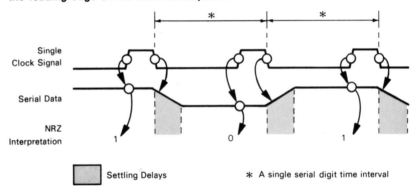

Settling Delays   * A single serial digit time interval

Look carefully at how the transmitted signal level is received:

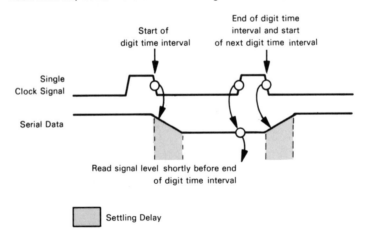

Settling Delay

The time interval during which the Serial Data signal represents a single binary digit is directly related to the speed at which data is being transmitted. Suppose 110 digits per second are being transmitted; this is a common transmission speed. Each serial digit will then endure for:

$$\frac{1}{110 \text{ digits/s}} = 9.091 \text{ milliseconds}$$

Baud Rate

However, the duration of a digit in a serial data stream is not the way in which serial data transfers are measured; instead, **we measure "bits per second," and refer to this number as the "baud rate."** For example, if 110 binary digits per second are transmitted, this is equivalent to a baud rate of 110.

Clock Signals

Our microprocessor already has a clock signal, used to time instruction execution within the CPU. Do not confuse the microprocessor clock with the serial data clock; the only thing these two signals have in common is that they are both clock signals. The serial data clock signal may or may not be derived from the microprocessor clock.

From a microprocessor user's point of view, speed is the most striking difference between the microprocessor clock and the serial data clock. A typical microprocessor clock may have a period of 500 nanoseconds (2 MHz) or less, whereas serial data transfer rates typically range from 110 to 9600 baud (110 Hz to 9.6 kHz). In other words, a fast serial data transfer rate (9.6 kHz) is approximately 200 times slower than a typical microprocessor clock.

Serial ×1 Clock Signal

The serial I/O clock does not necessarily have to pulse at exactly the baud rate, although frequently it does:

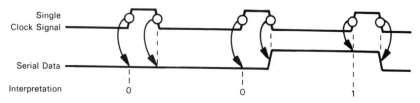

Serial ×16 Clock Signal

It is quite common for the serial I/O clock rate to be 16 times the baud rate:

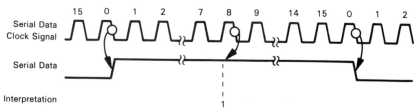

Serial ×64 Clock Signal

64 times the baud rate is also a frequent option:

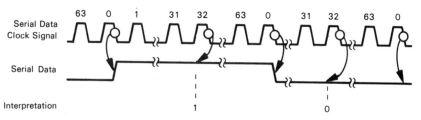

The reason for having ×16 and ×64 clocks is to get as close as possible to the center of a single-digit time interval when sampling the serial data signal.

The fact that serial data needs a companion clock signal does not necessarily mean that all serial I/O requires two signal lines. The accompanying clock signal does not actually have to be transmitted on a companion wire. If you set up a serial data communications interface, with a predefined baud rate, then **receiving device logic does not have to receive a companion clock signal.** Receiving device logic can create its own, local clock signal, synchronizing it with a transition in the serial data line:

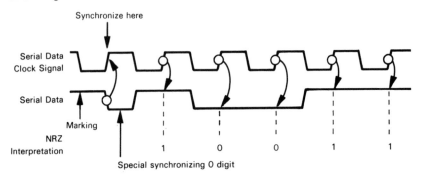

Marking In the illustration above, the Serial Data signal is permanently high when not transmitting data; this is often referred to as "Marking."

Note that when using a ×16 or ×64 clock signal, the receive clock can be one or two pulses out of phase with the transmit clock and no harm will be done. The receive sampling point will simply be skewed a little off center.

If a single synchronization binary digit is insufficient, how about a synchronizing digit pattern?

We can, for example, define a special synchronization serial data bit sequence and set up rules which state that every serial data stream must be preceded by a synchronization pattern. Here is an example:

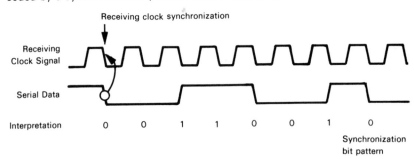

Sync Character Synchronization patterns such as the one illustrated above are called Sync characters.

Protocol in Serial Data Specifying that a serial data stream must use synchronization digits, or characters, is just the first of **many rules** that we must **impose on serial data streams in order to ensure that the receiving device correctly interprets the transmitted data. This set of rules** is referred to as "communications protocol."

Every serial I/O data link must have a communications protocol, since the serial data must be completely self-defining. Unlike parallel data, the serial data line cannot always be accompanied by control lines which tell the receiving device how to interpret the data at any instant.

TELEPHONE LINES

When transmitting serial data over telephone lines, two-way communication will almost always be required. At each end of the telephone line data will be transmitted and received.

Half Duplex

If a single telephone line is used to transmit data in two directions, but the telephone line can only transmit data in one direction at a time, then communication is said to be half duplex.

Full Duplex

If two telephone lines connect the transmitting and receiving devices, with each line being dedicated to data transfer in one direction only, **then communication is said to be full duplex.**

The advantage of full duplex telephone communication is that data transfer in both directions can proceed simultaneously.

ERROR DETECTION

Whether serial data is being transmitted over telephone lines, or directly between a transmitting and a receiving device, we must check for errors in transmission.

If spurious data signals find their way into the serial data line, the receiving device must have some means of determining that errors have crept into the data.

Parity Bit

At a primitive level, the parity bit does this job. **Since the parity bit has been set or reset to ensure that the total number of 1 bits in the data unit is either odd or even, then an odd number of 1 bits in an even parity data unit indicates that an error has occurred, as does an even number of 1 bits in an odd parity data unit. However, if multiple bits erroneously change, but happen to end up with the correct parity, the error will not be detectable through parity.** Here are some examples, assuming odd parity; in all illustrations, the parity bit is shaded and error bits are starred:

Transmitted	Received	Result
101101100	100101100	Even parity, error detected
101101100	110101100	Odd parity, no error detected
100101101	100101100	Even parity, error detected
100101101	011010011	Odd parity, no error detected

Cyclic Redundancy Character

An additional technique used to check for errors in transmission is to append a "cyclic redundacy character" at the end of data stream segments. The cyclic redundancy character is a number created by dividing the transmitted data stream by a fixed polynomial. Here is one commonly used, 17 binary digit divisor:

11000000000000101

The result of dividing this divisor into the transmitted data stream, treating the transmitted data stream as one continuous binary number, becomes the cyclic redundancy character. The receiving device multiplies the received data stream by the cyclic redundancy character. If the result is not the standard divisor, then an error must exist.

The cyclic redundancy character is just one rather simple method used to track down errors in transmission. Very complex methods have been devised not only to track down errors, but also to determine exactly what the error is, so that it can be corrected. Entire books have been written on the subject of error detection and correction, therefore we are not going to discuss the subject any further.

Block Check Character **The cyclic redundancy character is sometimes called a block check character.**

SERIAL INPUT/OUTPUT PROTOCOL

Let us now tie together the miscellaneous necessities of serial data transfer which have been described thus far.

Generally stated, serial data communications protocol can be divided into synchronous and asynchronous categories. You will find protocol easier to understand if you approach synchronous and asynchronous data communications as two separate and distinct entities — not minor variations of a single concept.

SYNCHRONOUS SERIAL DATA TRANSFER

The principal characteristic of synchronous data transfer is that data streams must be continuous.

Having once established a serial data transfer baud rate, the transmitting device MUST transmit a data bit at every character interval; therefore the receiving device knows exactly how to interpret the serial data signal:

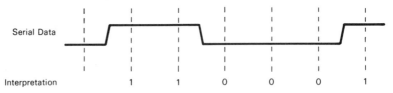

Synchronous serial data could be timed by a clock with a frequency that is 16 or 64 times the baud rate, but in practice it never is. The clock signal accompanying a synchronous serial data signal always has the same frequency as the serial data. In other words, a synchronous serial data clock will output one pulse in each bit time. Conversely, synchronous serial transmit logic, once it has started transmitting a message, is obliged to output a data bit on every transmit clock pulse until the end of the message has been reached. For example, if 300 baud serial synchronous data transfer has been specified, then the receiving device can slice the serial data signal into 3333-microsecond segments, interpreting each segment as a single binary digit. A companion clock transmitted by synchronous serial transmit logic would pulse once every 3333 microseconds, for a total of 300 clock pulses per second.

How is the receiving device to know the bounds of each data unit?

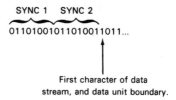

Sync Character

Synchronous protocol must define the length of individual data units — and must provide the receiving device with some way to synchronize on data unit boundaries. The Sync character is used for this purpose. **Every synchronous data stream begins with either one or two Sync characters:**

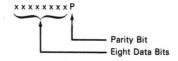

First character of data
stream, and data unit boundary.

The data unit in a synchronous serial data stream usually consists of data bits without parity; but a parity bit may be present. Here is an example of a 9-bit data unit; eight data bits and a parity bit:

x x x x x x x x P
Parity Bit
Eight Data Bits

Either odd or even parity may be specified.

Eight data bits need not always be transmitted; options allow 5, 6, 7, or 8 of the data bits to be meaningful. If less than eight data bits are meaningful, then the balance of high-order bits are ignored. Here is an example of a data unit in which only six data bits are significant:

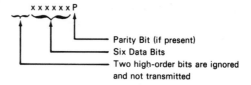

x x x x x x P
Parity Bit (if present)
Six Data Bits
Two high-order bits are ignored
and not transmitted

Serial Synchronous Hunt Mode

While waiting for synchronous serial data to start arriving, a receiving device will enter a ''hunt'' mode, during which the receiving device continuously scans the serial data input trying to match an incoming serial data stream with the standard Sync pattern. If the protocol calls for one Sync character, then the receiving device will start interpreting data as soon as it has matched a single Sync character. More frequently, protocol will call for two initial Sync characters, in which case the receiving device will not start decoding data until it has matched two sequential Sync characters.

We have already stated that synchronous data transmission requires that the transmitting device send data continuously. What if the transmitting device does not have data ready to send? Under these circumstances **the transmitting device will pad with Sync characters until the next real character is ready to transmit.** To illustrate this concept, **consider an operator entering data at a keyboard;** the keyboard transmits data using very slow, synchronous serial I/O. The operator has to enter the message:

GoodƀmorningƀMr.ƀSmith

ƀ represents a space character.

Since the operator will be entering data at variable speed, keyboard serial data transmission logic will insert a Sync character whenever the operator is slow; thus the message might get transmitted as follows:

GoʃoʃoʃʃdʃbʃʃmoʃrnʃsingbʃʃʃMʃrʃʃ.ʃbʃʃSmbbithʃ

ʃ represents a Sync character.

When the receiving device decodes a Sync character in the middle of a message, it will ignore the character, but it will remain in synchronization with the serial data stream, ready to interpret the next character.

Assuming that the message illustrated above is being transmitted in ASCII code, consider this portion of the message:

Mr.

The synchronous serial data stream may be illustrated as follows:

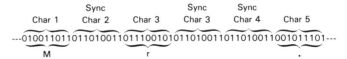

When this serial data stream is actually transmitted, characters are always transmitted beginning with the least significant bit (bit 0), and ending with the most significant bit. Nine-digit characters, including an odd parity bit, are illustrated.

If ASCII characters only are being transmitted, 8-digit characters, including seven data digits and a parity digit, may be used.

BISYNC PROTOCOL

A wide varity of arbitrarily defined protocols have been used to transmit and receive synchronous serial data. These protocols must allow for much more than the character synchronization which we illustrated above using the Sync character. Protocols must allow transmitting and receiving devices to exchange messages, and identify the start or end of individual data messages.

We will now summarize Bisync protocol, probably the most popular of the synchronous serial protocols. The discussion of Bisync protocol which follows is sufficient for you to understand the scope and intent of protocols, and that is all. It is not our intent to describe Bisync protocol in sufficient detail for you to design logic that incorporates this protocol.

Bisync protocol identifies the beginning, the end,and intermediate stages of a message using special control characters which are summarized in Table 5-3. A message itself consists of one or more data blocks; the first data block may optionally be preceded by a heading. The heading will consist of a number of characters that describe the message, without being part of the message. Figure 5-23 illustrates various Bisync messages.

Table 5-3. Bisync Protocol Special Characters

Character	USASCII*	EBCDIC	
SYNC	16_{16}	32_{16}	Sync Character
PAD	FF_{16}	FF_{16}	End of frame pad
DLE	10_{16}	10_{16}	Data link escape
ENQ	05_{16}	$2D_{16}$	Enquiry
SOH	01_{16}	01_{16}	Start of heading
STX	02_{16}	02_{16}	Start of text
ITB	$0F_{16}$	$0F_{16}$	End of intermediate transmission block
ETB	17_{16}	26_{16}	End of transmission block
ETX	03_{16}	03_{16}	End of text

* When using USASCII, only the seven low-order bits are used in detecting control characters. The high-order bit may be used for external odd parity checking.

Bisync protocol allows characters to be transmitted using USASCII or EBCDIC character codes. The serial data signal may be encoded using NRZ or NRZI interpretation; however, all characters must have eight data bits. Usually a ninth parity bit is added when EBCDIC code is used. The ninth parity bit is not needed with USASCII code where the eighth data bit may be used as a parity bit.

Bisync Non-transparent Mode

Bisync protocol allows messages to be sent in transparent or non-transparent modes. In non-transparent modes, Sync characters are discarded by the receiving device when detected in the middle of a message; we illustrated Sync characters earlier, imbedded in the message "Good morning Mr. Smith."

Bisync Transparent Mode

In transparent mode the DLE-SYNC character pair is discarded when detected.

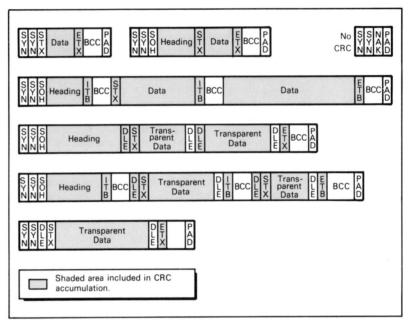

Figure 5-23. Bisync Serial I/O Protocol Message Formats

All Bisync messages begin with one of the following character sequences:

SYNC-SYNC-SOH   Start of heading in non-transparent mode. This means a heading will precede the data portion of the message.

SYNC-SYNC-STX   Start of text in non-transparent mode. This message will begin with data, not preceded by a heading.

SYNC-SYNC-DLE-STX   Transparent mode, start of text. Headings are always sent in non-transparent mode; therefore, if a message begins immediately in transparent mode it must begin with data. However, as illustrated in Figure 5-23, it is possible for a heading, transmitted in non-transparent mode, to be followed by data transmitted in transparent mode.

These character rules, **and all other rules surrounding Bisync mode, are utterly arbitrary.** Not one of them has any compelling reason to exist as compared to a hundred other ways of achieving the same objective. You simply have to learn the rules of a protocol, and live with them, without seeking any justification for their existence. Protocol rules also have frequent quirks. For example, the DLE character is an integral component of Bisync transparent mode, since all codes become character pairs, with the DLE character being the first of the pair. However, many variations of Bisync transparent mode detect an odd DLE character, or the last DLE character in an odd multiple sequence of such characters. In the illustration below, DLE characters which will be detected and recorded as characters are shaded; DLE characters which will be deleted are not shaded:

-DLE-   -DLE-DLE-   -DLE-DLE-DLE-

-DLE-DLE-DLE-DLE-   -DLE-DLE-DLE-DLE-DLE-

A message transmitted in Bisync protocol need not have data; data, if present, can be sent in one or more blocks.

A message with no data will usually consist of a command, or a response to a command. In Figure 5-23, a message consisting of the four characters SYN-SYN-NAK-PAD is illustrated. NAK is a "no-acknowledge" response from a receiver to a transmitter which was not able to accurately detect a received message.

If data is transmitted in multiple blocks, then intermediate blocks end with the ITB control character. The last data block of a message ends with either the ETB or the ETX control character. The ETB control character usually specifies another message to follow, whereas the ETX control character usually specifies the end of all messages for now. In Bisync transparent mode, the character pairs DLE-ITB, DLE-ETB, and DLE-ETX will end messages.

Bisync protocol requires messages to include cyclical redundancy characters, usually referred to as "block check characters." However, very arbitrary rules specify where the block check characters must appear, and which characters are or are not included in the block check character computation. Figure 5-23 shades the characters in a Bisync message which are included in the block check character computation.

Figure 5-24 illustrates a typical Bisync message, showing how the transmitter and receiver respond to the various portions of the message.

SDLC AND HDLC PROTOCOLS

Serial Data Link Control (SDLC) and High Level Data Link Control (HDLC) are synchronous serial data protocols; they are rapidly becoming world standards for synchronous serial data. We will now describe SDLC and HDLC protocols superficially. For a detailed description of SDLC and HDLC protocols refer to these two IBM publications:

1) IBM Synchronous Data Link Control General Information, GA27-3093-1.
2) IBM 3650 Retail Store System Loop Interface OEM Information, GA27-3098-0.

**SDLC/HDLC
Information
Field**

SDLC transmits data as a serial bit stream of any bit length, from 0 data bits to the largest number of data bits that a memory unit can handle. There are no implied character boundaries within the bit stream, which is called an information field, which may be illustrated as follows:

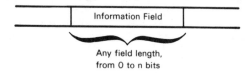

Information Field

Any field length,
from 0 to n bits

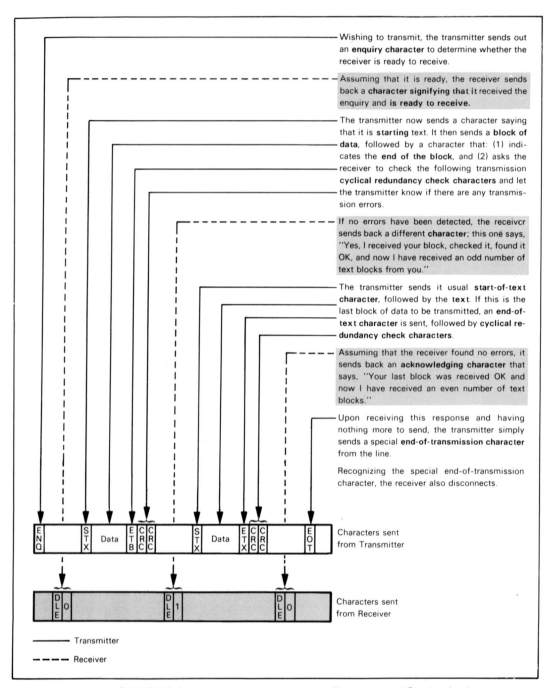

Wishing to transmit, the transmitter sends out an **enquiry character** to determine whether the receiver is ready to receive.

Assuming that it is ready, the receiver sends back a **character signifying that it** received the enquiry and **is ready to receive.**

The transmitter now sends a character saying that it is **starting** text. It then sends a **block of data**, followed by a character that: (1) indicates the **end of the block**, and (2) asks the receiver to check the following transmission **cyclical redundancy check characters** and let the transmitter know if there are any transmission errors.

If no errors have been detected, the receiver sends back a different **character**; this one says, "Yes, I received your block, checked it, found it OK, and now I have received an odd number of text blocks from you."

The transmitter sends it usual **start-of-text character**, followed by the text. If this is the last block of data to be transmitted, an **end-of-text character** is sent, followed by **cyclical redundancy check characters**.

Assuming that the receiver found no errors, it sends back an **acknowledging character** that says, "Your last block was received OK and now I have received an even number of text blocks."

Upon receiving this response and having nothing more to send, the transmitter simply sends a special **end-of-transmission character** from the line.

Recognizing the special end-of-transmission character, the receiver also disconnects.

Characters sent from Transmitter

Characters sent from Receiver

——— Transmitter

- - - - Receiver

Figure 5-24. BISYNC Protocol, and its Interpretation by Transmitter and Receiver Logic

**SDLC/HDLC
Zero Bit
Insertion**

Any protocol is going to need control characters. SDLC and HDLC protocols use a sequence of six or more 1 bits as the basis for all control characters. To prevent control characters from occurring by accident within the information field, SDLC and HDLC protocols will always insert a 0 bit following five adjacent 1 bits in a valid data stream. This is called zero bit insertion. The 0 bits are inserted by the transmitter, and are stripped by the receiver. Therefore zero bit insertion is transparent. This may be illustrated as follows:

```
7F3A ←From CPU
0 1 1 1 1 1 1 1 0 0 1 1 1 0 1 0  to transmitter
0 1 1 1 1 1 0 1 1 0 0 1 1 1 0 1 0  zero bit inserted by transmitter
0 1 1 1 1 1 0 1 1 0 0 1 1 1 0 1 0  to receiver
0 1 1 1 1 1 1 1 0 0 1 1 1 0 1 0  zero bit stripped by receiver
7F3A →To CPU
```

If you look at the description of synchronous serial data transmission given earlier, you will see that the transmitting device transmits data when it is available, and Sync characters when no data is available. In sharp contrast, SDLC and HDLC protocols do not allow breaks of any kind within an information field. These protocols assume that the transmitter will have data available, as needed, until the entire information field has been transmitted. The transmitter treats unavailable data as an error and aborts the transmission; it does not insert Sync characters, or any substitute for Sync characters.

**SDLC/HDLC
Address and
Control Fields**

The information field is always preceded by an address field and a control field. In SDLC protocol the address field and the control field are each exactly eight bits long. This may be illustrated as follows:

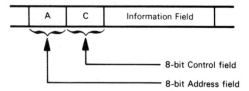

In HDLC protocol the address field may have any length and the control field may be eight bits or sixteen bits wide. The receiving station examines the high-order bit of each address field byte; if this bit is 0, another address byte is assumed to follow. If this bit is 1, it is assumed to be the last address byte. If the high-order bit of the first control field byte is 0, then a second control field byte is assumed. If the high-order bit of the first control field byte is 1, then an 8-bit control field is assumed. This may be illustrated as follows:

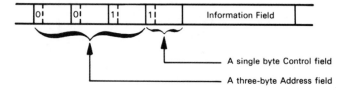

SDLC and HDLC protocols transmit all fields beginning with the least significant bit. This is of no consequence to you. You will write parallel data to the transmitting device, which will transmit the parallel data least significant bit first. The receiving device reassembles parallel data from the received serial data stream assuming that the least significant bit arrives first.

SDLC/HDLC
Frame Check
Character

SDLC/HDLC
Flag Character

SDLC/HDLC
Frame

Every transmitting device computes a 16-bit "frame check" character which is mathematically derived from the bit pattern of the combined address field, control field, and information field. The "frame check" character is equivalent to the cyclical redundancy character which we described earlier. The frame check character immediately follows the information field. **A "flag" character precedes the address field and follows the frame check field. The flag character has the bit pattern 01111110_2.** The entire information unit, from opening flag to closing flag, is called a "frame." **An SDLC/HDLC frame may be illustrated as follows:**

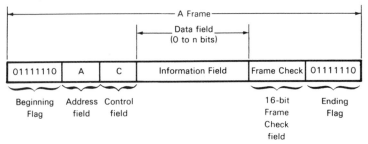

All information is transferred as frames by SDLC and HDLC protocol. Any information that is not a valid frame is assumed to be erroneous. A frame must have its beginning and ending flags, and the address, control, and frame check fields.

SDLC/HDLC
Networks

SDLC/HDLC
Point-to-Point
Network

All SDLC or HDLC communications networks assume the presence of one primary station and one or more secondary stations. Secondary stations communicate with the primary station. Secondary stations do not communicate directly among themselves.

Networks may be point-to-point:

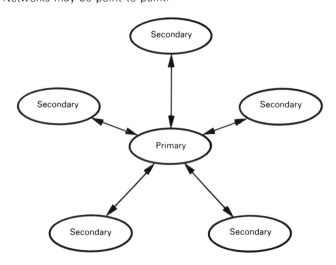

SDLC/HDLC Multipoint Network

or they may be multipoint:

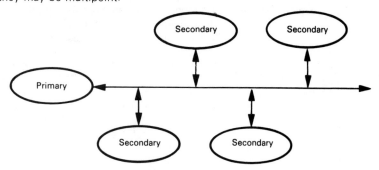

The structure of frames and the organization of SDLC/HDLC networks has some non-obvious repercussions.

The address field of a frame will always be the address of a secondary station. The primary station uses the address field of a transmitted frame to identify an intended secondary recipient, since there can be more than one secondary recipient. The secondary station uses the address field of a transmitted frame to identify itself as the transmitter. Since a secondary station can transmit only to the primary station, it does not need to identify the destination; but for the sake of the destination, it needs to identify the source.

All information must be transferred between stations as frames. Therefore some frames will transfer control information rather than data, while other frames will transfer data. Data frames can and usually will have accompanying control information contained in the control field.

A receiving station uses the frame check field in order to accept or reject the entire frame. SDLC and HDLC protocols operate on the basis of implied acceptance. That is to say, a transmitter assumes that the frame has been successfully received unless it receives back a message to the contrary. However, acknowledgment of correctly received messages must occur every n frames (n=7 in SDLC). This acknowledgment validates all frames prior to the one being acknowledged.

No data breaks are allowed within a frame. In between frames a transmitter may either output a sequence of flag characters or it may output a continuous high signal. The continuous high signal is called an idle signal.

Notice that SDLC and HDLC protocols impose no constraints on the data contained in a frame's information field. So far as the protocol is concerned, the information field is an unstructured serial sequence of bits. It is up to the transmitter and receiver to mutually agree on how the bits must be interpreted. It makes no difference to the protocol whether data is being transferred as bytes, words, or amorphous bit streams; it makes no difference whether the data is ASCII characters or a memory object code dump.

SDLC and HDLC protocols allow a serial data stream to be encoded and decoded using NRZ or inverted (NRZI) logic.

SDLC/HDLC Abort Characters

When a transmitter aborts a transmission it outputs a continuous high signal. In HDLC mode, seven contiguous 1 bits are interpreted as an abort character. In SDLC mode, eight contiguous 1 bits are interpreted as an abort character.

SDLC Loop Configuration

In SDLC mode, but not HDLC mode, **secondary stations can be configured as a loop,** rather than point-to-point or multipoint, as illustrated earlier. An SDLC loop may be illustrated as follows:

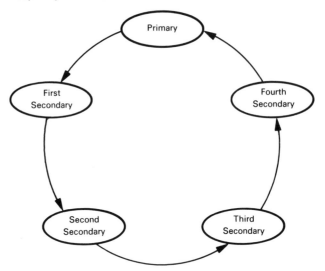

The primary transmits frames to the first secondary in the SDLC loop. The secondary retransmits the frame downstream. Of necessity, the secondary introduces a short delay when retransmitting a received frame. Each secondary in the loop receives its frame from the immediately upstream secondary; after an additional delay it retransmits the frame. Thus the primary will ultimately receive back any frame it transmits.

Secondaries may transmit a frame to the primary in response to a received frame, or by their own initiative.

These are the ways in which a secondary may respond to a received frame:

1) If a secondary's receive logic is enabled, then the secondary will examine the address byte at the head of the frame. If the address byte matches the address of the secondary, then the secondary will receive the frame; the secondary will also retransmit the frame downstream.

2) A frame received by a secondary may contain a command from the primary asking the secondary to transmit a frame back to the primary.

If the secondary wishes to transmit a frame, either in response to the primary, or on its own initiative, then it must wait until it can seize control of the SDLC loop before attempting to transmit a frame. Moreover, the secondary will transmit a frame to the primary via the downstream secondaries of the loop. If, for example, the second secondary in the illustrated loop wishes to transmit a frame to the primary, then the second secondary's frame is actually transmitted to the third secondary, which retransmits to the fourth secondary, which retransmits it to the primary.

A secondary cannot start transmitting a frame if it is receiving a frame from an upstream secondary, or is likely to be interrupted by an upstream secondary's transmission. In order to avoid both problems, the primary transmits a polling pulse around the secondary loop. This polling pulse is received by the first secondary, then the second secondary, and so on until it returns to the primary. **The polling pulse is called an "end of process" (EOP) character;** it is formed by the trailing 0 of a frame's closing flag followed by seven 1 bits. This may be illustrated as follows:

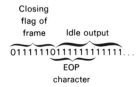

When the first secondary receives an EOP character, it has the option of transmitting the EOP character downstream to the second secondary, or it can transmit a frame before retransmitting the EOP character to the second secondary. After passing the EOP character on to the second secondary, the first secondary cannot transmit a frame again until the primary sends another EOP character around the loop.

When the second secondary receives the EOP character, it can either retransmit the EOP character directly to the third secondary, or it can transmit a single frame before retransmitting the EOP character to the third secondary. In this fashion the EOP character makes its way around the SDLC loop. The primary will ultimately receive back its polling frame, any frames that secondaries had to transmit, and finally the EOP character. **Suppose the second and third secondaries have frames to transmit, but not the first or fourth secondaries. The polling sequence may be illustrated as follows:**

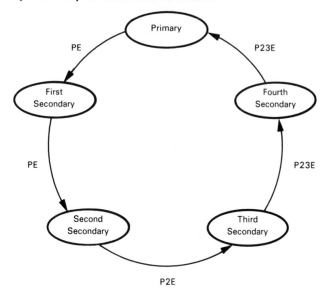

P	represents the polling frame that tells secondaries to transmit pending frames
2	represents the frame transmitted by the second secondary
3	represents the frame transmitted by the third secondary
E	is the EOP character

ASYNCHRONOUS SERIAL DATA TRANSFER

Mark
Signal
When serial data is transferred asynchronously, the transmitting device only transmits a character when it has a character ready to transmit. In between characters, a continuous mark signal (usually a high level) is output:

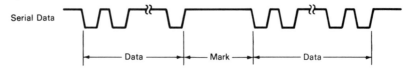

Framing

Start Bit

Stop Bit
Every data unit in an asynchronous data stream must carry its own synchronization information. An asynchronous data unit is therefore "framed" by a single start bit, and one, one and-a-half, or two stop bits:

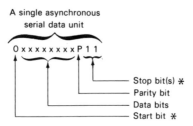

* Framing bits

Having a single 0 start bit is universally accepted in the microcomputer world.

There is a similarity between the synchronous data stream's Sync characters and the framing bits of an asynchronous data stream.

Sync characters frame a block of synchronous data characters. Start and stop bits frame every data character in an asynchronous a stream.

Asynchronous protocol allows a character to have five, six, seven, or eight data bits, as was the case with synchronous serial data. For example, if your protocol stipulates that there will only be five data bits in each transmitted asynchronous word, then the receiving device will only receive five data bits, and will interpret each received word as follows:

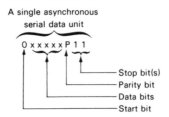

Thus a 9-bit unit is actually transmitted.

Parity Bit
The parity bit is always present. Either odd or even parity may be specified, or the parity bit may be always 0 or always 1.

Stop Bits   **1's are always used for stop bits.** Usually there will be two stop bits; one stop bit is sometimes specified. If you have two stop bits, then every serial 8-bit data word will contain 12 bits:

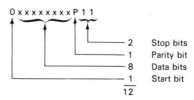

If you have one stop bit, then every serial 8-bit data word will consist of 11 bits.

Teletypewriter Serial Data Format   Teletypewriters use one start bit, seven data bits, a parity bit, and two stop bits — for a total of 11 bits per character. Teletypewriters operate at a standard 10 characters per second, which translates into 110 baud.

Some transmission protocols specify one-and-a-half stop bits. The stop bit width is one-and-one-half times the normal bit width.

Consider even parity, asynchronous serial data using two stop bits, with six data bits in each data unit. This is how a sequence of parallel data will be converted into a serial data stream:

```
 1       0       0       1  ← MSB
 1       1       1       0        Parallel
 0       1       0       0        Data
 1       0       1       1
 0       1       1       1
 0       0       0       1  ← LSB

 ... 000101111100101101110011010110111001011  ← Serial Data
```

If asynchronous serial data communication is occurring over telephone lines, then some form of handshaking protocol, as illustrated for synchronous telephone communications, is going to be required. In fact, there is nothing to prevent the identical handshaking protocol from being used. This protocol is simply a method of transmitting information between two devices via a single telephone line.

Framing Error   Notice that during asynchronous data transfer, the receiving device has an additional means of checking for transmission errors. The first binary digit of every data unit must be 0, representing the start bit; the last one or two binary digits of the data unit must be 1, representing the stop bits. **If the receiving device does not detect appropriate start and stop bits for any data unit in an asynchronous serial data stream, then it will report a framing error.**

A SERIAL I/O COMMUNICATIONS DEVICE

Let us now look at the requirements for a serial I/O interface device. **For our serial I/O communications device we are going to select a 28-pin DIP.** We can get away with this smaller number of pins because our serial I/O ports are going to shrink to one pin per port.

Logic Distribution

Synchronous and asynchronous serial I/O logic are going to share a single chip. The two sets of logic have enough in common for this to make a lot of sense. We will not include SDLC or HDLC capability in the devices we describe.

Our serial communications I/O device may be visualized as having three interfaces: one for the microprocessor, a second for received serial data, and a third for transmitted serial data. Each interface will, as usual, have data lines and control signals. For the serial I/O interface, control signals can be grouped into general controls and modem controls. General controls apply to any external logic, whereas modem controls meet the specific needs of industry standard modems — which does not prevent you from using modem controls for other external logic if you can.

The Microprocessor-Serial I/O Device Interface

Since the microprocessor interface is common to synchronous and asynchronous I/O, this is where we will begin.

The serial I/O device is going to communicate in parallel with the microprocessor via the external system bus data lines. **We must therefore provide eight data pins, backed up by a data bus buffer:**

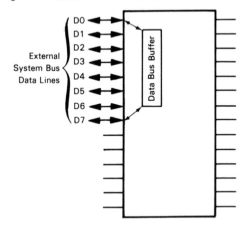

Other signals required by the microprocessor interface are no different from those we included in the parallel I/O interface device. We will use **Select and IORW.** Select is decoded off the address bus to select the serial I/O device; IORW selects either a "read to" the microprocessor or a "write from" the microprocessor. We will arbitrarily assume that IORW high specifies a read, while IORW low specifies a write.

Add clock, power, and ground, and our serial I/O interface device looks like this:

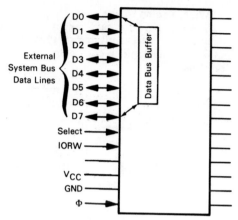

THE SERIAL I/O DEVICE

We are going to use separate pins to transmit and receive serial data. Since we have separate transmit and receive data pins, we will also need to input separate transmit and receive clock signals. Both clock signals are input by external logic to control the rate at which data is being transmitted or received:

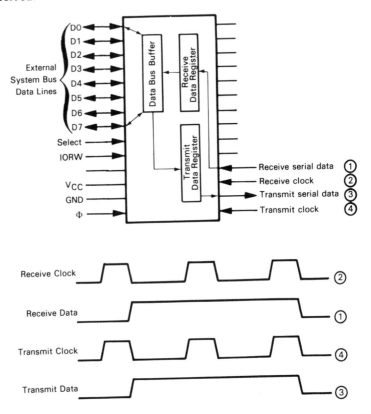

In the illustration above we show received data being assembled in the Receive Data register, while transmitted data is held in a Transmit Data register. The Data Bus buffer functions as a parallel data conduit for the Receive and Transmit Data registers.

When a single Receive Data register lies between the Data Bus buffer and the serial data input stream, and a single Transmit Data register lies between the Data Bus buffer and the serial transmit data stream, the serial I/O device is said to be "single buffered." usually serial I/O devices are "double buffered," in which case a Receive and Transmit Data buffer is interposed between the Data Bus buffer and the data stream. Double buffering may be illustrated as follows:

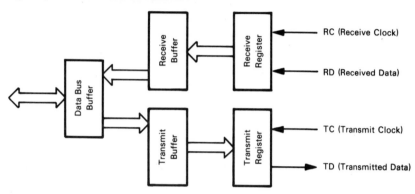

The disadvantage of single buffering is that it gives the microprocessor one bit time within which received data must be read out of the Receive Data register; the next character then begins to overwrite the contents of the Receive Data register. This may be illustrated as follows:

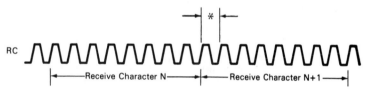

＊ Read character N in this time because character N+1 starts
being loaded into Receive Data register at end of clock period

Similarly, if transmit logic is single buffered, then following transmission of a character, the microprocessor has one bit time within which to write the next character to the Transmit Data register if continuous data transfer is to occur. This may be illustrated as follows:

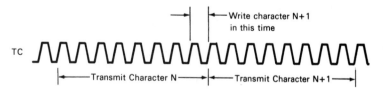

Double buffering, on the other hand, gives program logic one character time within which to process received data:

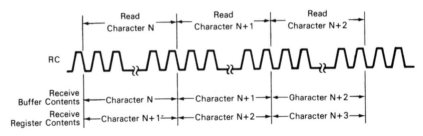

Similarly, program logic has one character time within which to write the next character to be transmitted:

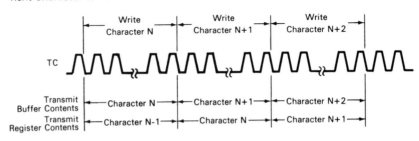

Occasionally you will come across serial I/O devices that are triple buffered. They give you two character times to read a received character or write a transmitted character.

Clock Signals

If external logic uses the same transmit and receive clock signal, you can derive both signals from the system clock Φ or from any other clock logic. In any case **these two clock signals are going to control the serial data baud rate.** Baud rate will not be determined by logic internal to the serial I/O interface device, and device logic will not generate or output clock signals.

You do not have to input transmit and receive clock signals to all serial I/O devices. Many serial I/O devices give you the option of program-ming a baud rate, in which case device logic computes serial data bit times using the microcomputer system clock signal in order to compute time in-tervals as specified by the selected baud rate. This can present a problem when the transmitting and receiving devices are physically far removed — which is the rule rather than the exception. The transmitting and receiving devices will have to compute serial bit time intervals using their local system clocks, which can never be absolutely accurate — and may have errors that com-pensate for each other, or combine to increase the overall error. Unless the receiving device has some internal logic that allows it to resynchronize itself with the arriving serial data at frequent time intervals, internally generated baud rates will quickly lead to timing errors.

In the discussion that follows, we will examine logic associated with serial data that has a companion clock signal.

Consider a synchronous data stream where every Receive Clock signal rising edge will strobe the Receive Data signal level, as a binary digit, into the Receive Data register. **Whenever the Receive Data register contains eight binary digits, its contents will be transferred to the Data Bus buffer.** Here is an illustration of serial data entry:

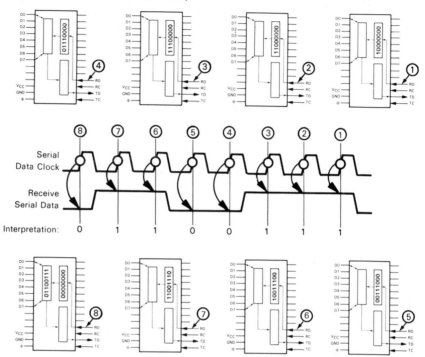

The Receive Data register is now empty, so the next receive data bit will start the loading process all over again.

Every Transmit Clock pulse trailing edge will strobe out a bit from the Transmit Data register. **The eight Transmit Data register bits will be output in ascending order, starting with bit 0.** As soon as bit 7 has been output, the Transmit Data register will be considered empty, so the Data Bus buffer contents will be loaded into the Transmit Data register, to continue the serial transmit process. Here is an illustration of serial data output:

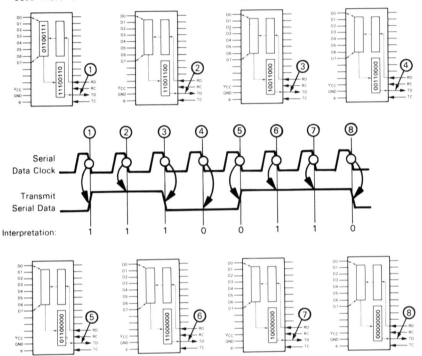

If asynchronous serial data were being transmitted, the relationship between data clock and serial data signals would change, but that is all. Remember, in an asynchronous data stream you may use a ×16 or ×64 clock, and you sample the data on the 8th or 32nd pulse — in the middle of the data bit.

SERIAL I/O CONTROL SIGNALS

A single Data Bus buffer cannot simultaneously receive assembled data bytes and transmit data bytes for disassembly. **Control logic and control signals which we are now going to describe determine which of the possible operations is occurring at any time.** The serial I/O interface device will simply ignore the clock signal if internal control logic has not been programmed to recognize it. Also, the Receive Data register contents will simply be lost if the Data Bus buffer is not ready to receive an assembled byte.

Let us consider the status and control signals which must be present to support serial data being transmitted and received.

First of all, consider transmit logic; it will need two status signals, one to indicate that the Transmit Data register is empty, the other to indicate that the Data buffer is ready to receive another byte of data. We will call these two signals TE and TRDY.

TRDY is active whenever one or more of the transmit buffers are empty. TRDY is used to determine when it is safe for the microprocessor to output another byte to transmit logic.

TE is active whenever the buffers are empty *and* the Transmit register is *completely* empty. TE is normally not used by the microprocessor, except with a half-duplex line where the microprocessor needs to know when the line becomes idle so it can be turned around.

TRDY and TE signal logic may be illustrated conceptually as follows:

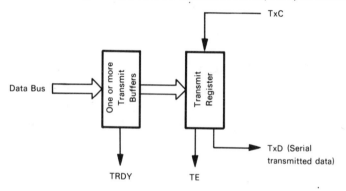

Receive logic uses a single Receive Ready signal which we will call RRDY. This signal tells the CPU that a byte of data has been loaded into the Data Bus buffer and can now be read.

Frequently, the TRDY and RRDY signals will be used to generate an interrupt request. The interrupt can be acknowledged by very simple instruction sequences that write the next data byte to the serial I/O device's Data buffer, or read the received data byte from the Data buffer.

When synchronous data is being received, remember that the serial I/O interface logic must detect either one or two Sync characters before acknowledging valid data. External logic must know when the serial I/O device has detected these Sync characters. **We will therefore add a SYNC status signal, which will be output true as soon as the Sync characters have been detected.** Some serial I/O devices allow the Sync status line to be bidirectional. In this case, rather than preceding synchronous data with Sync characters, **external logic can input a true SYNC control signal.** The serial I/O device uses this control input to start receiving synchronous data; this may be illustrated as follows:

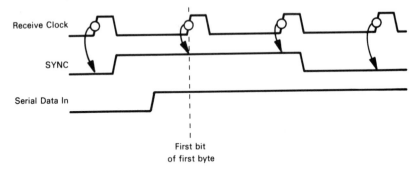

Receive Clock

SYNC

Serial Data In

First bit
of first byte

**External
Sync Detect**

This is called "external sync detect."

MODEM CONTROL SIGNALS

Only the modem control signals remain to be described. There are these four industry-standard modem control signals:

1) $\overline{DSR}$ (Data Set Ready) — The modem drives this signal low whenever it is ready to transfer data. The signal is input high at other times. Optionally, other external logic can use this signal as a master enable/disable. For example, a microcomputer system might generate $\overline{DSR}$. A video terminal could then test $\overline{DSR}$ to see if the microcomputer system is ready before attempting to communicate with it.

2) $\overline{DTR}$ (Data Terminal Ready) — This control signal is the serial I/O device's equivalent of $\overline{DSR}$; it is output by the serial I/O interface device to tell external logic that it is ready to communicate. Under program control you can set this signal high to inhibit all serial I/O operations, or you can set it low to initiate serial I/O operations.

3) $\overline{RTS}$ (Request To Send) — When the serial I/O device and the modem or other external logic are ready to communicate, $\overline{DSR}$ and $\overline{DTR}$ will both be low. Now the serial I/O device uses the $\overline{RTS}$ signal to indicate that it is ready to transmit data. Remember that the receiving device may be temporarily busy, even though it has been turned on.

4) $\overline{CTS}$ (Clear To Send) — When $\overline{DSR}$, $\overline{DTR}$ and $\overline{RTS}$ are all low and the modem or external logic is ready to receive data from the serial I/O device, the modem or other logic sets $\overline{CTS}$ low to indicate its readiness.

The interaction of $\overline{DSR}$, $\overline{DTR}$, $\overline{RTS}$, and $\overline{CTS}$ may be illustrated by the following program flowchart:

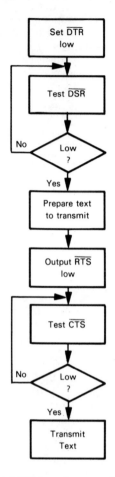

This is how our serial I/O interface device now looks:

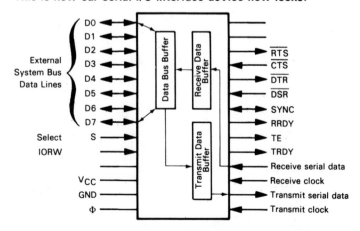

CONTROLLING THE SERIAL I/O INTERFACE DEVICE

Serial I/O Mode

Given the many options available when using the serial I/O interface device, we are going to need a Control register in order to select options — and in some cases to set the level of control signals being output.

First we must select synchronous or asynchronous I/O. Table 5-4 identifies the fundamental decisions we must make under program control. We will refer to Table 5-4 variables as mode parameters, since they are unlikely to be changed during the course of any serial I/O operation.

Table 5-4. Serial I/O Mode Parameters

Function	Asynchronous	Synchronous
Clock frequency	Baud rate x1, x16 or x64	Usually baud rate x1
Data bits per word	5, 6, 7, or 8	5, 6, 7, or 8
Parity	Odd, even, 0, 1 or none	Odd, even, 0, 1 or none
Stop bits	1, 1½ or 2	Does not apply
Sync characters	Does not apply	1, 2 or external Sync

Isosynchronous Serial I/O

Asynchronous I/O using a ×1 clock is sometimes called iso-synchronous I/O; the correct name for this serial I/O mode was, originally, "isochronous" serial I/O. This mode is equivalent to data using asynchronous character format (including framing bits) in an otherwise synchronous data stream.

Serial I/O Commands

Having selected mode parameters, you will still have to transmit commands to the serial I/O interface device. Commands must identify the direction of serial data flow (transmit or receive), or terminate current operations, allowing the mode to be modified. Commands must also set the condition of the $\overline{DTR}$ and $\overline{RTS}$ control signals, and respond to any error conditions.

Serial I/O Error Conditions

To identify error conditions we **will provide the serial I/O interface device with an 8-bit Status register.** Having eight bits, we can read a combination of eight signal statuses and error conditions. **The signals whose level we must be able to read are:**

Serial I/O Input Control Signals

1) $\overline{DSR}$ — Data set ready.
2) $\overline{CTS}$ — Clear to send. This signal's level is sometimes left out of the Status register; serial I/O interface device logic must then automatically wait for $\overline{CTS}$ true before initiating a serial data transfer.
3) SYNC — External synchronization.
4) TE — Transmit register empty.
5) TRDY — Transmit buffer ready to receive data from the CPU.
6) RRDY — Receive buffer ready to send data to the CPU. This signal may be connected to interrupt logic and left out of the Status register.

These are the error conditions that may be reported:

Framing Error

1) Parity error. The wrong parity was detected in a serial data unit.
2) Framing error. In asynchronous mode, start and/or stop bits were not correctly detected.
3) Overrun errors. The microprocessor did not read the contents of the Receive buffer within the allowed time. Receive logic overwrote the prior Receive buffer contents, which are now lost.
4) Underrun error. The microprocessor did not write the next character to the Transmit buffer within the allowed time. Transmit logic had no valid data to transmit after completing transmission of the previous character.

Normally an error condition does not cause a serial I/O interface device to abort operations. The error is reported in the Status register and operations continue undaunted. **Using commands, you must react to an error condition in one of these ways:**

1) In synchronous receive mode, send a NAK (no acknowledge) character back to the transmitting source.
2) In asynchronous mode, abort operations and set TD to its mark signal level.
3) Execute any other error recovery program.
4) Reset any error bits in the Status register of the serial I/O interface device.

To our serial I/O interface device we must now add a Mode/Control register and a Status register:

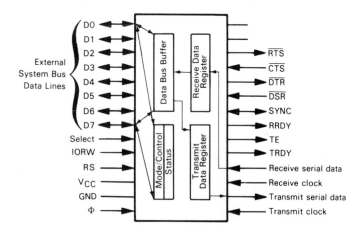

ADDRESSING THE SERIAL I/O INTERFACE DEVICE

The only aspect of the serial I/O interface device that we have not covered is how the device is going to be selected, and how its buffers and registers are addressed.

The microprocessor accesses the serial I/O interface device as a collection of addressable locations: the Data Bus buffer, the Control register, and a Status register.

The Receive Data register and Transmit Data register lie passively in the path of received and transmitted data, respectively; they communicate with the Data Bus buffer, therefore do not need additional direct access.

In reality the Control and Status registers can be looked on as a single addressable unit, since you can only write into a Control register and you can only read from a Status register.

Thus, we need two pins in order to access a serial I/O interface device. One pin (S) is the chip select, which we have already described; the other pin (RS) selects either the Data Bus buffer or the Control/Status register. Figure 5-24 illustrates our serial I/O interface device.

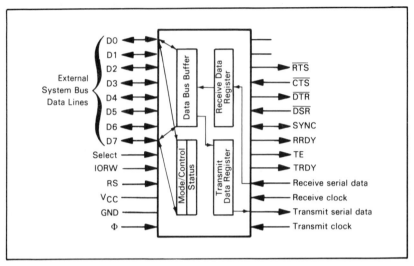

Figure 5-24. A Serial I/O Interface Device

In Figure 5-25 we can now illustrate one way in which a serial I/O interface device may be integrated into our microcomputer system.

In Figure 5-25 the transmit and receive control outputs TRDY, TE, and RRDY are shown connecting to the interrupt priority device's interrupt requests EXTIREQ2, EXTIREQ3, and EXTIREQ4, respectively. The serial I/O interface device does not receive any interrupt acknowledge signals; it does not need to, since it is not obliged to perform any specific operation following an interrupt acknowledge. The microprocessor transmits or receives data.

Notice that serial I/O interface device logic has IOSEL as an input. This signal (which we described earlier in this chapter) discriminates between memory accesses and I/O port accesses. Figure 5-25 shows the serial I/O interface device being accessed at I/O ports.

The interrupt logic in Figure 5-25 provides an excellent example of why interrupt priority devices usually have fairly elaborate enable/disable logic for the various interrupt requests which they support. TE and TRDY are shown connecting to interrupt request inputs. In many cases, one or the other, but not both of these interrupt requests will need to be active. The interrupt priority device will probably have a programmable register which allows you to selectively enable and disable external interrupt requests. Thus, you could make the interrupt request connections shown in Figure 5-25, yet by appropriately disabling specific interrupt requests within the interrupt Priority device, you could negate either the TE interrupt request, or the TRDY interrupt request, or both, or neither.

No connections are shown between external logic and the serial I/O device's data or clock lines. Also, no connections are shown for the modem control signals. These signals will connect with appropriate external logic in a variety of different ways that depend on whether the serial I/O device is being used in telephone communications, or as an interface for a low speed peripheral such as a teletypewriter or a magnetic tape cassette unit.

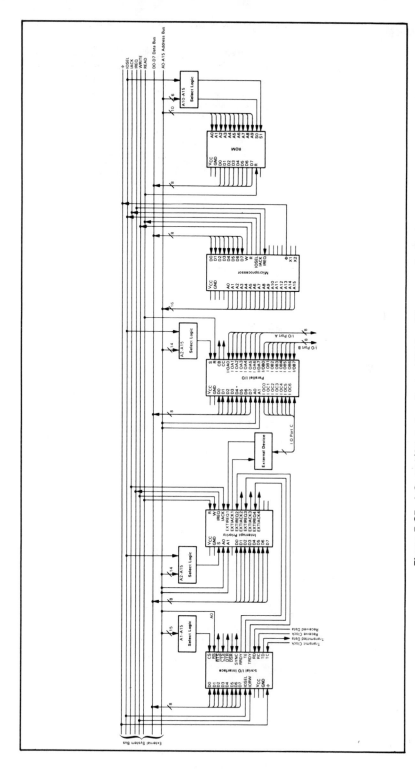

Figure 5-25. A Serial I/O Interface Device Within a Microcomputer System

PROGRAMMABLE COUNTER/TIMERS

Square Wave Signals

A programmable counter/timer is a device that can operate on square wave signals. Properly used, a programmable counter/timer can perform many useful tasks within a microcomputer system.

A square wave signal, as suggested by its name, is a signal that continuously switches between 0 and 1 levels; we can illustrate a square wave signal as follows:

In fact, all digital signals are square wave signals, but some of them are more useful to a programmable counter/timer than others.

A clock signal, for example, is a square wave signal with a fixed, unvarying frequency. A single data or address line on an external system bus is also a square wave signal, but its signal transitions would usually appear unpredictable.

These are the operations that a programmable counter/timer can perform using a square wave signal:

Event Counter

1) The programmable counter/timer can "count events," if each "event" is identified by a transition (either high-to-low or low-to-high) of an incoming square wave signal. This may be illustrated as follows:

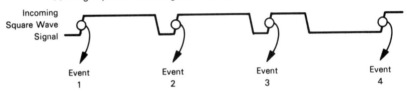

Time Intervals

2) A programmable counter/timer can measure time intervals by counting events using an incoming clock signal. For example, if a programmable counter/timer receives a clock signal with a 250 nanosecond period as an input, then every four events that it counts is equivalent to one microsecond:

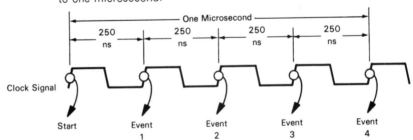

Of course, the computed time interval can only be as accurate as the clock signal. To measure real time of day, a very precise clock circuit is required.

3) A programmable counter/timer can generate and output square wave signals whose transitions are computed by counting events, or time, as described in 1) or 2) above. For example, a "slow" square wave signal might be generated and output by changing the signal level every 1000 clock periods. Alternatively, the square wave signal that is output might change level every ten events counted.

Let us examine how programmable counter/timers are used in real microcomputer systems.

Programmable counter/timers usually provide you with a reloadable Counter register. A reloadable Counter register has two parts: a register into which you write data, and a companion register whose contents can be automatically incremented or decremented by counter logic. If we refer to these two parts as a Counter buffer and a Counter register, we may illustrate them as follows:

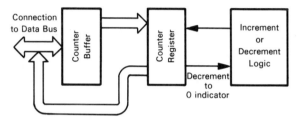

The logic illustrated above could generate a square wave output signal as follows:

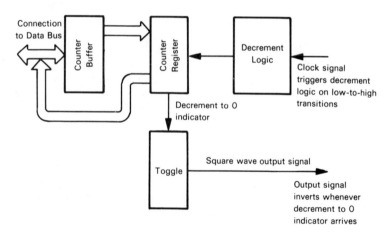

In order to specify the square wave frequency, you will write an appropriate initial value into the Counter buffer. Upon starting square wave logic (by writing an appropriate code to a companion control register), the Counter buffer contents will immediately be shifted to the Counter register; the Counter register contents will then decrement once every clock period. When the Counter register decrements to 0, a square wave output signal will change level; the Counter buffer contents will be transferred to the Counter register, which will start decrementing again. This sequence will continue endlessly, until you stop it by writing an appropriate code to the companion Control register. Let us assume an initial value of 0080_{16} is loaded into the Counter buffer. We can then illustrate square wave logic as follows:

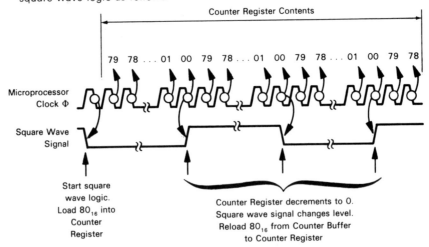

When you read from the Counter buffer/register, you will usually get the Counter register contents, as illustrated above. This lets program logic determine how far the next pulse has gone, by looking at the correct, decremented Counter register contents.

Thus, the real time clock device has generated a very low frequency clock signal.

Numerous variations of the logic illustrated above are provided by programmable counter/timers. Variations let you generate a wide variety of square wave signals; for example, you can change the shape or frequency of signals dynamically, by loading new values into the Counter buffer. Square wave signals are very useful. Microcomputer systems, and digital logic in general, are broadly controlled by clock signals and square wave signals.

Counting Events

The same logic can calculate time intervals or count events. Let us examine event counting. Rather than decrementing (or in this case incrementing) some register's contents when a clock signal makes an active transition, programmable counter/timer logic increments the counter when an external signal makes active transitions. Assuming that low-to-high signal level changes are active, event counting may be contrasted with time interval computation as follows:

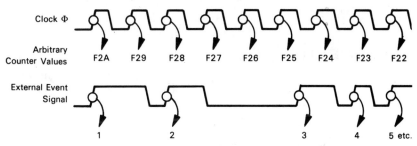

By combining event counting logic with real time clock logic, programmable counter/timers let you use an external signal to start or stop counter/timer logic. This may be illustrated as follows:

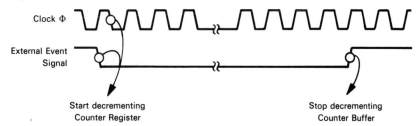

Pulse Width Measurement

The sequence illustrated above measures pulse width. Decrement logic starts when the external event signal makes a high-to-low transition; it stops when this signal subsequently makes a low-to-high transition. The programmable counter/timer has measured the time that the external event signal was low, reporting this time as the same number of Clock Φ pulses.

Endless variations of square wave signal outputs and control inputs can be configured around programmable counter/timer logic.

A programmable counter/timer can tell the microprocessor that a special event has occurred either by setting a Status register bit, or by requesting an interrupt. Usually the Counter register incrementing or decrementing to zero is the special event that triggers such action, but other special events may have the same effect; here are some possibilities:

1) An input signal might trigger an interrupt request or a status flag bit setting. For example, the input signal in the pulse width measurement illustration above might trigger an interrupt request when it makes a low-to-high transition marking the end of the pulse.

2) Periodic interrupt requests, or Status register bit settings may be triggered every n increments or decrements, where n is less than the number in the Counter register. For example, suppose a programmable counter/timer has a 16-bit Counter register; it might be programmed to generate an interrupt request once every 256 decrements — or, perhaps, once every 128 decrements. Sometimes the number of decrements separating such interrupt requests is a programmable option.

There are microprocessor support devices which provide programmable counter/timer logic only. Since this logic is quite simple (by microprocessor standards), such dedicated devices usually have two or more sets of counter/timer logic on a single chip. More often, programmable counter/timer logic is provided on a multifunction chip that includes one or more of the other capabilities described earlier in this chapter (we conclude this chapter with a discussion of such logic distribution options).

REAL TIME CLOCK LOGIC

Many microcomputer systems have logic which generates periodic interrupt requests using logic equivalent to the timer portion of the programmable counter/timer. For example, a microcomputer system may have special logic which generates an interrupt request every millisecond. **This logic is referred to as real time clock logic;** it is used most frequently with powerful microprocessors that are functioning as minicomputers. Typically, the real time clock will be used to guarantee service to a number of users or applications sharing a single central processing unit. For example, if ten users are time-sharing a single central processing unit, then the real time clock interrupt occurring every millisecond may trigger execution of a supervisory program which suspends service for one user and starts servicing the next user.

LOGIC DISTRIBUTION AMONG MICROCOMPUTER DEVICES

Microprocessors essentially reproduce a computer's central processing unit logic. We have described a number of support devices which, for the most part, provide one computer logic function per device. With the exception of interrupt logic occurring on a parallel I/O device, we have illustrated no combination devices. Such devices do exist — in almost every conceivable combination.

In the early days of microprocessors some manufacturers (Fairchild and Rockwell in particular) built microcomputer components with various complex logic distributions, far removed from the one-function-per-device descriptions given in this chapter; this was done not for any practical reason, but rather because the chip designers in question did not have computer backgrounds. These Fairchild and Rockwell parts with strange logic combinations were not commercially successful. Instead, the parts that gained popularity were single-function components of the type described in this chapter.

But a separate and distinct market developed in high volume consumer applications such as toys, home appliances, and automobiles. In these applications, the number of individual components that comprised the total microcomputer system was very important. Small savings in part or assembly costs were critical. Therefore, manufacturers started to combine a number of functions on a single chip.

Almost any commercial microcomputer system will need the following logic elements:

1) A central processing unit
2) Some read-only memory to hold programs
3) Some read/write memory to hold data
4) Parallel I/O ports
5) Interrupt logic
6) A programmable counter/timer

Were these logic elements to be provided by devices described in this chapter, five components would be required: the microprocessor, plus four support devices. Assuming that relatively primitive interrupt logic, and three parallel I/O ports would suffice, the parallel I/O device described in this chapter could provide both the interrupt and parallel I/O logic for the microcomputer system. If a small amount of RAM would do, a single N×8-bit RAM device could be used.

But five devices will, in fact, become more than five devices, since we have not taken into account bus buffers and incidental intermediate logic needed to connect the five major components in a configuration that will work. Therefore, the manufacturer will finish up with a printed circuit card that is expensive to produce and may be far too large to fit in a small consumer product.

We have already made three compromises in order to reduce the major component chip count to five. We assume that three parallel I/O ports are sufficient, interrupt logic is simple, and read/write memory is small enough to be contained on a single N×8-bit RAM device. In many commercial applications, the resulting configuration, far from being too primitive, is in fact much larger and more capable than the application demands. Therefore, the device count can be reduced further.

Multiple Function Devices

One obvious combination would be to put some read-only memory and some read/write memory on the same chip. Such parts exist. A more common combination puts read-only memory or read/write memory on the same chip with parallel I/O logic, real time clock logic, and interrupt logic. For example, the combination part may have read-only memory, two 8-bit I/O ports, and an interrupt request on it. Another component might have read/write memory, two I/O ports and a real time clock on it. These two combination devices, together with a microprocessor, would reduce our part count to three. This reduction would be very desirable, since it would also reduce the additional buffers and incidental logic needed to connect the major components.

One-Chip Microcomputer

But **the ultimate reduction in part counts generates a one-chip microcomputer. This single chip provides a central processing unit, read-only memory for programs, read/write memory for data, I/O ports and interrupt logic.** A wide variety of one-chip microcomputers exists.

We will not describe one-chip microcomputers or multifunction support parts in this book, since conceptually they add nothing to your understanding of basic concepts. Whether I/O ports are implemented on a parallel I/O device, or constitute part of a device that also contains ROM and RAM, has no bearing on your understanding of parallel I/O ports, per se. So long as you understand that there are no conceptual differences between logic implemented on single chips, or chips that combine numerous functions, it is sufficient that you understand that such variations exist.

6

Programming Microcomputers

Instructions are used to specify any logic sequence that may occur within a microcomputer system. For example, an instruction may complement the contents of the CPU's Accumulator register, move data from the accumulator to a memory word, or output data via an I/O port.

To use a microcomputer, therefore, you must first select the devices that will give you sufficient logic capability; then you must sequence the logic to meet your needs by creating a sequence of instructions which, taken together, select chip logic capabilities that satisfy the needs of your application. The instruction sequence is a program, and programming is the creation of the instruction sequences.

THE CONCEPT OF A PROGRAMMING LANGUAGE

The concept of a microcomputer program was introduced in Chapter 3, where a five-instruction binary addition program was described. In this chapter we will expand on the elementary concepts introduced by the binary addition program.

There are, in fact, two separate and distinct aspects to programming concepts: we must describe the types of instructions which any particular microprocessor has; but we must also discuss the way in which programs get written. These two aspects of programming concepts are really quite unrelated.

A microprocessor's instruction set identifies the individual operations that the microprocessor can perform. Each instruction represents one program building block. Every program is a network of interconnected instruction sequences that explicitly define the tasks a microcomputer system must perform.

But you will first explicitly define your microcomputer system's tasks in a human readable form. Next you will convert these task definitions into a computer program, which consists of instruction sequences. And you will recall that each instruction, in every sequence, will be represented by an instruction object code: a binary number. Therefore the computer program ultimately becomes a sequence of binary numbers that no human could make sense of.

How do you create the instruction sequences that constitute a program? And how do you convert these instruction sequences into binary object codes? That is the subject matter for the second of our two separate and distinct programming concept aspects: the way in which programs get written. And the way in which programs get written is not affected in any way by the first of our two separate and distinct programming concept aspects: the types of instructions which a particular microprocessor may have.

How Programs are Written

Let us begin by describing how programs get written.

There is nothing to prevent you from creating a computer program as a sequence of binary instruction codes, just as they will appear in memory or in the Instruction register. The addition program described in Chapter 4 can be written out using binary or hexadecimal digits as follows:

Program as a Binary Matrix	Hexadecimal Version of Program
10011100	9C
00001010	0A
00110000	30
01000000	40
10011100	9C
00001010	0A
00110001	31
10000000	80
01100000	60

Were you to generate your microcomputer program as a sequence of binary digits, the chances of misplacing a 0 or a 1 are very high, and the chances of spotting the error are low. This is unfortunate since it is not good enough for a program to be 99.99% accurate. Unless it is absolutely accurate, there is always the lurking possibility that the error will manifest itself at an inopportune moment, with disastrous consequences. It is this inherent necessity for perfection that causes programmers to grasp at any device which makes errors harder to create and easier to spot.

As compared to creating a program as a sequence of binary digits, the first and most obvious improvement would be to code the program using hexadecimal digits, then find some automatic way of converting the hexadecimal digits to their binary equivalents.

Writing the program in hexadecimal digits makes it harder to generate errors, because there is one hexadecimal digit for every four binary digits. On the theory that every digit offers an equal probability of being written down wrong, programming in hexadecimal digits is likely to generate one quarter of the number of errors, because there are one quarter the number of digits.

Programming in hexadecimal digits also makes errors easier to spot, since detecting a misplaced hexadecimal digit, while not the simplest thing in the world, surely beats spotting a wrong 1 or 0 in a mesmerizing binary pattern. The binary and hexadecimal programs are reproduced below, each having one error. See how long it takes you to find the errors:

Program as a Binary Matrix	Hexadecimal Version of Program
10011100	9C
00001010	0A
00110000	30
01000000	40
10011100	9C
00001010	A0
00011001	31
10000000	80
01100000	60

In the end, however, the program must be converted into a binary sequence, because that is how it is going to be stored in memory — and that is how each instruction must be represented in the Instruction register.

Object Program   **We use the name "object program" to describe the binary number sequence which is the final representation of any program.**

Source Program   **We use the name "source program" to describe the human readable form in which the program is written initially.**

In the illustration above the hexadecimal version of the program is a source program. The binary matrix is an object program.

SOURCE PROGRAMS

Let us examine how you might go about creating a source program, and equally important, how you might preserve the source program once you have created it.

You could create a source program by writing it on a piece of paper as a sequence of hexadecimal digits. That will give you a permanent record of the source program, but it will not help your microprocessor; microprocessors cannot read. In addition to creating a human readable source program, you must create a version that the computer can read; and that will require the assistance of a machine.

Of all available machines, the teletypewriter is the oldest and one of the cheapest. **The teletypewriter is primitive and undesirable, but it is easy to understand, so we will use it, without encouraging you to do likewise.**

You can type your source program at the teletypewriter keyboard. The teletypewriter can print whatever you type; it can also punch whatever you type on paper tape. The teletypewriter transmits whatever you type to the microcomputer, as data. Subsequently the teletypewriter can read the punched paper tape; it has a paper tape reader that performs this task. The paper tape reader reads the punched paper tape; it transmits what it reads to the microcomputer, as data, just as the keyboard did. Therefore if you print and punch your source program, you have it in human and machine readable forms.

But teletypewriters do not print or punch hexadecimal digits, they create ASCII character codes. Therefore our hexadecimal digit source program must be created first as a sequence of ASCII codes.

Hexadecimal digits are represented by the digits 0 through 9 plus the letters A through F. The ASCII codes for these digits are extracted from Appendix A:

Hexadecimal Digit	ASCII Code
0	0110000
1	0110001
2	0110010
3	0110011
4	0110100
5	0110101
6	0110110
7	0110111
8	0111000
9	0111001
A	1000001
B	1000010
C	1000011
D	1000100
E	1000101
F	1000110

Suppose you write the binary addition program on a piece of paper, using hexadecimal digits, as illustrated in Figure 6-1.

This is the binary addition source program.

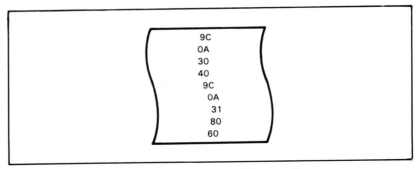

Figure 6-1. A Source Program Written on Paper

OBJECT PROGRAMS

This source program must be converted into a form that can be loaded into memory and executed. We have elected to do this using paper tape.

Paper Tape   **A paper tape has eight "channels," representing the eight binary digits of a byte.** A hole punched in any channel represents a 1, while the absence of a hole represents a 0. Ten bytes are represented by one inch of paper tape. In other words, every 0.1" of paper tape represents one byte, as follows:

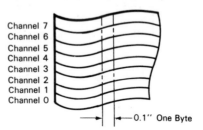

Usually a line of sprocket holes appears between Channels 2 and 3; the sprocket holes are used by a toothed wheel to advance the paper tape.

Our goal is to convert the source program into an object program paper tape, as illustrated in Figure 6-2. The paper tape in Figure 6-2 is an exact representation of the binary instruction codes that will be stored in memory; 1 digits are represented by holes, and 0 digits are represented by a lack of holes.

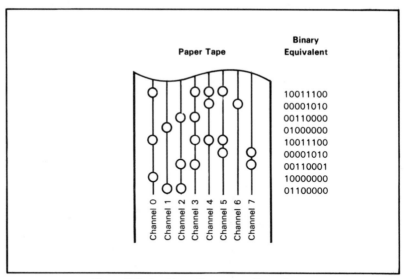

Figure 6-2. An Object Program on Paper Tape

Creating Object Programs

Converting the source program of **Figure 6-1** into the object program of **Figure 6-2** is a two-step procedure.

First the hexadecimal digits illustrated in **Figure 6-1** are entered at a keyboard. We have elected to use a teletypewriter keyboard. Each digit becomes an ASCII code on paper tape, as illustrated in Figure 6-3.

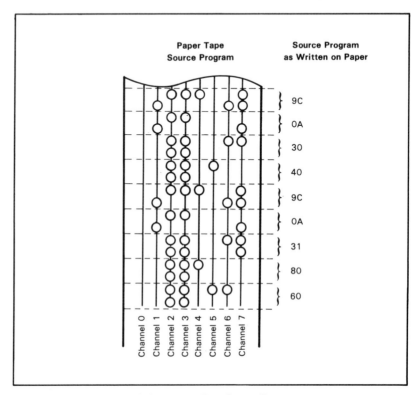

Figure 6-3. A Paper Tape Source Program

Editors

You could create the paper tape illustrated in **Figure 6-3** by simply turning on a teletypewriter punch, then depressing appropriate keys at the keyboard.

You could get a little more fancy by attaching the teletypewriter to a computer, which executes a program to read keyboard data and punch paper tape. This is a very simple-minded version of a program called an "editor."

Using an editor program to create source programs is a good idea. For example, the editor program could be written to ignore any key that is not a valid hexadecimal digit (0, 1, 2, 3, 4, 5, 6, 7, 8, 9, A, B, C, D, E, F). Since a teletypewriter can read as well as punch paper tapes, the editor can read old source program paper tapes, let you make corrections, then punch out the corrected version of the source program. This saves the time you would otherwise spend rekeying the error-free portions of the source program.

Converter Program

Having used an editor to create a source program on paper tape, as illustrated in Figure 6-3, you will then execute another program which automatically reads the source program and creates an object program equivalent; for the moment we will refer to this as a "converter program."

With reference to Figures 6-2 and 6-3, the logic of the converter program is quite simple; it must extract one hexadecimal digit from each ASCII character, then combine pairs of hexadecimal digits into instruction object code bytes. It does this as follows:

1) Combine the rightmost (low-order) four bits of every pair of source program bytes into one object program byte.
2) If Channels 0 through 3 of the source program contain 0011, discard these four bits and use Channels 4 through 7 as is.
3) If Channels 0 through 3 of the source program contain 0100, discard these four bits and use 9 plus the contents of the four bits in Channels 4 through 7.

These three logic steps may be illustrated as follows:

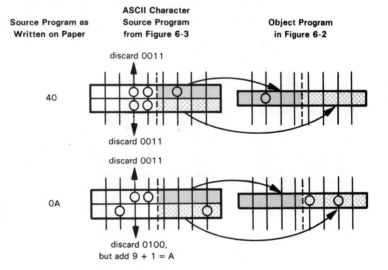

Source Program as Written on Paper | ASCII Character Source Program from Figure 6-3 | Object Program in Figure 6-2

discard 0011
40
discard 0011

discard 0011
0A
discard 0100, but add 9 + 1 = A

Data on the object program paper tape, as created by the converter program, can be loaded directly into memory, to be executed by the microprocessor.

You do not have to use paper tape as the medium for creating source and object programs; in fact, you should do whatever you can to avoid using paper tape. Only the simplest of microcomputer systems will use paper tape. **Usually a magnetic medium, such as a disk unit, is used to store source and object programs (or any other data).**

ASSEMBLY LANGUAGE

Why are ASCII coded hexadecimal digits more efficient than binary digits as a programming medium? Because ASCII coded hexadecimal digits make the programmer's job easier, leaving the hard job to the computer.

Easing the programmer's job — by making errors harder to introduce and easier to spot — is a goal worth striving for. And making the computer convert an ASCII coded hexadecimal source program into a binary object program — by executing a converter program — is a small price to pay, because the converter program will execute in seconds or (at most) a few minutes.

Let us take this line of reasoning a step further. **Instead of programming in ASCII coded hexadecimal digits, we will use a "programming language" which is even simpler for the human programmer to comprehend.**

A source program written in a "programming language" will be very unlike an object program binary digit sequence; so the converter program becomes more complex. But that remains a small price to pay.

A programming language tries to eliminate syntactical programming errors — the misplaced digit, the wrong instruction code — leaving only logic errors, specific to the application, as the programmer's responsibility.

Assembly language is the first step into programming forms more easily understood by the human programmer.

Assembly Language Syntax

The assembly language of any minicomputer or microprocessor consists of a set of instructions, each of which occupies one line of the source program. Each line may be divided into four parts, or fields, as follows:

Label	Mnemonic	Operand	Comment
	LD	DC0,#ADDR1	;Load the Source Address into DC
HERE	LDB	A0,@DC0	;Load Data Word into Accumulator
	ANDB	A0,#H'0F	;Mask Off High-Order Four Bits
	BZ	OUT	;Jump Out if Result is 0
	STB	A0,@DC0	;Store Masked Data
	INC	DC0	;Increment the Data Counter
	BR	HERE	;Return for Next Byte
OUT			;Next Instruction

Mnemonic Field   Every source program instruction represents one object program instruction.

Consider first the mnemonic field, which is highlighted as follows:

Label	Mnemonic	Operand	Comment
	LD	DC0,#ADDR1	;Load the Source Address into DC
HERE	LDB	A0,@DC0	;Load Data Word into Accumulator
	ANDB	A0,#H'0F	;Mask off High-Order Four Bits
	BZ	OUT	;Jump Out if Result is 0
	STB	A0,@DC0	;Store Masked Data
	INC	DC0	;Increment the Data Counter
	BR	HERE	;Return For Next Byte
OUT			;Next Instruction

The mnemonic field is the most important field in an assembly language instruction; it is the only field which must have something in it. This field contains a group of letters which constitute a code identifying the source program instruction.

Assembler   **The converter program used to convert assembly language source programs into binary object programs is called an "assembler."** The assembler reads the mnemonic field, as a group of ASCII characters, and substitutes appropriate binary digits in order to create part (or occasionally all) of the instruction's object code.

Consider the instruction specified by the mnemonic STB. This instruction performs the same operation as Instruction 5 of the binary addition program described in Chapter 4. STB specifies object code bits 7, 6, 5, 3, and 2 as follows: 011X00XX. Bits 4, 1, and 0, shown containing X, are determined by the contents of the operand field. The assembler must therefore have logic which generates instruction code bits 7, 6, 5, 3, and 2, as shown, upon encountering STB in the mnemonic field of a source program instruction:

Source Program	Binary form of ASCII mnemonic seen by Assembler	Binary form of Object program created by Assembler
S	01010011	
T	01010100 } Assembler logic →	011X00XX
B	01000010	

The assembler will fill in the X digits later, when it processes the operand field.

Note carefully that only the binary instruction codes of a microcomputer (that is, the object code) are sacred and unalterable. The source program mnemonics are arbitrarily selected and can be changed at any time simply by rewriting the assembler to recognize the new source program mnemonic.

Every microprocessor's instruction set is described in vendor literature using source program mnemonics. The selection of mnemonics is a very arbitrary business. This is demonstrated by the fact that only in rare cases will two different microprocessors use the same mnemonic to identify instruction codes that do the same thing. In fact, the selection of instruction mnemonics can become a very emotional issue.

Consider the use of more than one mnemonic to represent the same instruction.

We have just shown how the mnemonic STB is converted to the object program instruction code $011X00XX_2$. Another assembler could be written to convert the mnemonic XYZ to the same object code. A third assembler could be written to convert either STB or XYZ to $011X00XX_2$.

There is no reason why every microprocessor should have separate and distinct instruction mnemonics. The mnemonic variations that we see from microprocessor to microprocessor have no rational justification. Variations are aimed at marking products with a stamp of individuality; this aggrandizes individuals at the expense of the user public.

The Institute of Electrical and Electronic Engineers (IEEE) has a task force attempting to define a standard syntax to be used throughout the microprocessor industry. The most recent results of the task force are presented in Appendix C. IEEE proposed standard syntax is used throughout this chapter, and in Chapter 7. Future revisions of this book will include modifications to the IEEE standard syntax, until a final standard has been officially adopted.

It is critically important that all microprocessor users rally to a single assembly language standard. We must force a standard on the microprocessor manufacturers, with or without their cooperation. The alternative is that every microprocessor manufacturer will foist their own arbitrary rules on us, greatly increasing the complexity and expense of assembly language programming.

Next we will discuss an assembly language instruction's Label Field, which is highlighted as follows:

```
          LD     DC0,#ADDR1   ;Load the Source Address into DC
HERE      LDB    A0,@DC0      ;Load Data Word Into Accumulator
          ANDB   A0,#H'OF     ;Mask Off High-Order Four Bits
          BZ     OUT          ;Jump Out if Result is 0
          STB    A0,@DC0      ;Store Masked Data
          INC    DC0          ;Increment the Data Counter
          BR     HERE         ;Return For Next Byte
OUT                           ;Next Instruction
```

Label Field   The label field may or may not have anything in it. If there is anything in the label field, it is treated as a name which can be used subsequently to address the instruction. In other words, you do not identify an instruction by its location in program memory (as we did in Chapter 4), because at the time you are writing the program you may not know where in memory the instruction will finish up. This being the case, you give the instruction a name, or label.

Refer to the example above. The instruction labeled HERE must be identified, because later on there is an instruction which specifies a change of execution sequence. The instruction:

```
          BR     HERE         ;Return For Next Byte
```

specifies that the instruction labeled HERE is the next instruction to be executed. This is a Jump, or Branch instruction; it may be used to illustrate the function of a label by drawing the following picture of our program's execution sequence:

```
              LD     DC0,#ADDR1   ;Load the Source Address into DC
HERE →        LDB    A0,@DC0      ;Load Data Word into Accumulator
              ANDB   A0,#H'OF     ;Mask Off High-Order Four Bits
              BZ     OUT          ;Jump Out if Result is 0
              STB    A0,@DC0      ;Store Masked Data
              INC    DC0          ;Increment the Data Counter
              BR ───→ HERE ─┐     ;Return For Next Byte
OUT                          ;Next Instruction
```

The assembler will have to keep track of where in memory instructions finish up, because the assembler will ultimately have to replace every label with an actual memory address.

Suppose the object program corresponding to the above assembly language source program is going to occupy memory words as follows:

```
03FF, 0400, 0401      LD     DC0,#ADDR1   ;Load the Source Address into DC
0402             HERE LDB     A0,@DC0      ;Load Data Word into Accumulator
0403, 0404            ANDB   A0,#H'OF     ;Mask Off High-Order Four Bits
0405, 0406            B      OUT          ;Jump Out if Result is 0
0407                  STB    A0,@DC0      ;Store Masked Data
0408                  INC    DC0          ;Increment the Data Counter
0409, 040A, 040B      BR     HERE         ;Return For Next Byte
040C             OUT                        ;Next Instruction
```

The assembler will assign the value of 0402_{16} to the label HERE, and $040C_{16}$ to the label OUT.

The binary instruction code for the JMP instruction happens to be BC_{16}. If the label HERE has the value of 0402_{16}, then the assembler will convert the source program instruction:

```
          BR     HERE
```

to the three object program bytes:

```
BC
04
02
```

If you moved the program, so that the object code for

```
HERE        LDB
```

occupied a program memory byte with address 0C7A$_{16}$, then the assembler would convert:

```
BR          HERE
```

to the three program bytes:

```
BC
0C
7A
```

Operand Field

Next consider the Operand field, which is highlighted as follows:

```
            LD      DC0,#ADDR1    ;Load the Source Address into DC
HERE        LDB     A0,@DC0       ;Load Data Word into Accumulator
            ANDB    A0,#H'0F      ;Mask Off High-Order Four Bits
            BZ      OUT           ;Jump Out if Result is 0
            STB     A0,@DC0       ;Store Masked Data
            INC     DC0           ;Increment the Data Counter
            BR      HERE          ;Return For Next Byte
OUT                               ;Next Instruction
```

Let us look at the operand field contents in the program we are illustrating in this chapter:

DC0,#ADDR1   DC0 identifies the data counter into which immediate data must be loaded. ADDR1 is a label representing the address which must be loaded into the data counter. Because a # precedes ADDR1, the assembler will convert ADDR1 into a 16-bit binary data value.

A0,@DC0   occurring in the LDB instruction's operand field specifies that data will be loaded into Accumulator A0 from a memory location whose address is held in Data Counter Register DC0.

A0,#H'0F   specifies Accumulator A0 and an immediate, hexadecimal two-digit value 0F$_{16}$. ANDB specifies an 8-bit AND operation. Whatever is in Accumulator A0 is ANDed with the immediate value, in this case 0F$_{16}$. This has the effect of setting to zero the high-order four bits of Accumulator A0 while leaving the low-order four bits of the accumulator as they are.

OUT
and
HERE

appearing in operand fields, identify instructions with labels OUT and HERE. The instruction:

```
BZ      OUT           ;Jump Out if Result is Zero
```

uses the contents of the accumulator to decide which instruction gets executed after the ANDB instruction. If the ANDB instruction leaves zero in the accumulator, then the instruction with the label OUT gets executed after BZ. If the ANDB instruction leaves a non-zero value in the accumulator, then the next sequential instruction (STB) gets executed after BZ.

The BR instruction:

```
BR          HERE           ;Return For Next Byte
```

states unconditionally that the next instruction to be executed must be the instruction with the label HERE. The instruction with label OUT, since it follows sequentially, would otherwise have been executed next.

A0,@DC0 occurring in the Operand field of the STB instruction causes the contents of Accumulator A0 to be written into the memory location whose address is held in Data Counter DC0.

DC0 specifies the data counter whose contents are to be incremented.

Comment Field

The comment field contains information which makes the program easier to read but has no effect on the binary object program created by the assembler. In other words, the assembler ignores the comment field.

Field Identification

How is the assembler going to tell where one field ends and the next begins? Usually space codes are used to separate fields, but every assembler will have its own set of rules for specifying instruction fields. Here is one set of rules that are as good as any other, and better than none:

1) All characters from the first character on a line up to the first space code constitute the label field.
   If the first character is a space code, then the label field is presumed to be empty.
2) Contiguous space codes are treated as though they were one space code.
3) All characters between the first and second space code (or contiguous space codes) are interpreted as the mnemonic field.
4) If the mnemonic does not require an operand, the assembler quits here, assuming everything that follows is comment.
5) If the mnemonic does require an operand, then the assembler assumes that all characters between the second and third space codes (or contiguous space codes) constitute the operand field.
6) The comment field, if present, must begin with a semicolon.

Space code field delimiters may be illustrated, according to the above rules, as follows:

```
        LD        DC0,#ADDR1    ;Load the Source Address into DC
HERE    LDB       A0,@DC0       ;Load Data Word Into Accumulator
        ANDB      A0,#H'0F      ;Mask Off High-order Four Bits
        BZ        OUT           ;Jump Out If Result is 0
        STB       A0,@DC0       ;Store Masked Data
        INC       DC0           ;Increment the Data Counter
        BR        HERE          ;Return For Next Byte
OUT                             ;Next Instruction
```

ASSEMBLER DIRECTIVES

An assembly language program, such as the seven-instruction sequence we have been using to illustrate assembly language instruction fields, cannot be assembled as it stands. If the assembler is to give fixed binary values to labels OUT and HERE, then it must be told where in program memory the object program will eventually reside.

There is a class of instructions, referred to as "assembler directives," which you will use to provide the assembler with information that it cannot deduce for itself.

Origin Directive

In explaining how the labels OUT and HERE in the operand field would be interpreted by the assembler, we illustrated the object program occupying program memory locations beginning at 03FF$_{16}$. You **specify** this **origin to the assembler using an Origin assembler directive** as follows:

```
        ORG     H'03FF
        LD      DC0,#ADDR1      ;Load the Source Address Into DC
HERE    LDB     A0,@DC0         ;Load Data Word Into Accumulator
        ANDB    A0,#H'0F        ;Mask Off High-order Four Bits
        BZ      OUT             ;Jump Out If Result is 0
        STB     A0,@DC0         ;Store Masked Data
        INC     DC0             ;Increment the Data Counter
        BR      HERE            ;Return For Next Byte
OUT                             ;Next Instruction
```

The Origin assembler directive generates no object code. Its sole purpose in the program is to tell the assembler where the object code will be located in program memory, and thus how to calculate the real binary memory addresses that must be substituted for instruction labels.

End Directive

Another assembler directive that is always present, because it makes the job of creating an assembler easier, is **the END directive.** This is the last instruction in a program; **it tells the assembler that there are no more executable instructions.** The END assembler directive may be illustrated as follows:

```
        ORG     H'03FF
        LD      DC0,#ADDR1      ;Load the Source Address Into DC
HERE    LDB     A0,@DC0         ;Load Data Word Into Accumulator
        ANDB    A0,#H'0F        ;Mask Off High-Order Four Bits
        BZ      OUT             ;Jump Out If Result is 0
        STB     A0,@DC0         ;Store Masked Data
        INC     DC0             ;Increment the Data Counter
        BR      HERE            ;Return For Next Byte
OUT     :                       ;Next Instruction
        END
```

Equate Directive

Equate is another assembler directive that is always present. **You use the Equate assembler directive to assign a value to a symbol or a label.** Consider the instruction:

```
        ANDB    A0,H'0F         ;Mask Off High-Order Four Bits
```

The operand H'0F could be replaced by a symbol which is equated with the value $0F_{16}$. This is illustrated as follows:

```
VALUE   EQU     H'0F
        ORG     H'03FF
        LD      DC0,#ADDR1      ;Load the Source Address Into DC
HERE    LDB     A0,@DC0         ;Load Data Word Into Accumulator
        ANDB    A0,#VALUE       ;Mask Off High-Order Four Bits
        BZ      OUT             ;Jump Out If Result Is 0
        STB     A0,@DC0         ;Store Masked Data
        INC     DC0             ;Increment the Data Counter
        BR      HERE            ;Return For Next Byte
OUT                             ;Next Instruction
```

An Equate assembler directive could also be used to assign a value to the address labeled ADDR1. However, you would only do this if ADDR1 did not exist as an instruction label somewhere else within the program.

Define Constant

Define Address

There are two mnemonics that appear in every assembly language and are neither instructions nor assembler directives. These are the Define Constant and Define Address mnemonics.

The Define Constant mnemonic is used to specify a single byte of actual data. The Define Address mnemonic is used to specify two bytes of actual data. As an example of how these two mnemonics are used, the instruction sequence:

```
        ORG     H'0700
        DATA    H'3A
ADDR1   DATA    H'27AC
VALUE   DATA    H'0F
```

causes the assembler to create the following memory map:

```
0700    3A
0701    27
0702    AC
0703    0F
0704
0705
0706
```

MEMORY ADDRESSING

Programs are always stored in a microcomputer's memory; so is the data that a program uses. Much of a program's logic is therefore expended transferring data from memory to CPU registers, performing various operations using this data, then returning results to memory. Thus the operand field for many instructions contains information that identifies memory locations. **There are many ways in which memory locations can be identified; they are referred to, collectively, as memory addressing.**

We introduced memory addressing in Chapter 4, where some discussion of the subject was needed in order to define the registers which a CPU will require. We will now discuss memory addressing thoroughly, since it is a critical component of any microprocessor's programming logic. Furthermore, as we will see in Chapter 7, the memory addressing options offered by a microprocessor go a long way towards determining the "flavor" of the microprocessor's instruction set.

Microprocessor Memory Addressing —
Where it Began

Microprocessor memory addressing logic has evolved from three different sources: the Intel 8008 microprocessor, the PDP-8 minicomputer, and IBM mainframe computers.

All of today's popular 8-bit microprocessors have instruction sets and addressing logic that are descendents of the Intel 8008 microprocessor and the Datapoint 2200 minicomputer. These two have identical, very primitive CPU architecture and instruction sets, deliberately restricted by the designers who, in 1968, set about building an ultra low cost computer given the electronics technology available at that time.

The PDP-8 was the world's first low cost minicomputer. Introduced in 1965, it too had a very primitive CPU architecture, with restricted memory addressing modes and a limited instruction set, again aimed at minimizing product costs, given the level of electronics technology in the early sixties. Although the PDP-8 has been reproduced as a microprocessor, the Intersil IM6100, "mainstream" microprocessor evolution has bypassed the PDP-8. Nevertheless, the PDP-8 had a profound impact on minicomputer architectures in general, which, of necessity, have had tangential impact on microprocessors.

The most recent 16-bit microprocessors have cut loose from the artificial restrictions imposed by Intel 8008 and PDP-8 architectural concepts, embracing instead IBM 360/370 mainframe concepts.

We will refer to these three influences in the discussion of addressing modes that follows.

The Intel 8008 microprocessor and the Datapoint 2200 minicomputer have the same instruction set; but the Datapoint 2200 executes instructions approximately ten times as fast. Datapoint developed the 2200 CPU architecture and instruction set for the limited data processing environment of "intelligent terminals." Discrete logic replacement was not what they had in mind. The Datapoint 2200 instruction set was deliberately limited, to accommodate the confines of large scale integration (LSI) technology as it stood in 1968. **Datapoint 2200 memory addressing capabilities were primitive out of necessity, not desire.**

Intel, which initially developed the 8008 microprocessor at Datapoint's request, found a significant market for the product in discrete logic replacement — a market for which the instruction set was never intended.

Subsequent microprocessor instruction sets have evolved as a result of two competing influences:

1) Microprocessor designers have incorporated minicomputer features as fast as advances in LSI technology would allow, without analyzing the needs of any existing microprocessor customer base. This is where PDP-8 influence is occasionally evident.

2) Now that a definable microprocessor customer base is beginning to emerge, microprocessor designers are responding directly to their needs.

Influences 1 and 2 above do indeed differ. Microprocessor users' needs are not always well served by minicomputer instruction sets.

IMPLIED MEMORY ADDRESSING

Implied memory addressing was the only memory addressing option provided by the Intel 8008; in consequence it became the principal memory addressing method used by most early microprocessors.

An instruction that uses implied memory addressing specifies that the address of the selected memory location will be the contents of a data counter.

Implied memory addressing has been described in detail in Chapter 4; therefore, we will simply summarize this addressing mode.

Using the data counter to address memory is a two-step process:

1) First, the required memory address must be loaded into the data counter.
2) Next, the implied memory reference instruction is executed. The data counter contains the address of the memory location to be referenced.

Consider the first two instructions of the programming example we have been using in this chapter. Execution of the two instructions may be illustrated as follows:

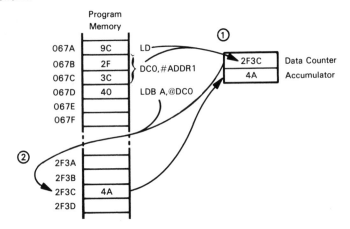

Object code for the first instruction (LD DC0,#ADDR1) occupies the three program memory bytes with addresses $067A_{16}$, $067B_{16}$, and $067C_{16}$. These program memory addresses have been selected arbitrarily. Byte $067A_{16}$ contains an 8-bit object program code which represents the LD DC0,#ADDR1 instruction mnemonic. This instruction specifies that the contents of the next two program memory bytes are to be loaded, as a 16-bit value, into Data Counter DC0. Recall that the actual binary code appearing in memory byte $067A_{16}$ will vary from microprocessor to microprocessor.

The second instruction, with mnemonic LDB, specifies that the contents of the memory location which is addressed by Data Counter DC0 are to be loaded into the accumulator. **We call this IMPLIED memory addressing, because the memory reference instruction, in this case LDB, does not specify a memory address; rather, it stipulates that the memory location whose address is contained in Data Counter DC0 is the memory location to be referenced.**

Many early microprocessors had Data Counter registers that were designed strictly to address data memory. Few modern microprocessors make such restrictive use of registers. Instead, modern microprocessors have a number of CPU registers, all of which can be used in a variety of ways; one use is to hold a memory address, doing the job of a data counter. This is how IBM 360/370 computers use CPU registers to address memory.

The term "implied" memory addressing makes sense when a data memory address is taken from a special Data Counter register. The address is neither described nor specified; it is the contents of the data counter, by default or implication.

"Register indirect" memory addressing is more accurate and descriptive than "implied" memory addressing when the data memory address can be taken from any one of many general purpose CPU registers. The instruction then specifies the data memory address indirectly, as the contents of a named CPU register. The logic of implied and register indirect memory addressing is identical, however.

DIRECT MEMORY ADDRESSING

An instruction with direct memory addressing provides the address of the memory location to be referenced, directly, as part of the instruction's object code. This is the principal addressing mode of the PDP-8 minicomputer.

Simple direct memory addressing has been described in Chapter 4 along with implied memory addressing. In terms of the instruction sequence we are using in this chapter, the LD and LDB instructions could be combined into one direct memory reference instruction as follows:

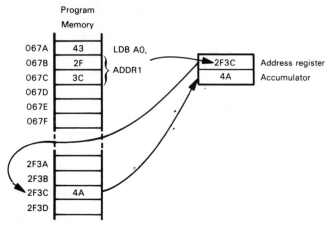

An Address register performs the same function as a data counter, but it does so transiently.

A direct memory reference instruction always starts with a memory address being computed and loaded into the Address register. This becomes the address of the memory location to be referenced.

Direct Versus Implied Addressing

By way of direct comparison, **a minicomputer Address register is referred to as a nonprogrammable register.** This means that a minicomputer has no instructions that merely load data into the Address register or modify the Address register's contents. **The process of changing the contents of the Address register is only one transient step in the course of executing a memory reference instruction.**

The data counter in a microprocessor is programmable. In fact, every microprocessor will have a number of instructions that simply load data into the data counter, or modify the data counter contents, but do nothing else.

All modern microprocessors provide both implied and direct memory addressing. Furthermore, modern microprocessors have no special Data Counter registers; they allow any one of many CPU registers to function as a data counter.

The earliest microprocessors used implied memory addressing only, because it was simple to design into the control unit; there was no other reason. But implied memory addressing carries a penalty; it takes two instructions to do what one direct memory addressing instruction could do. LSI technology has advanced to the point where microprocessor designers could do away with implied memory addressing, but they have not done so. Today most microprocessors use direct memory addressing extensively, but implied memory addressing remains; why? Because some aspects of direct memory addressing are very undesirable when programs are stored in ROM.

Variations of Direct Memory Addressing

We will first consider variations of direct memory addressing as they apply to minicomputers with 12-bit and 16-bit words. This is a good beginning, since direct memory addressing variations evolved from the PDP-8, a 12-bit minicomputer, to the general world of 16-bit minicomputers.

12-Bit Word Direct Addressing

A 16-bit word allows a minicomputer to have 65,536 different instructions in its instruction set. A 12-bit word allows a minicomputer to have 4096 different instructions in its instruction set. These are ridiculously high numbers. Minicomputers therefore separate instruction words into instruction code bits and address bits.

PDP-8

Consider first the 12-bit PDP-8. **The PDP-8's 12-bit word is used as follows:**

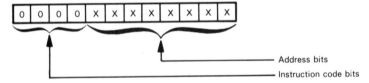

Eight address bits allow this instruction to directly address up to **256 memory words; 256 words constitute a very small memory.**

Will four instruction code bits be enough? Yes indeed. Remember, the above separation of twelve bits into four instruction code bits and eight address bits applies only to memory reference instructions. This is how the PDP-8 and IM6100 interpret memory reference instructions:

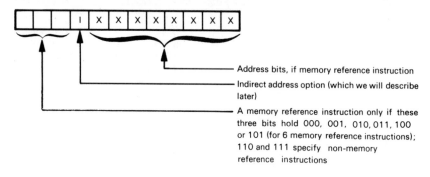

— Address bits, if memory reference instruction

— Indirect address option (which we will describe later)

— A memory reference instruction only if these three bits hold 000, 001, 010, 011, 100 or 101 (for 6 memory reference instructions); 110 and 111 specify non-memory reference instructions

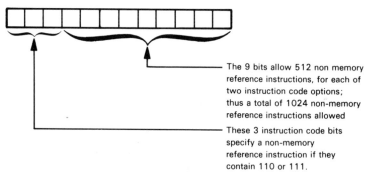

— The 9 bits allow 512 non memory reference instructions, for each of two instruction code options; thus a total of 1024 non-memory reference instructions allowed

— These 3 instruction code bits specify a non-memory reference instruction if they contain 110 or 111.

A 16-bit computer could address 4096_{10} memory words with 12 bits of an instruction word:

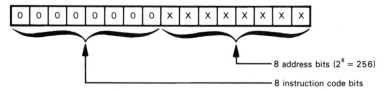

— 8 address bits ($2^8 = 256$)

— 8 instruction code bits

The 16-bit computer could offer more instruction code options, and a smaller addressing range, as follows:

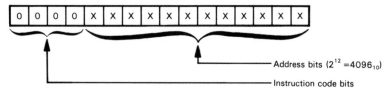

— Address bits ($2^{12} = 4096_{10}$)

— Instruction code bits

Most minicomputers divide their single-word instructions into eight address bits and eight instruction code bits, as illustrated above. An 8-bit microprocessor can easily achieve the same result, using two 8-bit words, as follows:

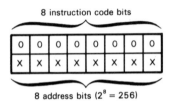

8 instruction code bits

8 address bits ($2^8 = 256$)

If a 16-bit computer uses two words per instruction, it can directly address $65,536_{10}$ words of memory:

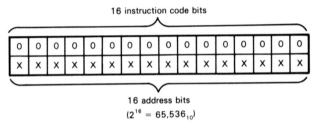

16 instruction code bits

16 address bits
($2^{16} = 65,536_{10}$)

Programming examples that we have used specify 16-bit memory addresses via three 8-bit object code words, as follows:

Word 1	0	0	0	0	0	0	0	0	8 instruction code bits
Word 2	X	X	X	X	X	X	X	X	16 address bits
Word 3	X	X	X	X	X	X	X	X	

Recently introduced 16-bit microprocessors can (optionally) generate memory addresses that are more than 16 bits wide. Memory addresses up to 24 bits wide are now available. A 24-bit memory address can access more than 16 million memory words. Are such large memory spaces necessary? In most cases they are not, but semiconductor technology has reached the point where it costs the chip designer very little to create such large memory addresses. Large memory spaces make impressive advertising copy; moreover, large memory spaces may well allow microprocessors to penetrate new markets, as the basis for products that make extensive use of large programs or data bases.

Address Bits — The Optimum Number

One way or another, instructions can have anywhere from 8 to 24 address bits. What is the optimum number? In minicomputer applications, statistically we find that 80% to 90% of Jump and Branch instructions only need an addressing range of ±128 words (addressable with eight address bits):

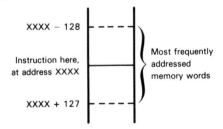

XXXX − 128

Instruction here, at address XXXX

XXXX + 127

Most frequently addressed memory words

Most minicomputers provide more than one instruction word format, including two or all three of the following:

Format 1 (limited addressing range)

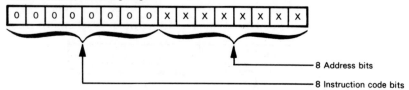

8 Address bits

8 Instruction code bits

Format 2 (limited addressing range)

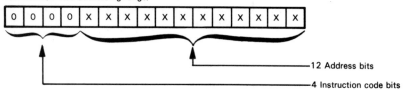

12 Address bits

4 Instruction code bits

Format 3 (extended addressing range)

0	0	0	0	0	0	0	0	0	0	0	0	0	0	0	0	16 Instruction code bits
X	X	X	X	X	X	X	X	X	X	X	X	X	X	X	X	16 Address bits

Instructions with a restricted addressing range are referred to as "Short Form" instructions. Instructions with 16-bit addresses are said to be "Long Form" instructions. Instructions that are more than 16 bits wide, and are generated from two 16-bit components, are often referred to as "Segmented Addresses." Segmented addressing is described later in this chapter.

Paged Direct Addressing

All computers provide some instructions with a limited addressing range. If all of a computer's instructions are subject to a limited addressing range, the computer is said to be "Paged."

To illustrate paging, consider a 12-bit minicomputer with eight address bits per instruction. Memory is effectively segmented into 256_{10} (100_{16}) word pages as follows:

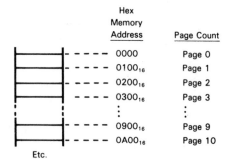

	Hex Memory Address	Page Count
	0000	Page 0
	0100_{16}	Page 1
	0200_{16}	Page 2
	0300_{16}	Page 3
	⋮	⋮
	0900_{16}	Page 9
	$0A00_{16}$	Page 10

Etc.

The eight address bits of an instruction word provide the two low-order hexadecimal digits of a four-digit memory address; the two high-order digits are taken from the program counter. Thus the instruction:

BR   H'3C

would be coded in one 12-bit word, as follows:

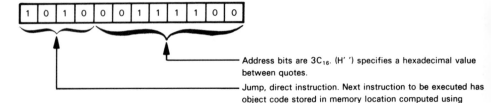

Address bits are $3C_{16}$. (H' ') specifies a hexadecimal value between quotes.

Jump, direct instruction. Next instruction to be executed has object code stored in memory location computed using address bits provided by the instruction word.

Effective Memory Address

Suppose the Jump instruction is stored in a memory word with the address 0709_{16}. After the Jump instruction has been fetched from memory, the program counter will contain the value $070A_{16}$. The effective memory address, therefore, is given by the two high-order digits of the program counter, plus the two low-order digits provided by the instruction, as follows:

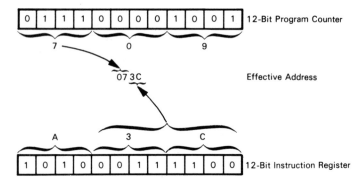

Page Number

The high-order digits, taken from the program counter, are called the page number. The low-order digits, supplied by the instruction code, are the address within the page. Combining the two portions of the address yields the effective memory address. The term "effective memory address" applies to any memory address that must be computed in some way using information provided by the instruction.

As illustrated below, the instruction:

BR   H'3C

will cause the value $073C_{16}$ to be loaded into the program counter, so the next instruction will be fetched from memory location $073C_{16}$.

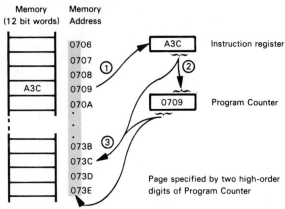

This illustration is described, with reference to the keys (1), (2), and (3), as follows:

(1) The program counter addresses memory word 0709_{16}. The contents of this memory word, $A3C_{16}$, are fetched and stored in the Instruction register. The program counter is incremented to $070A_{16}$; thus, it addresses the next sequential program memory word.

(2) The instruction code in the Instruction register is an unconditional jump. The two low-order digits of the Instruction register ($3C_{16}$) are moved to the two low-order digits of the program counter, which now contains $073C_{16}$.

(3) The next instruction will be fetched from memory location $073C_{16}$.

Consider another example. The instruction:

LDB   A0,H'6C

located on Page $2F_{16}$ would cause the contents of memory location $2F6C_{16}$ to be loaded into the accumulator. The same instruction on Page $1C_{16}$ would cause the contents of memory location $1C6C_{16}$ to be loaded into the accumulator.

Page Boundary Error   **With many paged computers a devious error occurs at the page boundaries.** Recall that the program counter is incremented after an instruction has been fetched. Therefore the page number is acquired from the high-order digits of the program counter, AFTER the program counter has been incremented. Suppose the instruction:

LDB   A0,H'6C

were located at a memory word with address $2FFF_{16}$. After this instruction has been fetched, the program counter will contain 3000_{16}. Now the contents of the memory word with address $306C_{16}$ would be loaded into the accumulator, instead of the memory word with address $2F6C_{16}$.

The most severe restriction imposed by fixed pages is that an instruction cannot reference any memory word outside of the page on which the instruction is located: to read data, to write data, or to execute a program branch or jump. Therefore, **programs cannot reside across a page boundary:**

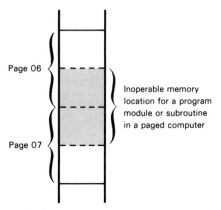

Page 06

Page 07

Inoperable memory location for a program module or subroutine in a paged computer

Paging is wasteful of computer memory, because it requires programs to access all data on or via addresses stored on the program's page. Thus numbers used commonly by programs on many different pages must be stored repeatedly on each page, or else we must add some new flexibility to paged addressing.

Also, when writing program modules and subroutines, it is difficult to contrive that every module exactly fills one page. As a result, a small portion of memory at the end of each page is wasted, since it is too small to accommodate even the smallest subroutine. Thus **a programmer must frequently waste a lot of time juggling the sizes and memory locations of program modules and subroutines.**

Consider, for example, a program with the following modules:

Program	Size (words)
MAIN	88_{16}
SUB1	22_{16}
SUB2	78_{16}
SUB3	52_{16}
SUB4	38_{16}
SUB5	50_{16}
SUB6	66_{16}

We can map the program into memory as follows:

Program	Memory Location
MAIN	$0300_{16} - 0387_{16}$
SUB2	$0388_{16} - 03FF_{16}$
SUB3	$0400_{16} - 0451_{16}$
SUB4	$0452_{16} - 0489_{16}$
SUB5	$0490_{16} - 04FF_{16}$
SUB6	$0500_{16} - 0565_{16}$
SUB1	$0566_{16} - 0585_{16}$

But beware of an error in subroutine SUB3 that requires you to increase its size (by two instructions, say). Subroutines SUB3, SUB4, and SUB5 no longer fit on one page, and correcting SUB3 will require remapping the whole program in memory.

Base Page   **One method of eliminating some of the restrictions imposed by paged addressing is to provide the computer with a "base page."** This is what the PDP-8 does, so let us look at this specific case. In order to give itself one more option, the PDP-8 uses just seven of the eight address bits to compute addresses within a page; in other words, the PDP-8 page is not 256 words long, it is 128 words long. However, the eighth bit allows you to address either the current page (that is, the page on which the instruction is located) or the base page (that is, one of the first 128 words of memory). This is illustrated as follows:

12-Bit Program Counter

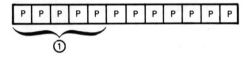

12-Bit Instruction Register

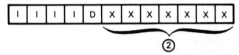

Effective memory address, D = 1

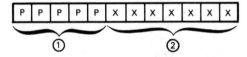

Effective memory address, D = 0

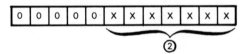

In the above illustration, symbols are used as follows:

P   represents individual binary digits of the program counter.

I   represents the instruction code bits of the Instruction register.

X   represents individual address bits of the instruction word.

D   is the page select bit. If this bit is 0, then the effective memory address is computed by moving the X bits into the low-order bits of an Address register and inserting 0s in the five high-order bits of the Address register; in other words, memory locations from 0 to 127 may be addressed. This is referred to as the base page of memory. If the D bit is 1, then the five high-order bits of the Address register are taken from the five high-order bits of the program counter; only memory locations within the 128-word page in which the instruction resides may be referenced.

Program Relative Paging

A more flexible variation of paging is **PROGRAM RELATIVE** paging, in which it is assumed that the address bits of an instruction represent a signed binary displacement, which must be added to the program counter contents.

A program relative page may be illustrated as follows:

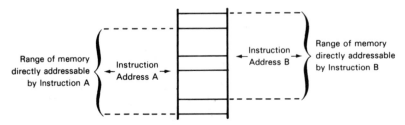

Program relative addressing allows an instruction to address memory in a forward (positive) or backward (negative) direction with a range in each direction of half a page. Consider again an 8-bit address, this time in a 16-bit word:

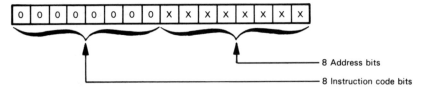

Assume that the high-order address bit is a sign bit; if the instruction is located at memory word $24AE_{16}$, and the eight address bits contain $7A_{16}$, then the effective memory address is given by:

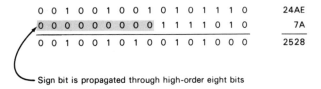

0 0 1 0 0 1 0 0 1 0 1 0 1 1 1 0	24AE
0 0 0 0 0 0 0 0 1 1 1 1 0 1 0	7A
0 0 1 0 0 1 0 1 0 0 1 0 1 0 0 0	2528

Sign bit is propagated through high-order eight bits

This example of forward memory addressing may be illustrated using assembly language instructions as follows:

Memory Address	Object Code	Source	Program	Instruction
24AD	BC7A		BR	HERE
2528		HERE	LDB	A0,THERE

In the above illustration, BC represents the BR instruction code. (The LDB instruction's object code is irrelevant to the discussion at hand, so it is left out.) The assembler will compute the address bits of the BR instruction by subtracting the value in the program counter, after the JMP instruction has been loaded, from the value associated with the label HERE:

Label HERE is equivalent to		2528
PC contents after instruction load	=	24AE
Difference	=	007A

If the assembler computes a value greater than $7F_{16}$, the BR instruction is invalid, and an error message will be transmitted to the errant programmer by the assembler.

Suppose the two instructions were reversed; we would now have:

Memory Address	Object Code	Source Program Instruction		
24AD		HERE	LDB	AO,THERE
2528	BC84		BR	HERE

The assembler will compute address bits of the BR instruction in the same way, by subtracting the value in the program counter, after the BR instruction has been loaded, from the value associated with label HERE:

$$\begin{array}{rl} \text{Label HERE is equivalent to} & \text{24AD} \\ \text{PC contents after instruction load} = & \underline{\text{2529}} \\ \text{Difference} = & -7\text{C} \end{array}$$

$-7C$ is stored in its twos complement form:

$$\begin{array}{rl} 7C = & 0 1 1 1 1 1 0 0 \\ \text{Ones complement} = & \underline{1 0 0 0 0 0 1 1} \\ \text{Twos complement} = & 1 0 0 0 0 1 0 0 = 84 \end{array}$$

The effective memory address provided by the JMP instruction is computed as follows:

$$\begin{array}{ll} 0 0 1 0 0 1 0 1 0 0 1 0 1 0 0 1 & 2529 \\ 1 1 1 1 1 1 1 1 1 0 0 0 0 1 0 0 & \text{FF84} \\ 0 0 1 0 0 1 0 0 1 0 1 0 1 1 0 1 & \text{24AD} \end{array}$$

Sign bit is propagated through high-order eight bits.

Direct Memory Addressing in Microcomputers

Variations of direct addressing which are useful in minicomputer applications are not always useful in microcomputer applications. Let us carefully examine why this is the case.

Consider first a three-byte, direct memory reference instruction, which we have represented as follows:

Instruction code

Two address bytes generated
16-bit address

This instruction format will certainly work. The two address bytes allow any memory location to be addressed directly either to store, read, or otherwise manipulate data, or to change program execution sequence by executing a Jump or Branch instruction. But the two address bytes cannot be changed if the program is in read-only memory.

Here is an example of an instruction sequence that moves data from one memory buffer to another memory buffer:

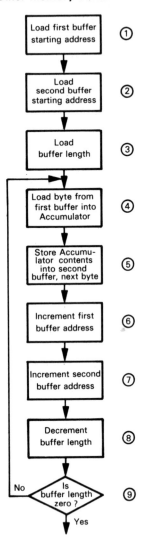

Consider how the above program logic sequence would be executed by a microprocessor that has two data counters (DC0 and DC1) and two accumulators (A0 and A1). Assume that Buffer 1 begins at memory location 0470_{16}, Buffer 2 begins at memory location $08C0_{16}$, and each buffer is eight bytes long. Illustrating CPU Data register contents, this is what happens:

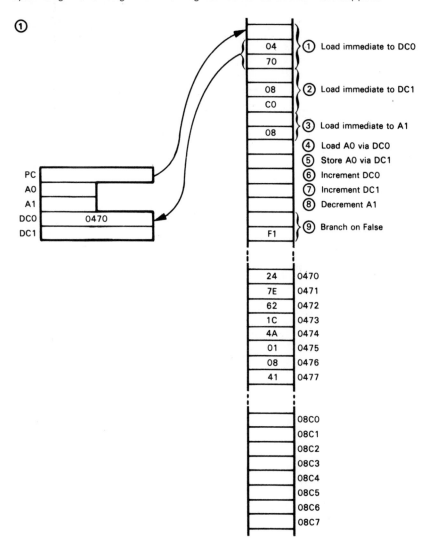

①

04	① Load immediate to DC0
70	
08	② Load immediate to DC1
C0	
08	③ Load immediate to A1
	④ Load A0 via DC0
	⑤ Store A0 via DC1
	⑥ Increment DC0
	⑦ Increment DC1
	⑧ Decrement A1
F1	⑨ Branch on False

PC
A0
A1
DC0 0470
DC1

24	0470
7E	0471
62	0472
1C	0473
4A	0474
01	0475
08	0476
41	0477

	08C0
	08C1
	08C2
	08C3
	08C4
	08C5
	08C6
	08C7

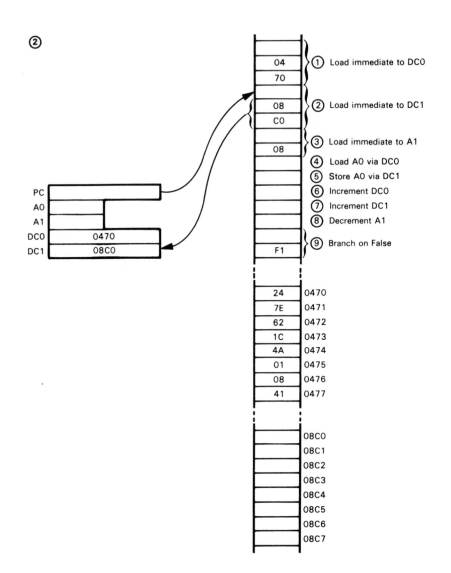

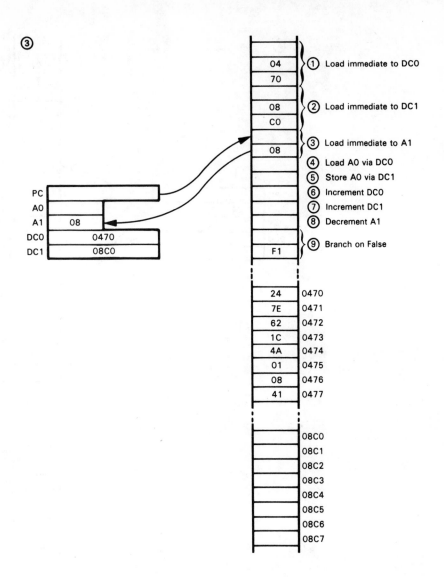

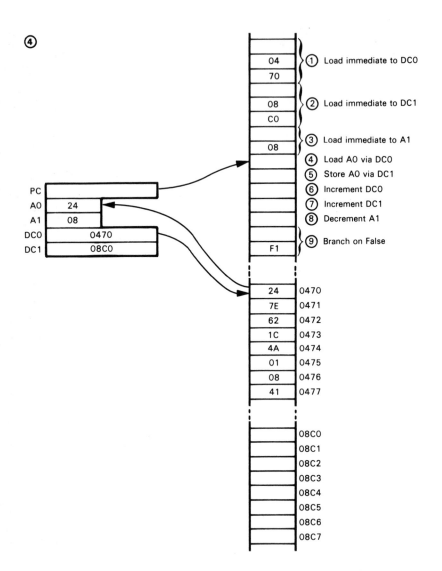

④

04	① Load immediate to DC0
70	
08	② Load immediate to DC1
C0	
08	③ Load immediate to A1
	④ Load A0 via DC0
	⑤ Store A0 via DC1
	⑥ Increment DC0
	⑦ Increment DC1
	⑧ Decrement A1
F1	⑨ Branch on False

PC
A0 24
A1 08
DC0 0470
DC1 08C0

24	0470
7E	0471
62	0472
1C	0473
4A	0474
01	0475
08	0476
41	0477

	08C0
	08C1
	08C2
	08C3
	08C4
	08C5
	08C6
	08C7

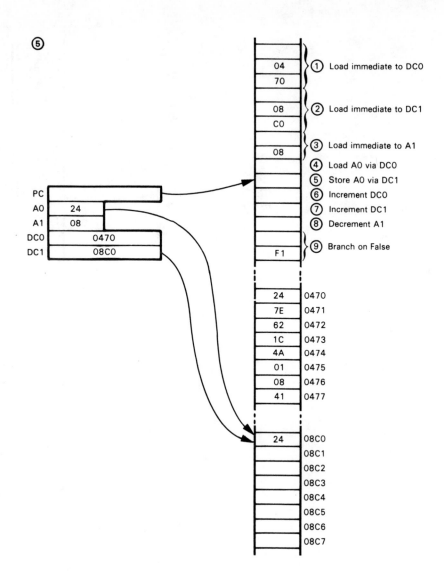

④

04	① Load immediate to DC0
70	
08	② Load immediate to DC1
C0	
08	③ Load immediate to A1
	④ Load A0 via DC0
	⑤ Store A0 via DC1
	⑥ Increment DC0
	⑦ Increment DC1
	⑧ Decrement A1
F1	⑨ Branch on False

PC	
A0	24
A1	08
DC0	0470
DC1	08C0

24	0470
7E	0471
62	0472
1C	0473
4A	0474
01	0475
08	0476
41	0477

24	08C0
	08C1
	08C2
	08C3
	08C4
	08C5
	08C6
	08C7

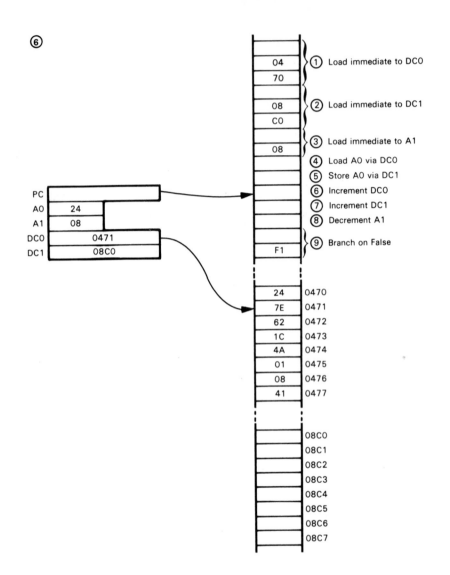

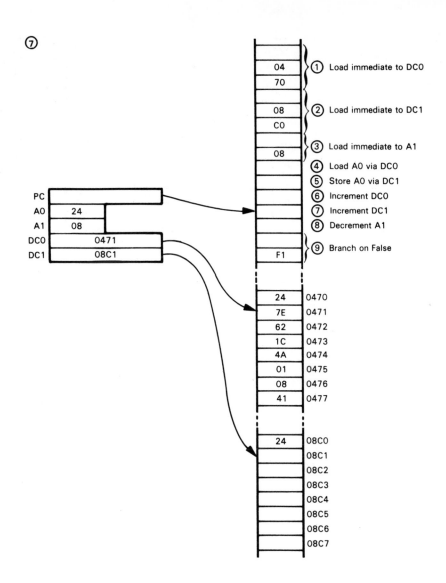

⑧

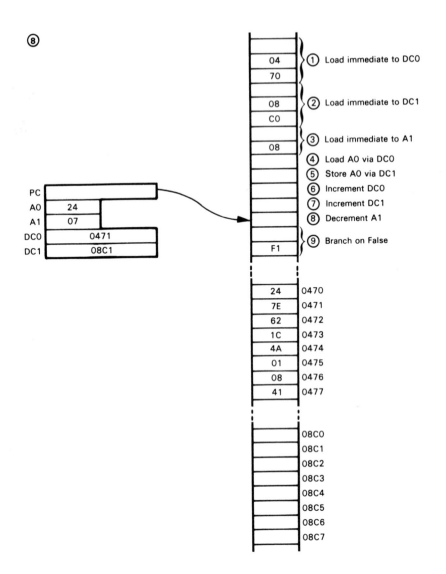

04	①	Load immediate to DC0
70		
08	②	Load immediate to DC1
C0		
08	③	Load immediate to A1
	④	Load A0 via DC0
	⑤	Store A0 via DC1
	⑥	Increment DC0
	⑦	Increment DC1
	⑧	Decrement A1
F1	⑨	Branch on False

PC	
A0	24
A1	07
DC0	0471
DC1	08C1

24	0470
7E	0471
62	0472
1C	0473
4A	0474
01	0475
08	0476
41	0477

	08C0
	08C1
	08C2
	08C3
	08C4
	08C5
	08C6
	08C7

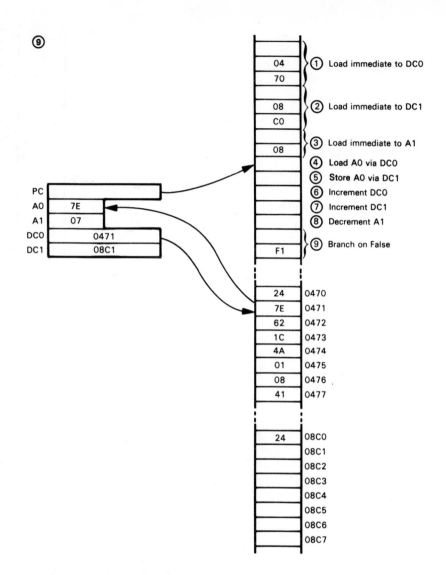

⑨

04	① Load immediate to DC0
70	
08	② Load immediate to DC1
C0	
08	③ Load immediate to A1
	④ Load A0 via DC0
	⑤ Store A0 via DC1
	⑥ Increment DC0
	⑦ Increment DC1
	⑧ Decrement A1
F1	⑨ Branch on False

PC
A0   7E
A1   07
DC0   0471
DC1   08C1

24	0470
7E	0471
62	0472
1C	0473
4A	0474
01	0475
08	0476
41	0477

24	08C0
	08C1
	08C2
	08C3
	08C4
	08C5
	08C6
	08C7

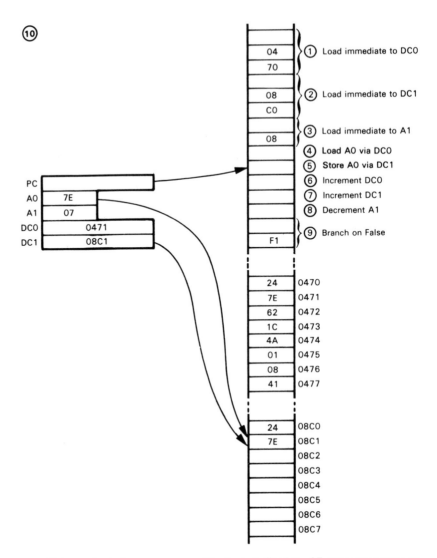

Observe that the program, as illustrated, fits into **15 program memory bytes. Instructions 4 through 9 are reexecuted eight times.** This is possible, since with each pass through instructions 4 through 9 the memory addresses, which are held in the data counters, are changed. This is the virtue of implied memory addressing.

How would the same program logic be implemented by a minicomputer that has direct addressing but no implied addressing? If the program is in ROM, it will have to consist of a pair of three-byte instructions repeated eight times:

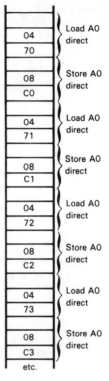

Total program length will be 48 bytes. Implied memory addressing has saved memory by allowing a set of instructions to be reexecuted, and by allowing memory reference instructions to occupy a single byte:

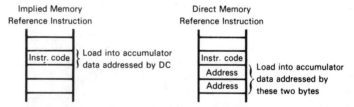

Paged Direct Addressing   **Addressing problems associated with microprocessors become more severe if you try to use any type of paged direct addressing.** Minicomputer designers use paged direct addressing in order to reduce the number of address bits that are part of each memory reference instruction. Pages may be absolute or program relative, as we have just described.

The problem is that if a program is to be stored in ROM, any form of paged direct addressing can only be used by Jump and Branch instructions or memory read instructions. This form of addressing simply cannot be used for memory write instructions. ROM usually comes in 1024-byte (or larger) modules. Pages are either 128 or 256 bytes long. Therefore, an entire page will be in either ROM or RAM. It is not possible to have the program area of a page in ROM and the data area of the same page in RAM:

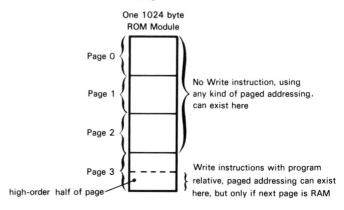

It would certainly be possible to have memory reference instructions that read data out of program memory, but this memory would then have to be divided into a checkerboard of program and data areas, as follows:

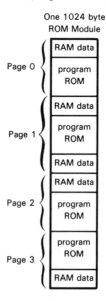

This type of complex memory mapping greatly increases the cost of creating microcomputer programs, plus the potential for introducing programming errors. As a result, microcomputer programs are almost always written with separate program and data areas of memory, as follows:

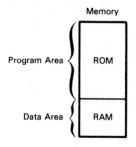

So universal is this division of memory into program and data areas that **some microprocessors address separate memory modules for programs and data. That is to say, the program counter addresses a memory module which the data counter cannot address; and conversely, the data counter addresses a memory module which the program counter cannot address.**

Paged direct addressing was designed into some early minicomputers at a time when memory and CPU electronics were still very expensive. But today memory and CPU electronics are very inexpensive, and they are becoming more inexpensive all the time. No minicomputer has been designed in recent years with paged direct addressing, and no 8-bit or 16-bit microprocessor has ever been designed with such limitations. But there are a few microprocessors that exactly reproduce early minicomputers, or were heavily influenced by them, and have absolute (or program relative) direct memory addressing. Some of these microprocessors have sold relatively well, because they were able to execute programs that had been written over many years for the minicomputers they reproduced. Two examples are the Intersil IM6100 which duplicates DEC's PDP-8, and the Fairchild 9440 which duplicates Data General's NOVA 1200.

Auto-Increment and Auto-Decrement

In the data movement example we just described, observe that the two addresses, stored in the two data counters, must be incremented after each memory reference.

It is easy to imagine program logic that starts at the other end of a data buffer, so the memory address must be decremented after every memory access. In either case, **we can create a single one-byte instruction that specifies a memory reference operation, plus a memory address increment or decrement:**

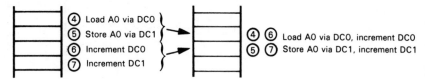

Many microprocessors include auto-increment and/or auto-decrement options among their addressing modes.

THE STACK

There is a variation of implied memory addressing which has existed in many minicomputers and is implemented in one form or another by almost every microprocessor: it is known as stack addressing. The concept of a stack was introduced at the end of Chapter 4, in connection with Chip Slice Control Unit addressing logic.

Memory Stacks

Stack Pointer

The more common stack architecture sets aside some area of data memory for transient storage of data and addresses. The stack is addressed by a data counter type of register, called a stack pointer.

Only two stack operations are usually allowed: writing to the top of the stack (referred to as a Push), and reading from the top of the stack (referred to as a Pop, or a Pull).

The stack gets its name from the fact that it may be visualized as a stack of data words, where only the last data word entered into the stack or the first empty data word at the top of the stack may be accessed. In either case the stack is accessed via an address stored in the stack pointer.

PUSH

A Push operation, which writes into the stack, will cause data from the accumulator (or some other CPU register) to be written into the memory word currently addressed by the stack pointer (SP); the stack pointer contents are then automatically incremented (or decremented) to address the next free word, at the new top of the stack. The following illustration shows the stack pointer being incremented following a Push:

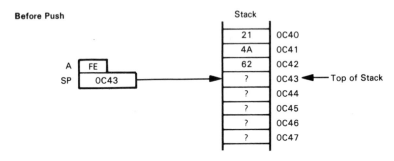

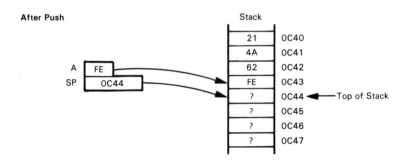

POP   A Pull or Pop operation is the exact reverse of a Push; the Stack register contents are decremented (or incremented) to address the last word written into the top of the stack, then the contents of the memory word addressed by the stack are moved to the accumulator or some other CPU register. This may be illustrated as follows:

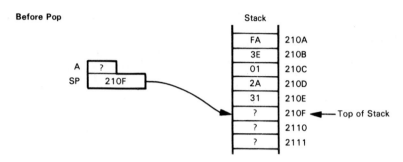

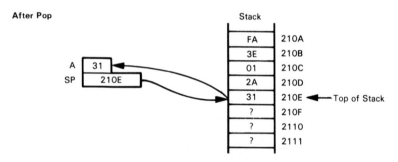

In the illustration, the stack pointer is decremented before the Pop.

Observe that at the end of a Pop operation the stack pointer is again addressing the first unused memory word at the top of the stack; once data has been read out of the top of the stack, the data word is assumed to be empty.

The parallel between implied memory addressing, using a data counter, and stack memory addressing, using a stack pointer, is self-evident. In fact, the only difference between the two is that the stack pointer contents MUST be incremented (or decremented) for a write and MUST be decremented (or incremented) for a read.

There is, of course, nothing to stop a stack being implemented in memory in the opposite direction from that illustrated above; that is, the bottom of the stack is at a larger address than the top. Now the stack will be decremented for a write and incremented for a read. Otherwise nothing changes.

The Cascade Stack

Cascade
PUSH

There is an alternative stack architecture that is less frequently seen. This architecture provides a limited number of registers (it is commonly 8 or 16) in the CPU. When a byte of data is pushed onto the stack it cascades down as follows:

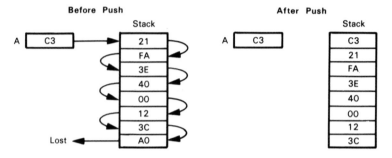

Cascade
POP

When a byte of data is pulled or popped from the top of the stack, data cascades up as follows:

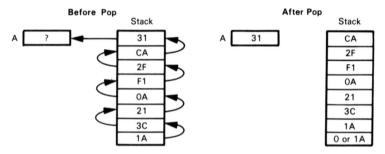

This stack architecture requires no stack pointer, since at all times data is being written onto or read out of the same register at the top of the stack.

How a Stack is Used

The stack is a great convenience to minicomputer users; it is an absolute necessity in microprocessor applications.

Subroutines

Consider the use of subroutines. Most programs, whether they are written for a minicomputer or a microprocessor, consist of a number of frequently used instruction sequences, each of which is recorded once, somewhere in program memory. The routine is then accessed as a subroutine.

An 8-bit microprocessor may require arithmetic to be performed on 32-bit numbers, occupying four contiguous bytes as follows:

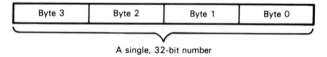

A single, 32-bit number

Subroutine
Call

The most efficient way of handling this type of arithmetic is to write four separate programs to perform 32-bit addition, subtraction, multiplication, and division. Now **every time you want to perform addition (for example), you will use an instruction which CALLS the subroutine.** A call may be illustrated as follows:

Program Memory Used by Main Program

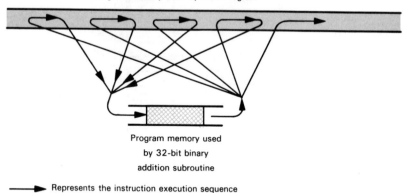

Program memory used
by 32-bit binary
addition subroutine

Represents the instruction execution sequence

Suppose you did not use subroutines; the instruction sequence needed to perform 32-bit binary addition would have to be repeated every time program logic specified 32-bit binary addition. The program would now appear as follows:

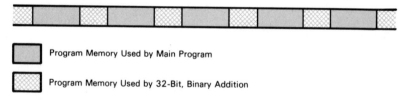

☐ Program Memory Used by Main Program

▨ Program Memory Used by 32-Bit, Binary Addition

Most programs, whether they are written for minicomputers or microprocessors, eventually become nothing more than a large network of calls to subroutines. Provided the importance of subroutines in all microprocessor programs is accepted at face value, you need not understand any more about subroutines at this point. However, let us consider what happens when a subroutine is called, and how program logic handles a return from a subroutine.

The PDP-8 minicomputer (and a number of other old minicomputers) use the first memory word of a subroutine as the location where the return address is to be stored. For example, suppose instructions for our 32-bit, binary addition subroutine occupy memory locations $4C2_{16}$ through $4E0_{16}$. The PDP-8, being a 12-bit minicomputer, stores only 12-bit addresses. Memory word $4C2_{16}$ is the first word of the subroutine, and must be left empty. If the subroutine is called from memory location $72A_{16}$, the following sequence of events occurs:

1) The current contents of the program counter are stored in memory location $4C2_{16}$.
2) The address of the first subroutine instruction, $4C3_{16}$, is loaded into the program counter.
3) Program execution proceeds at the instruction stored in memory location $4C3_{16}$.

This may be illustrated as follows:

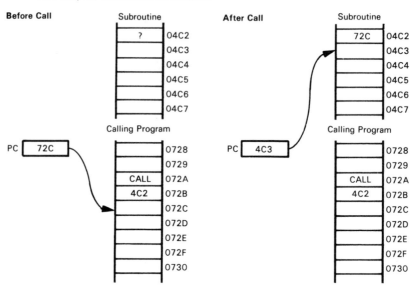

Subroutine Return   **The last instruction executed within the subroutine must be a return instruction.** This instruction moves the address (72C$_{16}$) stored in the first word of the subroutine (at 04C2$_{16}$) back into the program counter, thus causing program execution to continue at the instruction following the subroutine call.

This scheme for calling subroutines obviously cannot work in most microprocessor applications, since the subroutine is likely to be stored in read-only memory; this being the case, the return address cannot be stored in the first word of the subroutine. Microprocessors store subroutine return addresses in the stack. The 32-bit binary addition subroutine call would be executed as follows:

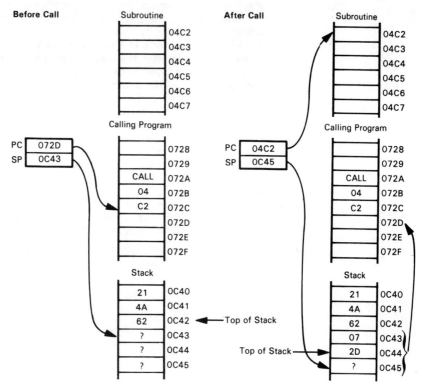

In the above illustration, note that 8-bit memory words are assumed. Since addresses are all 16 bits long, two memory words are required to store each address.

In order to return from a subroutine, it is only necessary to pop the top two bytes of the stack into the program counter. Execution will then proceed with the instruction following the call to the subroutine.

Nested Subroutines and Use of the Stack

A "Nested Subroutine" is defined as a subroutine which has been called by another subroutine.

Recursive Subroutines

There is nothing at all unusual about one subroutine calling another. In fact, subroutines are frequently nested to a level of five or more. The most efficient way to program some mathematical routines is to have subroutines that call themselves. **A subroutine that can call itself is referred to as a recursive subroutine.**

So long as the stack is being used to preserve return addresses, subroutines can be nested in any way, or they can call themselves; and providing the return path follows the call path exactly, the correct return address will always be at the current top of the stack.

Were this book a programmer's guide, we would now prove the above statement with extensive illustrations. However, in order to understand microcomputer concepts and microcomputer programming, you can take at face value the fact that a stack guarantees the return path for any subroutine call sequence. Should you still be curious, you can prove this for yourself by defining a number of subroutines located in various areas of memory. Arbitrarily place calls to other subroutines at random locations within each subroutine. Draw a stack on a piece of paper, and for each call perform a push of the return address. For each return, pop the return address into the program counter. You will find that you always come out of nested subroutines in exactly the same sequence as you entered them, and it does not matter how complex the subroutine call sequences may be.

Double Stacks

Many recently introduced microprocessors have two stack pointers, and therefore the ability to maintain two separate and distinct stacks. These microprocessors compete with, and can substitute for minicomputers.

System Software

Application Programs

Having two stacks is very useful when a microprocessor functions as the central processing unit of a minicomputer type product. Such products are designed to be programmed, usually using a language that puts a lot of distance conceptually between the programmer and the microcomputer hardware. This logical separation is manifest as "system software" — a set of programs that perform all routine tasks required by the microcomputer itself. In contrast, the programmer will write "application programs" that pay no attention to the physical characteristics of the microcomputer system, instead addressing themselves entirely to the application which the programmer wishes to define. **This concept may be illustrated as follows:**

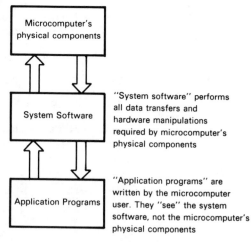

Microcomputer's physical components

System Software

"System software" performs all data transfers and hardware manipulations required by microcomputer's physical components

Application Programs

"Application programs" are written by the microcomputer user. They "see" the system software, not the microcomputer's physical components

When a microprocessor is to be used in a minicomputer type application, one stack supports system software, while the other stack supports application programs.

Privileged Mode

Normal Mode

Privileged Instruction

Many minicomputers, and a few recent microprocessors, take the two-stack concept a step further by allowing programs to be executed in a normal mode or a privileged mode. System software executes in privileged mode, while application programs execute in normal mode. Each mode will use a different stack — and a different stack pointer. Also, a number of instructions will be privileged. **A privileged instruction can be executed in privileged mode, but not in normal mode.** Typically, all input/output instructions are privileged since input/output is microcomputer hardware dependent, and therefore controlled entirely by programs that become part of system software. Application programs have their input/output requirements met at the system software interface by calling appropriate system software subroutines in some predefined way.

The real advantage of separating system and application programs is that it makes it harder for an errant application programmer's mistakes to damage system software. This becomes a particular problem in time-shared microcomputer systems, where two or more users can access one microcomputer system simultaneously. Users would be very displeased if one programmer was allowed to make an unfortunate mistake in an application program, modifying everyone else's I/O, and causing the entire microcomputer system to stop functioning.

Privileged Memory

It is particularly important that time-shared computers be designed so that no application program error can conceivably affect system software. The application programming error that most frequently affects system software is the "wild store," where the application program inadvertently writes data into an area of read/write memory that has been assigned to system software. A wild store will almost certainly cause the entire microcomputer system to stop functioning. Therefore **microcomputer systems designed for time-sharing applications will frequently allow blocks of memory to be referenced only in privileged mode. Programs executed in normal mode will not be able to access privileged memory; in fact, privileged memory will appear not to exist to programs executed in normal mode. A program executed in normal mode will receive the same lack of response if it attempts to reference a memory location assigned to privileged mode as it would if it tried to reference a memory location that did not exist.**

Multiple Stacks

The most recent 16-bit microprocessors (such as the Z8000) have "stack oriented" architectures. They allow many CPU registers to function as stack pointers. **This architecture encourages (but does not force) you to organize data memory as a large collection of small stacks.** Stack addressing and stack access instructions then become the principal means of accessing data.

INDIRECT ADDRESSING

Indirect Address An **INDIRECT ADDRESS** specifies a memory word which is assumed to hold the required direct address.

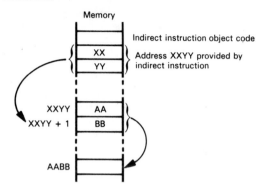

The first of these two memory bytes is at address XXYY, and the two bytes contain AABB.

This memory byte is at the memory address AABB, and is the addressed memory location.

Indirect Address Computation

For indirect addressing, the effective address is given by the equation:

$$EA = [XXYY]$$

Effective Memory Address

where:

EA stands for Effective Memory Address.

[ ] signifies the contents of the memory word whose address is enclosed by the brackets.

Consider the following indirect memory reference:

```
            LDB              A0,@HERE
             .
             .
             .
             .
HERE    DA               XXYY
```

In the LDB (Load 8-bit Accumulator) instruction, HERE identifies the memory word which holds the required address and "@" specifies indirect addressing. Memory location HERE contains an address XXYY which becomes the effective memory address.

If a microprocessor has absolute, paged direct memory addressing, its indirect addressing instructions will occupy two bytes. The effective memory address is now computed as follows:

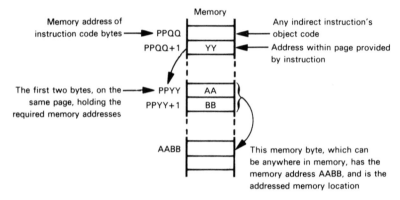

Memory address of instruction code bytes → PPQQ

PPQQ+1 — YY

Any indirect instruction's object code

Address within page provided by instruction

The first two bytes, on the same page, holding the required memory addresses → PPYY — AA

PPYY+1 — BB

AABB

This memory byte, which can be anywhere in memory, has the memory address AABB, and is the addressed memory location

The PDP-8, being a 12-bit minicomputer, uses the following variation of paged indirect addressing:

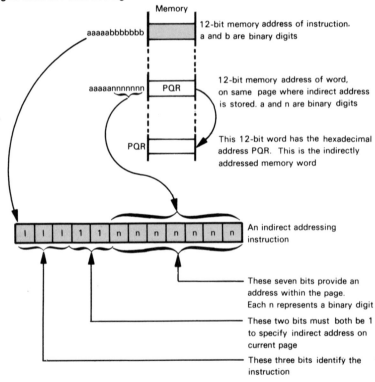

Memory

aaaaabbbbbbb

12-bit memory address of instruction. a and b are binary digits

aaaaannnnnnn — PQR

12-bit memory address of word, on same page where indirect address is stored. a and n are binary digits

PQR

This 12-bit word has the hexadecimal address PQR. This is the indirectly addressed memory word

| l | l | l | 1 | 1 | n | n | n | n | n | n | n |

An indirect addressing instruction

These seven bits provide an address within the page. Each n represents a binary digit

These two bits must both be 1 to specify indirect address on current page

These three bits identify the instruction

The PDP-8, and any other paged computer that has a base page, will use a large part of the base page to store addresses; these addresses will be referenced indirectly. For example, suppose in the above illustration the object code at memory location aaaaabbbbbbb is xxx10nnnnnnn, instead of being xxx11nnnnnnn. Now the address stored in memory location 00000nnnnnnn would be chosen, not the address stored in memory location aaaaannnnnnn.

Another variation of indirect addressing sets aside certain memory locations as auto-increment or auto-decrement locations. For example, the PDP-8 minicomputer (and IM6100 microprocessor) sets aside memory locations 008_{16} through $00F_{16}$, on the base page, as auto-increment locations. If an address is stored in any auto-increment location, then the address will be incremented whenever it is referenced indirectly.

With reference to the most recent illustration, if aaaaannnnnnn were 000000001000 (i.e., 008_{16}), then after the indirect addressing instruction had executed, memory location 008_{16} would contain PQR + 1. On the next execution of the indirect addressing instruction, PQR + 1 would be the effective memory address, not PQR. An auto-decrementing indirect address would have generated PQR − 1 rather than PQR + 1.

Observe that the PDP-8 base page must be implemented in read/write memory if addresses stored in the base page are to change.

Program Relative, Indirect Addressing

A computer that uses program relative, direct addressing can also have program relative, indirect addressing. This is what happens:

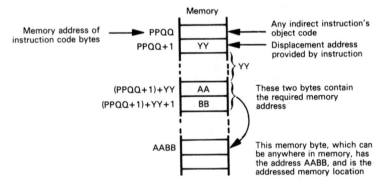

Indirect Addressing — Minicomputers Versus Microcomputers

In the world of minicomputers, even if the minicomputer's direct addressing is not paged, indirect addressing is a great convenience since it allows one Load or Store instruction to access a number of different memory locations, depending on the current contents of the indirect memory address word. Consider the following example:

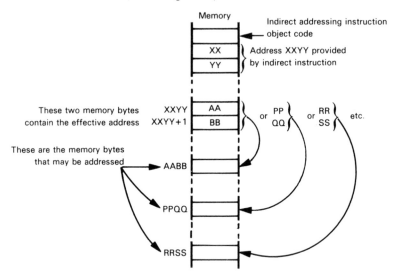

Why would you want to change the indirect address AABB to PPQQ or RRSS?

Many minicomputers are time-shared; in consequence, a single minicomputer may be executing many programs, attending to each one for a few milliseconds before going on to the next. Each program will use parts of memory to store programs and data that are needed for immediate execution, while the bulk of programs and data will remain on disk. A program or data table may occupy completely different areas of memory on each reexecution. This is because the area of memory that is free for use may be affected by totally unrelated programs that were executing in preceding milliseconds by the time-sharing system. **Variable indirect addressing is one of the ways in which minicomputers are able to cope with the fact that programs and data tables may occupy different areas of memory from one execution of the program to the next.** It is necessary to change only a few addresses, such as AABB, in order to change the location of a data table or a program. **While this justification for indirect addressing makes a lot of sense in complex minicomputer applications, it makes absolutely no sense in simple microprocessor applications.** When an entire microcomputer system, complete with memory, costs a hundred dollars or less, it will be cheaper to give each user his own microprocessor and memory, rather than go to the extra programming expense required to share the use of such a low-cost item as a microcomputer.

Non-time sharing applications can also make effective use of variable indirect addressing. For example, a single data area may be used by a number of data tables of variable length. Consider a simple telecommunications application. Data is arriving over a telephone line at some random rate; as data arrives, it is stored in read/write memory. At fixed intervals, a microprocessor program is executed to process the most recent chunk of raw data. Observe that each time the microprocessor program is executed, the data on which it must operate will reside in a different area of read/write memory. If the microprocessor program references read/write memory via indirect addressing, then by simply loading the new beginning address of the data area into the indirect address space, the microcomputer program can access the next segment of data — wherever it may be:

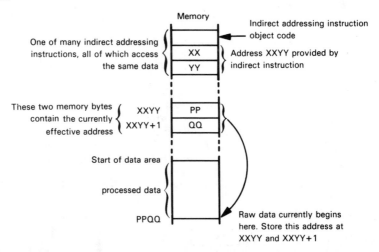

Memory

Indirect addressing instruction object code

One of many indirect addressing instructions, all of which access the same data

XX
YY

Address XXYY provided by indirect instruction

These two memory bytes contain the currently effective address

XXYY
XXYY+1

PP
QQ

Start of data area

processed data

PPQQ

Raw data currently begins here. Store this address at XXYY and XXYY+1

Of course, XXYY and XXYY + 1 must be read/write memory locations.

Very few microprocessors provide indirect addressing. Even the most recent, powerful 16-bit microprocessors have no indirect addressing capability. Instead, they make extensive use of indexed addressing, and variations of indexed addressing, which we will describe next.

INDEXED ADDRESSING

An INDEXED ADDRESS is the sum of a direct address and an implied address. This may be illustrated as follows:

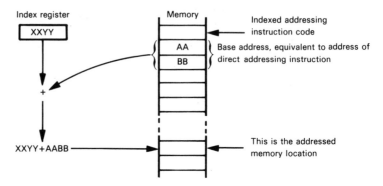

Index Register

The Index register is functionally equivalent to a data counter. Some microprocessors have no Index registers and no indexed addressing; most do. Some microprocessors have special Index registers, designed specifically to support indexed addressing. But it is preferable for a microprocessor to have a number of multifunction CPU registers, each of which can perform many tasks, including the task of an Index register. This is the way IBM 360/370 computers use their CPU registers.

16-bit microprocessor indexed addressing may be illustrated as follows:

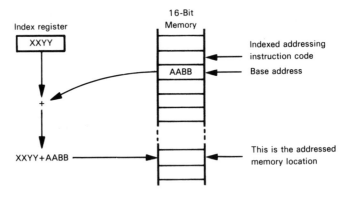

16-bit microprocessors also have a "short form" of indexed addressing that may be illustrated as follows:

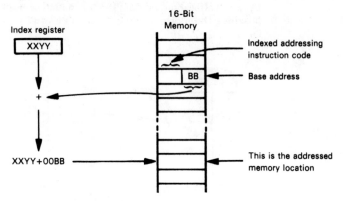

The Index register derives its name from the fact that its contents are likely to change (for example, while it indexes an area of memory being treated as a data table). This may be illustrated for a 16-bit microprocessor as follows:

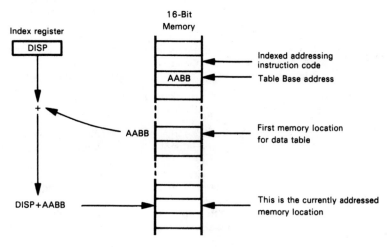

Pre-Indexing   **Indexed addressing may be combined with indirect addressing;** this gives rise to two possibilities: the index may be added to the base address before or after indirect logic is applied. **When the index plus the base address provides the indirect address, we talk of pre-indexed addressing.** This may be illustrated as follows:

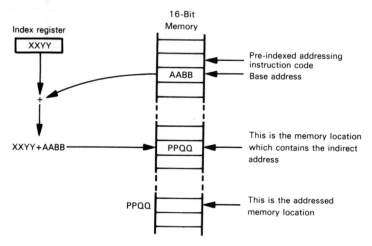

Pre-Index
Effective
Address

For pre-indexed addressing, the effective memory address (EA) is given by the equation:

$$EA = [BASE + INDEX]$$

The square brackets denote "contents of." In the above illustration:

$$EA = [AABB + XXYY] = PPQQ$$

Suppose the Index register contains $213A_{16}$ and the base address is $413C_{16}$; the effective memory address is given by:

$$EA = [413C_{16} + 213A_{16}] = [6276_{16}]$$

Therefore the effective memory address is the contents of the memory word with the address 6276_{16}.

Post-Indexing   **When the index is applied to the indirect address, we talk of post-indexed addressing.** This may be illustrated as follows:

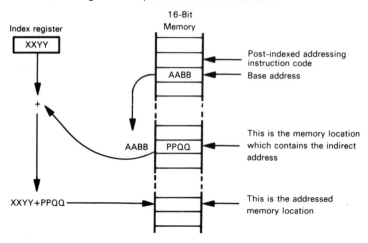

Post-Index Effective Address

For post-indexed addressing, the effective memory address (EA) is given by the equation:

$$EA = [BASE] + INDEX$$

Again the square brackets denote "contents of." In the above illustration:

$$EA = [AABB] + XXYY = PPQQ + XXYY$$

Again suppose the Index register contains $213A_{16}$ and the base address is $413C_{16}$; the effective memory address is given by:

$$EA = [413C_{16}] + 213A_{16}$$

Therefore the effective memory address is the contents of the memory word with address $413C_{16}$, plus $213A_{16}$.

Let us look at indexed addressing for an 8-bit microprocessor. This may be illustrated as follows:

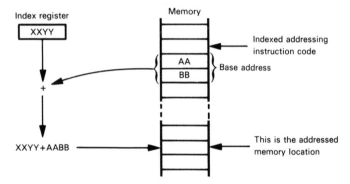

Clearly there is some redundancy in indexed addressing, as illustrated above. XXYY + AABB cannot sum to more than $FFFF_{16}$, since this is the largest value that a 16-bit address can acquire. Any valid indexed address can therefore be rewritten as follows:

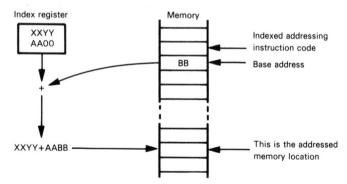

This is the effective memory address:

$$EA = XXYY + AA00 + 00BB$$
$$= XXYY + AABB$$

We have saved a byte in our indexed addressing instruction and given up nothing. In terms of indexing data tables, this representation of indexing may be illustrated as follows:

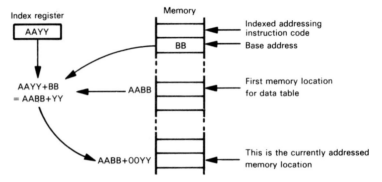

Since we have a 16-bit Index register, but only an 8-bit memory word, in effect, we create the table base address out of the Index register high-order byte plus the base address byte. The Index register low-order byte becomes the table index.

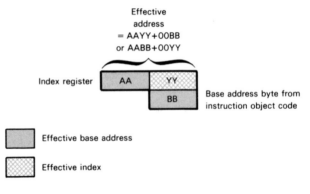

BASE RELATIVE ADDRESSING

Base
Register

Recently introduced 16-bit microprocessors use a second register much like an Index register; it is referred to as a "Base register." A Base register will be the same size as an Index register, and in simple addressing schemes it will be indistinguishable from an Index register. The difference between the two, however, is that the Base register's contents are not modified during any address computation, whereas the Index register's contents might be modified, for example, by auto-increment or auto-decrement logic. Also, when (and if) microprocessors with Base registers and Index registers gain indirect addressing logic, the Base register's contents should be treated as a pre-index, while the Index register's contents should be treated as a post-index. (Pre-indexing and post-indexing were described earlier.)

Conceptually we can differentiate the intended purpose of Base and Index registers by looking at how each might be used to address data tables. This difference may be illustrated as follows:

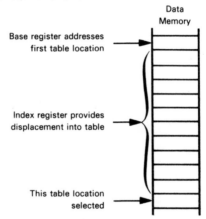

In the illustration above, the required data memory location's address would be computed as the sum of the Base and Index registers' contents. This may be illustrated as follows:

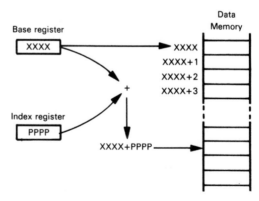

Since the Base and Index registers are both 16 bits wide, you may well ask what purpose is served by summing the contents of two 16-bit registers. Since the sum of these two registers cannot be more than 16 bits, why not make the initial Index register contents equal to the sum of the Base and Index register values, as illustrated above? The Index register's initial value would then be PPPP + XXXX, and this sum could be incremented or decremented.

Having separate Base and Index registers makes program logic cleaner; if data tables need to be moved in memory, it is logically simpler to separate origin addresses from distances into the table. Thus, the Base register becomes a convenience and an aid to elegant programming, rather than a necessity.

Address Displacement

An effective memory address can be the sum of three addresses: the Base register contents, the Index register contents, and an address provided by the instruction object code, which is usually referred to as a displacement. For a 16-bit microprocessor we can illustrate an effective memory address computed from these three parts as follows:

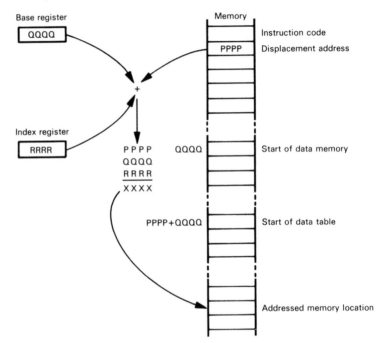

When effective memory addresses are computed from three parts, as illustrated above, the Base register usually provides the origin address for an entire data area of memory. Individual data tables are identified using the displacement, which gives the distance of the first table location from the beginning of data memory. The index then identifies a location within the table, as illustrated above.

Specific 16-bit microprocessors have other addressing variations which differentiate Base registers from Index registers. These are peculiarities of the specific microprocessor's addressing logic, and you should make sure that you understand them before using the microprocessor.

MEMORY SEGMENTATION

Segment
Register
    Some recent 16-bit microprocessors have been designed to directly address as much as sixteen million bytes of memory. One addressing technique uses a 16-bit Segment register to compute a 20-bit address as follows:

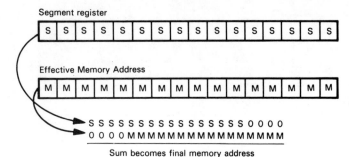

Sum becomes final memory address

    The Intel 8086 uses this segmented memory addressing scheme.

    Microprocessors that use segmented memory will usually have more than one Segment register. In the case of the 8086, one Segment register provides the base for program memory, while another Segment register provides the base for data memory, a third Segment register provides the base for Stack memory, and a fourth Segment register is used to access text strings.

    Some microprocessors generate large memory addresses by having a few Base registers that are more than 16 bits wide. The Intel 8089 I/O Processor uses this technique. Other microprocessors allow large addresses to be computed by concatenating two 16-bit registers, which, for address generation purposes, are treated as one 32-bit register. The Zilog Z8000 and the Motorola 68000 use variations of this 32-bit Address register concept.

7

An Instruction Set

We are now ready to create a hypothetical microprocessor instruction set. The instruction set we are now going to create will not copy any existing microprocessor's instruction set. Rather, it will contain features representative of all of them.We will justify each feature.

Recently introduced 16-bit microprocessors have very complex instruction sets. Rather than dealing with the advanced concepts embodied in these instruction sets, we will first look at a relatively primitive 8-bit microprocessor architecture; at the end of this chapter we will show how simple concepts have been expanded, and will likely continue to grow as more advanced microprocessors are introduced.

We will consider the impact of putting our 8-bit instruction set into a one-chip microcomputer. This is an important consideration, since a one-chip microcomputer's instruction set must pay attention to economical memory utilization. This is because a one-chip microcomputer imposes unique memory restrictions on programs. As discussed in Chapter 3, memory is cheap and getting cheaper all the time. When designing a general purpose microprocessor instruction set, no one would waste much time saving object code bytes simply to reduce memory costs. Soon the most economical memory chip is going to be a 16K-bit device, which means that memory will be added in 16K-byte modules. That leaves little economic incentive to shave bytes from instruction object codes. But few one-chip microcomputers have more than 2048 bytes of program memory. One-chip microcomputers are most frequently used in consumer applications, where there is a big economic incentive to keep the entire application within the one-chip microcomputer, preferably a simple one with a small price, rather than letting programs expand into additional chips. In order to accommodate the additional restrictions of a one-chip microcomputer, therefore, **we will develop an 8-bit microprocessor instruction set that does pay attention to economical memory utilization.** However, we will identify those places in our discussion where the instruction set is indeed being tailored for a potential one-chip microcomputer application.

CPU ARCHITECTURE

The first prerequisite, before we can discuss individual instructions, is to select the number and type of registers, plus the number and type of addressing modes that our hypothetical 8-bit microprocessor will have. We will start with registers.

Number of Registers

We cannot simply select a large number of registers — more than enough for any situation. Remember, every register must become chip logic, using up limited real estate on the CPU chip; also, if we have many registers, we will use up more instruction code bits simply identifying which register is to be referenced. Therefore we must carefully justify every single register we elect to have.

Accumulators

We are going to select two accumulators (A0 and A1). Having two accumulators, rather than one, simplifies 16-bit data operations, since the two accumulators can be visualized as the upper and lower bytes of a single 16-bit unit:

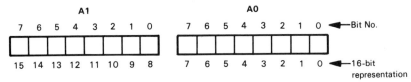

16-bit data operations are seen frequently enough to justify having two accumulators.

Having two accumulators is also useful when data from two tables must be read and processed in parallel; this is easier and faster with two accumulators, which in effect provide two independent channels for data transfer.

Will two accumulators be sufficient? The argument favoring many accumulators, or general purpose registers, is that they make programming easier; the argument against is that more object code bits are needed to select one of many general purpose registers.

Modern microprocessors have at least eight general purpose registers, and as many as sixteen. One-chip microcomputers have one or two accumulators. We will stick with two accumulators because it makes our hypothetical instruction set simple, and therefore easier to follow.

Data Counters

We will provide our microprocessor with three 16-bit data counters (DC0, DC1, and DC2). A microprocessor with eight or more general purpose registers will have no separate data counters; rather most, or all of the general purpose registers will be allowed to function as data counters. The advantage of having separate data counters is that object codes can be shorter if bits are not needed to specify the way in which a selected general purpose register is to be used.

Why have three data counters? The answer is that it greatly simplifies processing data out of tables. Frequently data from two source tables is combined in some way (the most obvious example is multibyte addition) and the result is stored in a third table. Microprocessors with less than three data counters (or equivalent general purpose registers) must shuffle addresses between temporary storage in memory, or must otherwise circumvent the limitations of having only one (or two) data counters.

Consider the simple case of multibyte addition. Having three data counters, this operation, and similar operations, may be easily handled as follows:

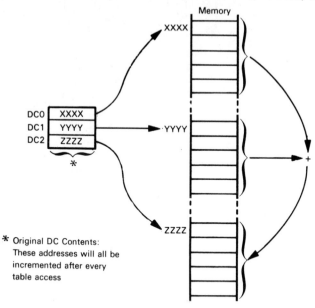

* Original DC Contents:
These addresses will all be
incremented after every
table access

Having two data counters, we would have to move one of the source data
buffers (beginning at either XXXX or YYYY) into the answer buffer, then add as
follows:

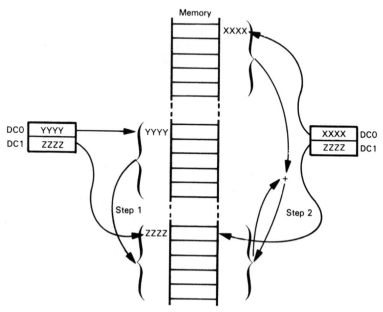

A microprocessor with only one data counter would have to store the three table addresses somewhere in read/write memory, then load each address into the data counter before accessing each table.

A microprocessor with indirect addressing could store the three table addresses in read/write memory, then access tables indirectly via the three addresses:

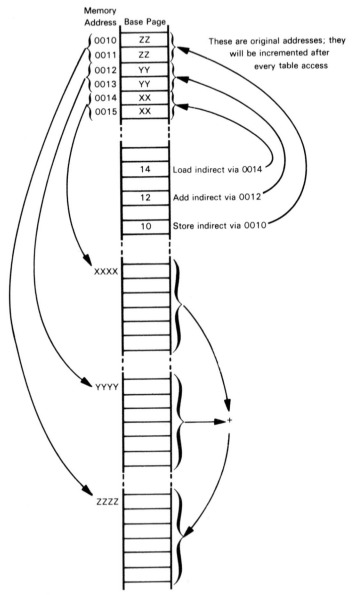

We will give our microprocessor a stack pointer (SP) and a program counter (PC). Our complement of registers looks like this:

8-bit	Accumulator A0
8-bit	Accumulator A1
16-bit	Data Counter DC0
16-bit	Data Counter DC1
16-bit	Data Counter DC2
16-bit	Stack Pointer SP
16-bit	Program Counter PC

Status Flags

In Chapter 2 we described status flags and how they are used. We will provide our hypothetical microprocessor with the four status flags Z (Zero), C (Carry), O (Overflow), and S (Sign).

Addressing Modes

A microprocessor's addressing modes will be influenced by the number and type of registers which have been selected. For example, a microprocessor with only one data counter is likely to provide indirect addressing as an alternative means of simultaneously accessing a number of data areas. This was illustrated in our discussion of data counters.

Since we have three data counters, we will save on instruction code bits, and CPU chip logic, by having no indirect addressing; rather, we will include auto-increment and auto-decrement. **Instructions that reference memory will be divided into two categories as follows:**

1) **Load and Store instructions.** Because they are frequently used, these two instructions will have a complete and flexible set of addressing options.
2) **Other memory reference instructions,** being less commonly used, will have a more limited memory addressing ability.

The complete memory addressing capability offerred by the Load and Store instructions may be represented as follows:

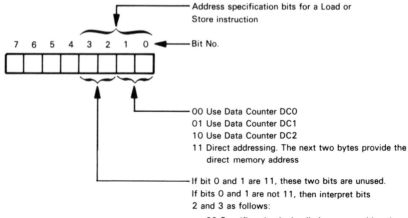

Address specification bits for a Load or Store instruction

7 6 5 4 3 2 1 0 ◄── Bit No.

00 Use Data Counter DC0
01 Use Data Counter DC1
10 Use Data Counter DC2
11 Direct addressing. The next two bytes provide the direct memory address

If bit 0 and 1 are 11, these two bits are unused.
If bits 0 and 1 are not 11, then interpret bits 2 and 3 as follows:

00 Specifies simple, implied memory addressing
01 Increment contents of specified Data Counter at conclusion of instruction
10 Decrement contents of specified Data Counter at conclusion of instruction
11 Increment and branch feature described with Load and Store instructions)

Memory reference instructions, other than Load and Store, will offer this limited subset of addressing options:

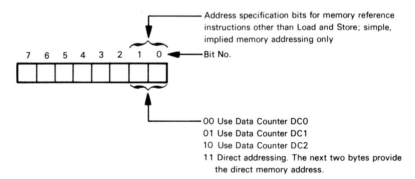

Address specification bits for memory reference instructions other than Load and Store; simple, implied memory addressing only

7 6 5 4 3 2 1 0 ◄── Bit No.

00 Use Data Counter DC0
01 Use Data Counter DC1
10 Use Data Counter DC2
11 Direct addressing. The next two bytes provide the direct memory address.

A DESCRIPTION OF INSTRUCTIONS

There are two competing perspectives which we must maintain while designing our 8-bit microprocessor's instruction set. First, we must decide what instruction types are vital, very useful, or simply desirable. Next, we must select instructions that use the 256 possible combinations provided by an 8-bit instruction code; we could have more than this number of options by going to two-byte object codes, but to keep things simple we will not.

In order to balance our two perspectives in the following discussion, we are going to create a complete, but hypothetical, microprocessor instruction set. This means that we must justify each instruction or instruction type, and we must specify the object code pattern which is to be interpreted by the control unit as identifying the specified instruction.

Assembly Language Syntax Used in This Chapter

Syntax used by all instructions described in this chapter conforms to the proposed microprocessor assembly language standard currently being developed by the Institute of Electrical and Electronic Engineers (IEEE Task T694/D11). The December, 1979 draft of this standard is presented in Appendix C.

Syntax rules specified by the proposed IEEE standard make our simple 8-bit microprocessor instruction set look more complex than it really is. The assembly language syntax presented in previous editions of this book used shorter instruction mnemonics combined with fewer and simpler operands. The primary reason we elect to describe our instruction set using the new IEEE standard syntax is to stress the need for such a standard.

Few programmers will spend their entire careers writing assembly language programs for a single microprocessor. Any programmer so restricted should seek wider experience writing programs for different microprocessors, if only to further their careers. Adopting syntax which describes instructions using a fixed set of rules will then go a long way towards making instructions recognizable. This will cut down on syntax errors.

If assembly language syntax describes the nature of instructions according to a fixed set of rules, then programs are easier to read. Elaborate, but descriptive syntax increases the legibility of programs, as compared to very economical syntax. For example, suppose a microprocessor has a single accumulator and two data counters. Two instructions allow data to be loaded from memory into the accumulator; either of the data counters can provide the address of the source data memory location. These two instructions could be identified using the following simple syntax:

```
LD1              ; Load data addressed by DC1 into A
LD2              ; Load data addressed by DC2 into A
```

Or we could use the following more elaborate syntax:

```
LD    A,@DC1     ; Load data addressed by DC1 into A
LD    A,@DC2     ; Load data addressed by DC2 into A
```

Why bother with an operand field at all? We only need to specify data counter DC1 or DC2 as supplying the data memory address. And why state that Accumulator A is to receive the data when there are no other possibilities? The answer is that the more complex syntax is easier to read.

But more complex syntax raises the possibility of more syntax errors. In the illustration above, for example, requiring an operand field with two entries in it gives you two more opportunities to make mistakes. A well-written assembler will usually take care of such problems by substituting the correct syntax when your error raises no ambiguities. In the illustration above, for example, it does not matter what the first parameter in the operand field may be, there is only one valid option: Accumulator A. A well-written assembler would likely insert the correct syntax upon finding something different, with a warning message identifying the substitution. (Assemblers allow you to change syntax rules in which case substitutions would not occur).

We have elected to use the most descriptive options allowed by the IEEE syntax standard. For example, byte versions of instructions have a B added to the instruction mnemonic; for ADD, this may be illustrated as follows:

```
ADD      A,B                    ; Add the contents of 16-bit
                                ; registers A and B
ADDB     A,B                    ; Add the contents of 8-bit
                                ; registers A and B
```

There is no reason why an 8-bit microprocessor should use ADDB (or any equivalent byte mnemonic) when it has no word version of the same instruction. We nevertheless elect to use the byte version of the mnemonic, although it is one character longer. But an assembler for this instruction set would be designed to accept the byte or word version of the instruction mnemonic, for those instructions that have only a byte version.

Perhaps the most compelling reason for using complex syntax rules with our simple 8-bit microprocessor instruction set is the fact that the rules are more realistic than the instruction set. The proposed assembly language standard must take into account real microprocessors, which are becoming ever more complex. Our instruction set must remain as simple as possible to be easily understood.

With each group of instructions we describe syntax used by the group. For a complete syntax definition, see Appendix C.

Input/Output Instructions

A microprocessor would be useless if it did not provide means for receiving data from, and transmitting data to, external devices; this is input/output, and is specified via input/output (I/O) instructions.

An input/output instruction needs to specify three things:

1) Is the instruction reading data from an external device (input), or is it transmitting data to an external device (output)?
2) As we discussed in Chapter 5, most microcomputer systems have, or at least allow, more than one port through which data can be transferred between external devices and the microcomputer system. We must identify the I/O port via which the input or output operation is to occur.
3) What is the source (for output) or destination (for input), within the microcomputer system, for data being transferred via I/O instructions?

Input/output operations are very frequently used in one-chip microcomputer applications. In order to save memory we will therefore include a few single-byte object code I/O instructions.

We could use just four of the 256 object code options — two for input (one for each accumulator as the destination), the other two for output (one for each accumulator as the source) — then specify one of 256 possible I/O ports in an immediate data byte to follow:

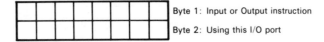

Byte 1: Input or Output instruction

Byte 2: Using this I/O port

This scheme for I/O instructions is better:

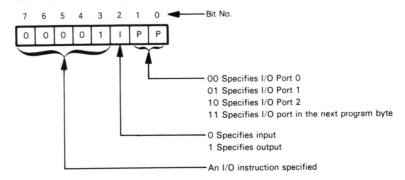

We have used up eight object code options without specifying which accumulator is involved in the data transfer. These are the eight object code options used by I/O instructions:

00001000	Input via I/O Port 0
00001001	Input via I/O Port 1
00001010	Input via I/O Port 2
00001011	Input via I/O port addressed by next byte
00001100	Output via I/O Port 0
00001101	Output via I/O Port 1
00001110	Output via I/O Port 2
00001111	Output via I/O port addressed by next byte

It is going to take an additional bit to specify one of the two accumulators as the data source or destination in I/O instructions. The eight object code options illustrated above would have to be repeated (perhaps with bit 4 set to 1) in order to represent two sets of I/O instructions, one set accessing Accumulator A0, the other set accessing Accumulator A1. As a result, 16 object code options would be consumed by I/O instructions, and that is unnecessarily extravagant. Instead we will stipulate that Accumulator A0 will always be the source or destination of data for I/O instructions.

Primary Accumulator

This preferred use of Accumulator A0 will occur frequently in our instruction set, since it is an easy way of reducing the number of object code options used up by any instruction type. By making one accumulator always more accessible, rather than treating the two accumulators equally, the programmer can think and program in terms of a primary accumulator (A0) and a secondary accumulator (A1).

Input Short

We will use the following mnemonics for our I/O instructions:

For Input:

INB   P

P is the instruction operand; if it is 0, 1, or 2, then one of the three I/O ports allowed by a single-byte I/O instruction is selected. The assembler will automatically create a one-byte object code.

Input
Long
    If P has any value from 3 through 255, a two-byte instruction will be generated as follows:

0	0	0	0	1	0	1	1	Input to A0
								Via this I/O port

Output
Short
    For Output we will use the mnemonic:

        OUTB P

    This is identical to the Input instruction, except that data will be output from Accumulator A0. If the specified I/O port is 0, 1, or 2, then the assembler will generate one byte of object code. If the I/O port is 3 through 255, then the assembler will generate a two-byte object code.

Output
Long
    By making I/O instructions access only Accumulator A0 as the source or destination for a data transfer, we have decided that it is more important to specify a limited number of ports within a one-byte I/O instruction, rather than allowing either of the two accumulators to be the data source or destination.

    Referring to the shower temperature controlling example, let us assume that temperature readings arrive through I/O Port 0, while controls are output to the hot water valve via I/O Port 1. I/O Port 2 is used as a common status port for inputs and outputs. Information at these I/O ports will be interpreted as follows:

    I/O Port 0:   A voltage, ranging from 0 mV through 255 mV. Temperature, in °F, may be approximated as follows:

$$°F = 30 + (0.45) \text{ (Port 0)}$$

This equation has been selected arbitrarily for purposes of illustration.

    I/O Port 1:   A signed binary number, specifying that the hot water valve must be opened (positive) or closed (negative). The amount of valve movement will be proportional to the absolute value 0 through 127.

    I/O Port 2:   Bits of this port will be interpreted as follows:

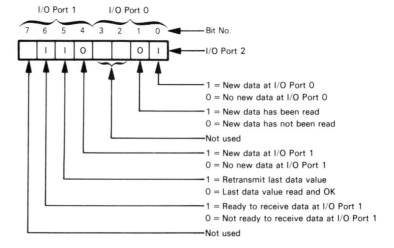

In the Port 2 illustration, I represents bits input by an external device; O represents bits output by the microprocessor. We are assuming that bits of I/O Port 2 can be assigned individually to input or output.

Memory Reference Instructions

If data arriving from a temperature sensor arrives in multibyte units, each data byte that is loaded into A0 by an input instruction must immediately be stored in read/write memory. Data output to the hot water controller must be read from memory, loaded into A0, then output via an output instruction. The data output to the hot water controller depends on the data input from the temperature sensor; in the process of computing the data to be output, any program will have to constantly reference data in memory — to load, store, add, perform logical operations, etc.

The basic architecture of any computer, mini or micro, provides a very limited data storage capacity in CPU registers, and a (relatively) enormous data storage capacity in memory external to the CPU. This makes memory reference instructions the next most vital, after I/O instructions. Recall from Chapter 5 that some microprocessors treat I/O instructions as a subset of memory reference instructions, by assigning specific memory addresses to I/O ports.

As might be expected, **the two most commonly used microprocessor memory reference instructions merely move data to or from memory; these are the Load and Store instructions.**

Load A Load instruction moves data from a memory location to an accumulator.

Store A Store instruction moves data from an accumulator to a memory location.

Load and Store are two of the most commonly used memory reference instructions; therefore we will allocate the bits necessary to include very flexible Load and Store addressing modes.

Load and Store instruction object codes will appear as follows:

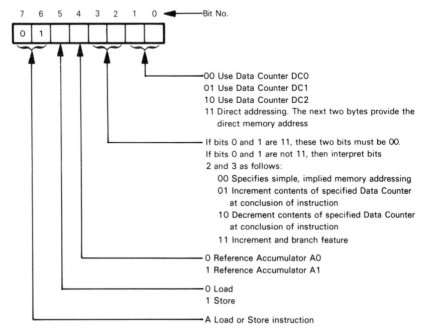

7 6 5 4 3 2 1 0 ◄—— Bit No.

| 0 | 1 | | | | | | |

00 Use Data Counter DC0
01 Use Data Counter DC1
10 Use Data Counter DC2
11 Direct addressing. The next two bytes provide the direct memory address

If bits 0 and 1 are 11, these two bits must be 00.
If bits 0 and 1 are not 11, then interpret bits 2 and 3 as follows:
 00 Specifies simple, implied memory addressing
 01 Increment contents of specified Data Counter at conclusion of instruction
 10 Decrement contents of specified Data Counter at conclusion of instruction
 11 Increment and branch feature

0 Reference Accumulator A0
1 Reference Accumulator A1

0 Load
1 Store

A Load or Store instruction

Let us now look at the complete addressing capabilities offered by the **Load and Store instructions, starting with the simplest.**

After describing what the addressing modes are, we will justify each one.

A Load or Store instruction with direct addressing will have ones in bits 0 and 1, and the direct address will be provided in the two bytes that follow. Observe that bits 2 and 3 are not used for direct addressing; they must, however, have a definite value. We will therefore specify that bits 2 and 3 must both be 0 for a direct addressing Load or Store instruction; these instructions will now have the following object code:

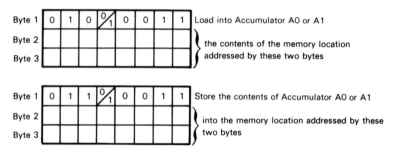

Byte 1 | 0 | 1 | 0 | 0/1 | 0 | 0 | 1 | 1 | Load into Accumulator A0 or A1
Byte 2 — the contents of the memory location
Byte 3 — addressed by these two bytes

Byte 1 | 0 | 1 | 1 | 0/1 | 0 | 0 | 1 | 1 | Store the contents of Accumulator A0 or A1
Byte 2 — into the memory location addressed by these
Byte 3 — two bytes

The following object codes have nothing to do with Load or Store instructions:

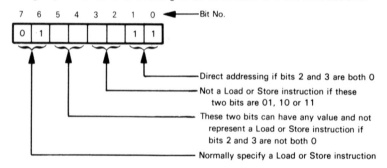

7 6 5 4 3 2 1 0 ◄——— Bit No.

0 · 1 | | | | | 1 | 1

—— Direct addressing if bits 2 and 3 are both 0

—— Not a Load or Store instruction if these two bits are 01, 10 or 11

—— These two bits can have any value and not represent a Load or Store instruction if bits 2 and 3 are not both 0

—— Normally specify a Load or Store instruction

Number of Load and Store Instructions

There are 64 object code combinations resulting from 01XXXXXX, where X may be 0 or 1; these are the Load and Store instruction object codes. Twelve of the combinations do not represent Load or Store instructions, as illustrated above (3 combinations of bits 2 and 3, times 4 combinations of bits 4 and 5, equals 12 combinations). Therefore, there are 52 variations of the Load and Store instructions.

Implied Addressing

Load and Store instructions with implied memory addressing can have any of the following object codes:

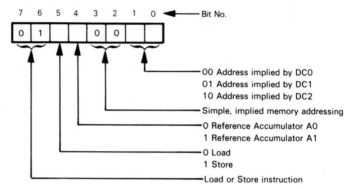

The effective memory address used by the Load or Store instruction is the contents of Data Counter DC0, DC1, or DC2, whichever has been specified by bits 0 and 1.

Auto-Increment

Auto-Decrement

The auto-increment and auto-decrement features are quite easy to understand; the auto-increment feature says that the implied memory address — that is, the contents of the specified data counter — will be incremented by 1 at the conclusion of the memory reference instruction's execution. Conversely, the auto-decrement feature specifies that the data counter contents will be decremented by 1 at the conclusion of the instruction's execution.

For an auto-increment instruction object code bits 2 and 3 will be 01; the equivalent auto-decrement instruction will have 10 in bits 2 and 3.

Increment-and-Branch

Increment-and-Branch, specified by having ones in bits 2 and 3, is not a common microprocessor feature. We are going to create Load and Store instructions with the following format:

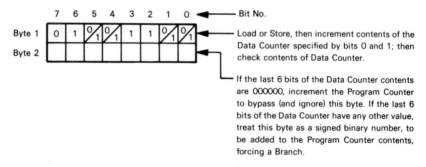

The most effective way of illustrating the necessity for the various addressing modes is with short program sequences. Let us therefore first describe the instruction mnemonics which will be used for the Load and Store instructions.

Load Direct

Store Direct

Load and Store Direct will use these mnemonics:

LDB	A0,ADDR	;Load direct into A0
LDB	A1,ADDR	;Load direct into A1
STB	A0,ADDR	;Store direct from A0
STB	A1,ADDR	;Store direct from A1

Load Implied

Store Implied

ADDR is any label representing a memory location from which data will be read or to which data will be written. A0 and A1 represent Accumulators A0 and A1, respectively.

LDB	A0,@DCX	;Load into A0 from the memory ;location addressed by DCX
LDB	A1,@DCX	;Load into A1 from the memory ;location addressed by DCX
STB	A0,@DCX	;Store the contents of A0 into the ;memory location addressed by DCX
STB	A1,@DCX	;Store the contents of A1 into the ;memory location addressed by DCX

DCX specifies one of the three data counters and therefore must be DC0, DC1, or DC2.

Load/Store with Auto-Increment or -Decrement

The Load or Store with Auto-Increment or Auto-Decrement instructions are identical to Load/Store Implied, as described above, except that the specified data counter contents will be incremented or decremented. We will use @DCX+ in the operand field for Load or Store with Auto-Increment, and @DCX− in the operand field for Load or Store with Auto-Decrement.

Load/Store with Auto-Increment-and-Branch

Load and Store instructions with Auto-Increment-and-Branch will be specified by the following instruction mnemonics:

LDBNZ	A0,@DCX,LABEL	;Load into A0
LDBNZ	A1,@DCX,LABEL	;Load into A1
STBNZ	A0,@DCX,LABEL	;Store contents of A0
STBNZ	A1,@DCX,LABEL	;Store contents of A1

DCX identifies the Data Counter holding the implied memory address; it must therefore be DC0, DC1, or DC2.

LABEL identifies the instruction which will be executed next if, after DCX is incremented, the last six binary digits are not all zeros.

In order to demonstrate the Load and Store instructions, let us look at a simple problem which moves data from one buffer to another. Assuming that the starting addresses of the source and destination buffers are in Data Counters DC0 and DC1, and assuming that the buffer length is stored in Accumulator A1, the problem may be illustrated as follows:

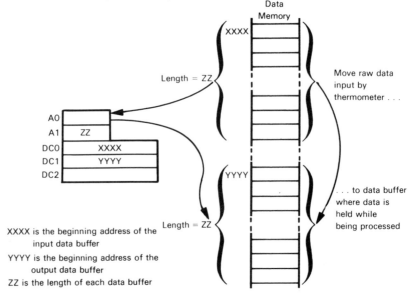

XXXX is the beginning address of the
    input data buffer

YYYY is the beginning address of the
    output data buffer

ZZ is the length of each data buffer

The following instruction sequence will perform the required data move:

```
                Load initial address into DC0
                Load initial address into DC1
        LOOP    LDB     A0,@DC0         ;Load next input data byte
                STB     A0,@DC1         ;Store in next destination buffer
                                        ;byte

                Increment DC0 contents
                Increment DC1 contents
                Decrement A1 contents
                If A1 contains 0, branch to LOOP
```

Instructions which we have not yet described are written out in words, rather than using unfamiliar instruction mnemonics.

Auto-Increment or -Decrement Justification

Now we will introduce the auto-increment feature, and this is what happens to our instruction sequence:

```
                Load initial address into DC0
                Load initial address into DC1
        LOOP    LDB     A0,@DC0+        ;Load next input data byte.
                                        ;Increment address
                STB     A0,@DC1+        ;Store in next destination buffer
                                        ;byte. Increment address

                Decrement A1 contents
                If A1 contains 0, branch to LOOP
```

Auto-Increment and -Branch Justification

Two instructions have been removed from the eight-instruction sequence and two bytes of program object code have been saved.

Now assume that the destination buffer ends at memory location $08C0_{16}$; the last six binary digits of this address are all zeros:

$$08C0_{16} = 0000100011\underbrace{000000}$$

Tested for auto-branch

We can now compress our data move program to these four instructions:

```
                Load initial address into DC0
                Load initial address into DC1
        LOOP    LDB     A0,@DC0+        ;Load next input data byte.
                                        ;Increment address
                STBNZ   A0,@DC1,LOOP    ;Store, increment and branch on end
```

The two instructions within the reexecuted loop occupy three bytes, as follows:

0	1	0	0	0	1	0	0	Load A0 via DC0; increment DC0
0	1	1	0	1	1	0	1	Store A0 via DC1; increment DC1 and branch
1	1	1	1	1	1	1	0	Twos complement of 2 .

We no longer need to hold the buffer length in Accumulator A1. Nor do we need to explicitly decrement the buffer length or increment memory addresses. After the Store, Increment, and Branch instruction increments the destination buffer address, it tests the incremented value. If the incremented value does not end in six binary zero digits, execution will return to the Load instruction. This two-instruction loop will be continuously reexecuted until the Store, Increment, and Branch instruction increments the destination address to $08C0_{16}$. At this point the branch will be bypassed and the instruction which immediately follows the above data movement loop will be executed.

A minicomputer programmer would recoil at an addressing scheme such as the auto-increment-and-branch. The idea that data tables must be placed at memory addresses nding in six binary zeros poses more problems than it offers advantages. For one thing, larger data tables must be processed in 64-byte blocks.

While the minicomputer programmer may see the neatness of instruction loops that require no special end-of-loop logic, problems associated with data relocation would be horrible; if a program were to be reused in another application, or if it were part of a time-sharing system, the programmer would constantly have to worry about ensuring that data tables ended at correct memory boundaries — or else the program would simply not work.

We return once again to the old minicomputer programmer's axiom: ''Remember that whatever you do today may impact tomorrow.'' But remember that in the world of microprocessors there may be no tomorrow. For one-chip microcomputer applications in particular, whatever you do today becomes a ROM chip and will never again change. Mapping data tables onto memory address boundaries is only a minor inconvenience, since memory mapping will be a significant part of every one-chip microcomputer programming assignment anyway.

The auto-increment-and-branch feature offers very significant advantages in a microcomputer application because it saves on object program bytes, while the penalty paid — having to map data tables onto address boundaries — is part of a job that might have to be done in any event.

Many microprocessors provide a variation of the increment/decrement and branch as part of indexed memory addressing. This popular variation causes a branch to occur whenever the Index register contents increment (or decrement) to zero. Basing branch and loop logic on the contents of an Index register is not only more common, it is also more useful than the more primitive technique we have described, where branch and loop logic is based on the implied memory address value.

Direct Addressing Justification

We have not yet justified the need for direct addressing instructions. Are they necessary?

There is nothing a direct addressing instruction does which could not be done with an implied addressing instruction. However, in certain cases direct addressing instructions use less memory. Consider the buffer length which we were going to load into Accumulator A1 and then decrement. In the end we eliminated this logic sequence from our data movement example, but there are going to be many instances in which this type of logic cannot be eliminated. How does the buffer length, or any similar number, get loaded into an accumulator? A three-byte direct addressing instruction will do the job as follows:

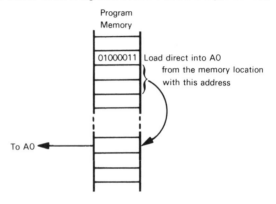

Using implied memory addressing, the operation will require four bytes and will temporarily use a data counter as follows:

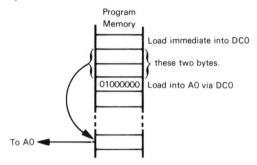

The three-byte immediate instruction which is needed to load data into a data counter is an unnecessary expense when it is followed by a single memory reference, such as the one-time load of an index into another register. As we have seen earlier in this chapter, the three bytes needed to load an address into a data counter result in a great memory savings, but only if the address in the data counter is going to be reused many times.

If a microprocessor is to have either direct or implied addressing, but not both, then implied addressing is the more desirable. For example, the Intel 8008, which was the predecessor of the Intel 8080, has implied addressing but no direct addressing. But no modern microprocessor designer is faced with this restrictive choice.

Most programs load single values (such as counters and indexes) into registers frequently enough to make direct addressing justifiable.

Note that if the counter or index to be loaded into a register has a value that will never change, you would use neither direct nor implied addressing to load the value into a register. You would use immediate addressing:

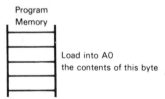

Secondary Memory Reference (Memory Reference Operate) Instructions

Let us now look at memory reference instructions other than Load and Store. In each case an operation will be performed using the contents of one of the accumulators, plus the contents of an addressed memory location. The result will always be stored in the identified accumulator, erasing whatever value had previously been in the accumulator (the Compare instruction described below is an exception). The Zero, Sign, Carry, and Overflow status flags will be set or reset to reflect the result of the operation. For example, the "Add memory to A1" instruction will add the contents of the addressed memory location to the contents of Accumulator A1. The previous contents of the memory are not changed.

With the exception of the Store instruction, microcomputer instructions will avoid modifying memory since that implies the presence of read/write memory.

Add

Add Decimal

Subtract Decimal

AND

OR

XOR

Compare

We will include these secondary memory reference instructions:

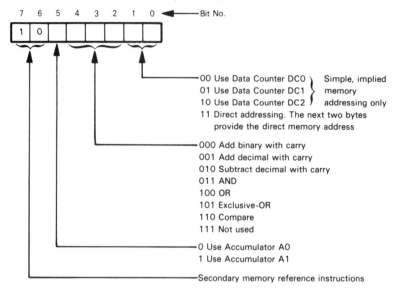

The lack of a Subtract Binary instruction is a nuisance, but not the problem it appears to be. This will be discussed later.

These are the instruction mnemonics we will use:

ADDCB	Add Binary with Carry to A0 or A1
ADDCDB	Add Decimal with Carry to A0 or A1
SUBCDB	Subtract Decimal with Carry from A0 or A1
ANDB	AND with A0 or A1
ORB	OR with A0 or A1
XORB	Exclusive-OR with A0 or A1
CMPB	Compare A0 or A1 with memory

The code "10" in bits 7 and 6 specifies that the remaining six bits represent secondary memory reference instructions. However, only seven of the eight combinations possible for bits 2, 3, and 4 are used for secondary memory reference instructions. Therefore, only 56 of the 64 bit combinations are, in fact, secondary memory reference instructions.

In each case, the instruction will be written out like this:

MNEM   AY,@DCX

where MNEM is one of the mnemonics listed above (e.g., ADDCB), AY is A0 or A1, DCX is one of the data counters (DC0, DC1, or DC2).

The direct memory referencing version of the instruction will look like this:

MNEM   AY,ADDR

where ADDR is the direct address.

Here are two examples. The instruction:

ADDCB   A0,@DC1

uses binary addition to add the Carry status and the contents of a memory location to the contents of A0. Data Counter DC1 contains the address of the memory location. This is the object code generated:

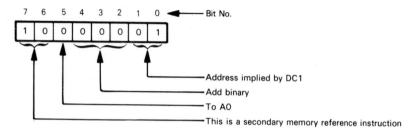

The following is a direct memory referencing instruction:

XORB   A1,ADDR

The contents of A1 are Exclusive-ORed with the contents of the memory location addressed by the label ADDR. These three object program bytes will be created:

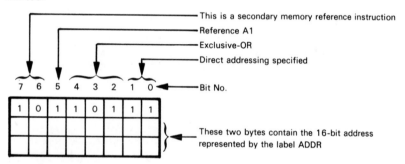

Only three of the seven secondary memory reference instructions described above need any comment.

The add and subtract instructions all include the Carry status in the addition. This may be illustrated as follows:

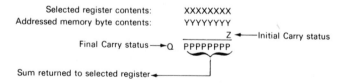

P, Q, X, Y, and Z represent any binary digits.

The Carry status is included in the addition so that these add and subtract instructions can be used to perform multibyte arithmetic. Consider the very simple example of two 16-bit numbers which must be added in byte increments. Program logic must add the two low-order bytes with no carry, and the two high-order bytes with the carry, if any, from the low-order byte sum. This may be illustrated as follows:

```
PPPPPPPPQQQQQQQQ
XXXXXXXXYYYYYYYY
J-------K-------0  ◄────── Carry Status
RRRRRRRRSSSSSSSS
```

J, K, P, Q, R, S, X, and Y represent any binary digits.

We can convert an Add with Carry instruction into a simple addition by first clearing the Carry status. If the Carry status is guaranteed to be 0, then it plays no part in the addition.

Add and subtract decimal perform decimal addition or subtraction, using three or two binary steps, as described for binary-coded decimal arithmetic in Chapter 2.

We perform decimal subtraction using a separate instruction, since the logic sequence is sufficiently different from a decimal add to make the extra instruction worthwhile.

Binary Subtract

We do not provide a separate binary subtract instruction, since this is simply a twos complement followed by an add, as described in Chapter 2.

Decimal Adjust

Note carefully that the decimal addition and subtraction instructions are not the same thing as a decimal adjust instruction. The decimal adjust instruction is used with binary addition to create binary coded decimal addition. For example, consider the decimal addition:

$$
\begin{array}{r}
86 \\
+49 \\
\hline
135
\end{array}
$$

If you add 86_{16} and 49_{16} using binary addition, this is what you get:

$$
\begin{array}{r}
10000110 \\
01001001 \\
\hline
11001111
\end{array}
$$

The sum is CF_{16}; the decimal adjust instruction will convert this result, or the binary sum of any two valid binary coded decimal numbers, to the correct binary coded decimal result. In this instance, the decimal adjust instruction will convert CF_{16} to 35_{16} with the Carry status set to 1. We described decimal adjust logic in Chapter 2.

Compare

The Compare instruction subtracts the contents of the addressed memory location from the specified accumulator. The result of the subtraction is discarded — it is not stored in the specified accumulator. However, all of the status bits are set or reset to reflect the result of the subtraction. **This is a very useful instruction since it allows the program execution sequence to be determined by the relative magnitude of data items.**

The Branch-on-Condition instructions, described later in this chapter, take advantage of and are used in conjunction with the Compare instruction.

Secondary Memory Reference Instructions Justification

Are the secondary memory reference instructions necessary? There are two parts to this question:

First, are the operations performed by the secondary memory reference instructions necessary?

Second, must these operations be performed using secondary memory reference instructions?

The operations described — addition, Boolean logic, and compare — are such basic steps in any logic sequence that a microprocessor that did not offer these logic capabilities, one way or another, would be worthless.

There is, however, no reason why these operations have to be part of memory reference instructions. For example, it would be possible to load the two operands into Accumulators A0 and A1, then perform the same operations, register-to-register. Microprocessors which have many accumulators, such as the Intel 8080, 8085, and Zilog Z80, favor register-to-register instructions over register-to-memory instructions; microprocessors with fewer accumulators, such as the Motorola MC6800 and the MOS Technology 6502, use register-to-memory instructions as we have described.

Let us look at a simple example.

Multibyte Addition

Suppose two buffers, beginning at XXXX and YYYY, each hold a single, multibyte number. The number in the buffer beginning at XXXX could be added to the number in the buffer beginning at YYYY as follows:

```
        Load address into DC0
        Load address into DC1
LOOP    LDB      A0,@DC0+        ;Load the next input byte and increment
        ADDCB    A0,@DC1         ;Add binary from answer buffer,
                                 ;with carry
        STBNZ    A0,@DC1,LOOP    ;Store the result, increment and branch
```

The three-instruction program shown above assumes that the buffer beginning at YYYY (this address is stored in DC1) contains one of the numbers to be added, but at the end of the addition this buffer will contain the answer. This logic works, since the answer is going to over-store the byte which was just added; therefore, information is destroyed only when it will not be needed in the future. This may be illustrated as follows:

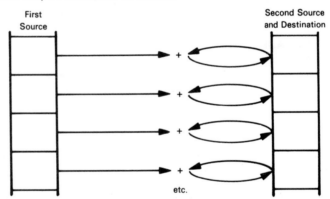

First Source

Second Source and Destination

etc.

Another instruction loop can perform a binary addition where the result is stored in a third buffer, which we will assume is addressed by DC2. The instructions will look like this:

```
        Initially clear the Carry status
LOOP    LDB      A0,@DC0+        ;Load next augend byte
        ADDCB    A0,@DC1         ;Add corresponding addend byte, with carry
        Increment DC1 contents
        STBNZ    A0,@DC2,LOOP    ;Store the result, increment and branch
```

This instruction loop would be more useful and more flexible if branch and loop logic were based on the contents of an Index register, rather than depending on the data counter; but branch and loop logic would be the same in both cases.

**Boolean
Logic
Justified**

**Switch
Change
Tests**

We will now look at Boolean logic instructions.

An example of the usefulness of the Boolean secondary memory reference instructions is to test switches seeking any changes in settings.

Suppose the statuses of eight switches are input to I/O Port 4; the previous settings for these eight switches are stored in memory at a location addressed by the label SWITCH. The following instruction sequence identifies which switches have changed settings and how the settings have changed:

```
INB        4                 ;Input new switch settings
XORB       A0,SWITCH         ;Identify changed switches
Save contents of A0 in A1
ANDB       A0,SWITCH         ;Identify switches that turned off
```

This is what the above three instructions do:

The first instruction inputs the new switch settings to A0. Suppose these settings are:

01100101

where 0 represents an "off" switch and 1 represents an "on" switch.

Suppose the previous switch settings, stored in the memory location identified by the label SWITCH, are:

10101101

Switches 7 and 3 were "on," and are now "off." Switch 6 was "off," and is now "on." Switches 5, 4, 2, 1, and 0 have not changed.

The XRA instruction leaves the Exclusive-OR of the old and new switch settings in A0:

```
Old Settings:    10101101
New Settings:    01100101
        XRA:     11001000 gives changed switches
```

The changed switches are identified by 1 bits, and are stored in A1.

The AND instruction leaves the AND of the old and the changed switch settings in A0:

```
Changed Settings:    11001000
Old Settings:        10101101
        ANA:         10001000 gives on-to-off switches
```

Load Immediate Instructions, Jump and Jump-to-Subroutine

The concept of immediate addressing has been discussed frequently as a means of loading data or addresses into registers. How vital are immediate addressing instructions to a microprocessor instruction set?

Immediate Instructions Justification

We cannot use implied memory addressing to load an address into a data counter, since implied memory addressing requires that a data counter already hold an address. Direct addressing could do the job. A base address stored in two memory bytes could be directly addressed and loaded into a data counter as follows:

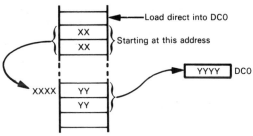

But the above illustration clearly has some redundant bytes; the address being loaded into the data counter could just as easily be stored in the two bytes that hold the direct memory address. This may be illustrated as follows:

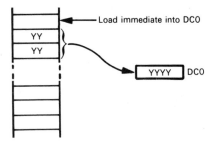

Immediate instructions are not absolutely vital to a microprocessor instruction set, but they are certainly a great convenience. Every modern microprocessor has some immediate instructions in its instruction set. We will therefore include eight immediate addressing instructions: to load data into the three data counters, the stack pointer, the program counter (with two variations), or the two accumulators. These will be either two-byte or three-byte instructions. Since the accumulators are only one byte long, immediate instructions that load data into an accumulator will be followed by just one byte of immediate data. The data counters, the program counter, and the stack pointer are all two bytes long, therefore immediate instructions that load data into any of these registers will be followed by two bytes of immediate data. **The following object code patterns will specify immediate instructions:**

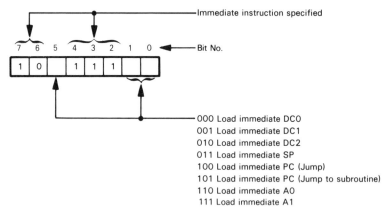

000 Load immediate DC0
001 Load immediate DC1
010 Load immediate DC2
011 Load immediate SP
100 Load immediate PC (Jump)
101 Load immediate PC (Jump to subroutine)
110 Load immediate A0
111 Load immediate A1

Since there are eight immediate instructions, and there were eight unused object code combinations from within the secondary memory reference instruction group, we use these eight unused combinations for immediate instructions, as illustrated above.

Jump Instruction

Special attention must be given to the two instructions which load immediate data into the program counter. These are the Jump and Jump-to-Subroutine instructions. Unlike the other immediate instructions, these two modify the program execution sequence; the next instruction executed is going to be fetched from the memory location whose address was loaded immediately into the program counter.

In its simplest form, this is an Unconditional Jump (or Branch) instruction:

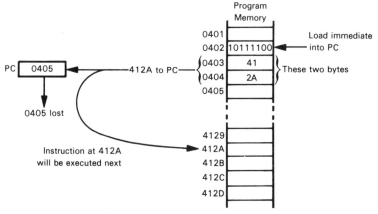

Jump-to-Subroutine Instruction

A Jump-to-Subroutine instruction differs only in that the current program counter contents must be saved before the new immediate data is loaded into the program counter. Since our microprocessor has a stack, the program counter contents will be pushed onto the stack before the immediate data is loaded into the program counter:

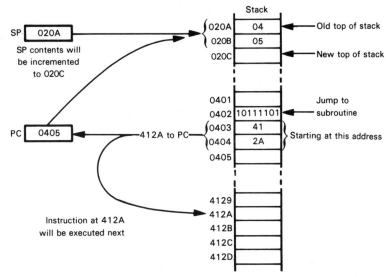

Microprocessor instruction set descriptions do not describe Jump and Jump-to-Subroutine instructions as immediate instructions; however, instruction logic is almost identical.

Load Immediate

Immediate and Jump instruction mnemonics will differ. For Load Immediate we will use the following mnemonics:

```
LDB    AY,#DATA
LD     R,#DATA
```

AY must be A0 or A1.

R must be DC0, DC1, DC2, or SP. DATA must be a number, or a symbol representing a number: it must be equivalent to an 8-bit value for LDB; it must be equivalent to a 16-bit value for LD.

Jump

The Jump instruction will appear as follows:

```
BR     ADDR
```

ADDR must be the label of the instruction which is to be executed next.

Jump-to-Subroutine

The Jump-to-Subroutine instruction will appear as follows:

```
CALL   SNAME
```

SNAME must be the label of the first instruction executed within the subroutine.

We will now create a subroutine.

Subroutines   Let us return to the data move program that illustrated the Increment-and-Skip instruction. Written out fully, this program would include instructions to load addresses into data counters, as follows:

```
BUFA    EQU     XXXX
BUFB    EQU     YYYY
        -
        -

        LD      DC0,#BUFA       ;Load source initial address
        LD      DC1,#BUFB       ;Load destination initial address
LOOP    LDB     A0,@DC0+        ;Move data from source
        STBNZ   A0,@DC1,LOOP    ;to destination
```

Equate
Assembler
Directive

The EQU mnemonics represent Equate assembler directives.

Recall that an assembler directive is not an instruction, and it generates no object code; instead it provides the assembler with information without which the assembler could not generate an object program.

The Equate directive tells the assembler that wherever the symbol in the label field occurs, the number in the operand field must be substituted. For example, it tells the assembler: "Use the hexadecimal value XXXX wherever you see the symbol BUFA."

We could just as easily rewrite our program as follows:

```
        LD      DC0,#XXXX
        LD      DC1,#YYYY
LOOP    LDB     A0,@DC0+
        STBNZ   A0,@DC1,LOOP
```

Value of
Assembler
Directives

The advantage of having the Equate is that the symbol BUFA (or BUFB) may appear many times within a program. If the value associated with the symbol changes, all you have to do is change one Equate in the source program. When you reassemble the source program, every reference to the changed symbol will be corrected in the new object program which the assembler creates.

Without the Equate directive, you would have to find every source program instruction that references the changed symbol, then you would have to correct each source program instruction, with no guarantee that you found them all.

Subroutine
Call

We convert the data move program into a subroutine by providing the instruction which is to be executed first with a label. Also, we add an instruction that executes a return from the subroutine:

```
MOVE    LD      DC0,#BUFA       ;Load source initial address
        LD      DC1,#BUFB       ;Load destination initial address
LOOP    LDB     A0,@DC0+        ;Move data from source to
        STBNZ   A0,@DC1,LOOP    ;destination
        Return from subroutine
```

Entry
Point

We use the term "entry point" to describe the instruction in a subroutine that gets executed first.

The Return-from-Subroutine instruction is described with the Stack instructions. We will ignore this instruction for now.

Other programs can call the move subroutine with this one instruction:

```
JSR     MOVE
```

Subroutine MOVE can be called by any other program, any number of times.

Immediate Operate Instructions

A limited number of Immediate Operate instructions will be very useful; these instructions will perform operations on the contents of an accumulator using the immediate operand. The result is stored back in the specified accumulator. Consider these instructions:

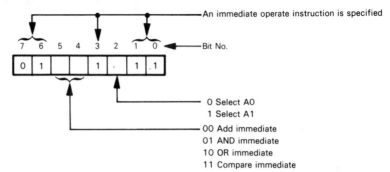

Many programmers are very fond of immediate operate instructions and would roundly condemn this instruction set for only having four such instructions.

Each instruction describes an operation that will be performed using the contents of an accumulator and the byte following the instruction code:

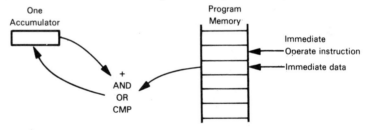

The status flags C, O, Z, and S will be set or reset to reflect the results of the operation.

Observe that we have used eight of the twelve unused object code combinations from the 64 Load/Store patterns 01XXXXXX. These four combinations still remain unused within this pattern:

> 01000111
> 01010111
> 01100111
> 01110111

These four combinations may be represented by 01XX0111.

Add Immediate
AND Immediate
OR Immediate
Compare Immediate

We will use the following mnemonics for the Immediate Operate instructions:

ADDB	A0,#DATA	Add immediate to A0
ADDB	A1,#DATA	Add immediate to A1
ANDB	A0,#DATA	AND immediate to A0
ANDB	A1,#DATA	AND immediate to A1
ORB	A0,#DATA	OR immediate to A0
ORB	A1,#DATA	OR immediate to A1
CMPB	A0,#DATA	Compare immediate with A0
CMPB	A1,#DATA	Compare immediate with A1

In each case DATA is a number (or a symbol) that becomes an 8-bit value. In each case two bytes of object code will be generated. For example, the OIB instruction will create this object code:

Byte 1	0	1	1	0	1	1	1	1

OR immediate with A1

Byte 2								

the data in this byte

Immediate Operate Instructions Justified

We will now demonstrate the value of the Immediate Operate instructions. Look again at how, in the I/O instruction description, Port 2 was defined as a combination control and status port.

These two instructions determine if there is new data at I/O Port 0:

```
IN      2              ;Input status
ANDB    A0,#H'01       ;Mask out all but bit 0
```

H'01 means 01 hexadecimal.

The ANDB instruction resets to 0 all bits in Accumulator A0 other than bit 0:

```
                        A0 Contents
IN      2              XXXXXXXX
ANDB    A0,#H'01       0000000X
```

X represents either 0 or 1.

If the result is zero, bit 0 must have been zero, and no new data is at I/O Port 0. If the result is not zero, bit 0 must have been 1, so there is new data at I/O Port 0.

Recall that the Z status will record whether the NIA instruction generates a zero or a non-zero result.

After reading data from I/O Port 0, the program can reset bit 0 of I/O Port 2 to 0, and can set bit 1 to 1, using these four instructions:

```
IN      2              ;Input status
ANDB    A0,#H'FE       ;Clear bit 0
ORB     A0,#H'02       ;Set bit 1 to 1
OUT     2              ;Return the result
```

This is what happens:

```
                        A0 Contents    I/O Port 2 Contents
IN      2              XXXXXXXX        XXXXXXXX
ANDB    A0,#H'FE       XXXXXXX0        XXXXXXXX
ORB     A0,#H'02       XXXXX10         XXXXXXXX
OUT     2              XXXXX10         XXXXX10
```

Again X represents any binary digit (0 or 1).

If you are unclear on how the AND and OR work, refer again to Chapter 2. All we are doing is ANDing I/O Port 2 contents with 11111110, then ORing the result with 00000010.

Branch-on-Condition Instructions

Up to this point, status flags Zero (Z), Carry (C), Overflow (O), and Sign (S) have been useless curiosities, because the microprocessor provides no way to take advantage of the status flags.

What is the logical way of using status flags?

The answer is to provide instructions which allow program execution sequence to depend on the condition of a status flag.

We have already seen two examples of how status flags can determine the subsequent course of a program's execution. In the Immediate Operate instruction description, bit 0 of I/O Port 2 is tested for a zero or non-zero value. If this bit has a zero value, program execution must branch to some instruction sequence which does not attempt to read new data from I/O Port 0. If this bit is 1, the program execution sequence must branch to a routine which will input data from I/O Port 0.

The discussion of Load and Store instruction categories started out with a routine that loads buffer length into Accumulator A1, then decrements the contents of A1 as a means of testing whether the last buffer byte has been moved. So long as A1 has not decremented to zero, program execution returns to the beginning of the data move loop; as soon as the contents of A1 decrement to zero, program execution must continue and not branch back:

```
        LDB     A1,#LENGTH      ;Load buffer length
        LD      DC0,#BUFA       ;Load source buffer starting address
        LD      DC1,#BUFB       ;Load destination buffer starting address
LOOP    LDB     A0,@DC0+        ;Load next input data byte, increment DC0
        STB     A0,@DC1+        ;Store next input data byte, increment DC1
        ADDB    A1,#H'FF        Add H'FF to A1; this decrements A1
```

If A1 does not contain 0, return to LOOP
If A1 contains 0, continue with next instruction

While the ADDB instruction (which has already been described) in effect decrements the contents of A1, a Register Operate instruction (which has not yet been described) does the job in one byte, instead of two.

Branch-on-Condition Instruction Justification

Branch-on-Condition instructions are vital to a microprocessor because they are the means of testing status flags. Status flags in turn are vital to a microprocessor because they are the means for determining what happens when an instruction is executed with more than one possible result.

There are two philosophies concerning Branch-on-Condition instructions; one uses Branches, the other uses Skips.

Branch Philosophy

A Branch-on-Condition instruction, as the name implies, has a one-byte or two-byte displacement following the instruction code (just like immediate data). If a specified condition is met, then the displacement is added to the contents of the program counter as a signed binary number and thus a program branch is executed. If the specified condition is not met, the program counter has incremented beyond the displacement bytes and the next sequential instruction is executed.

This may be illustrated as follows:

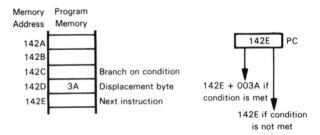

Skip Philosophy

The Skip-on-Condition instruction has no following address displacement. The logic of this instruction states that if the specified status conditions are met, then the next sequential instruction will be skipped; if the specified status conditions are not met, then the next sequential instruction will be executed. This may be illustrated as follows:

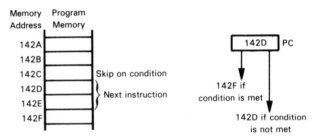

In the illustration above, observe that the "Next instruction" happens to be a two-byte instruction. Were it a one-byte instruction, the program counter would be incremented to $142E_{16}$, if the condition was met. Were "Next instruction" a three-byte instruction, the program counter would be incremented to 1430_{16} if the condition was met.

By placing an Unconditional Jump instruction directly after a Skip-on-Condition instruction, you create the inverse of a Branch-on-Condition instruction:

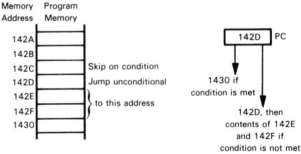

Observe that the auto-increment-and-branch logic available with Load and Store instructions is a form of Branch-on-Condition instruction.

Should our microprocessor include Branch-on-Condition or Skip-on-Condition instructions? We will choose Branch-on-Condition instructions because they are a little more economical with this type of two-way execution sequence:

Branch Logic		Skip Logic	

Data Movement Program Loop

```
LOOP  LDB   A0,@DC0+          LOOP  LDB   A0,@DC0+
      STB   A0,@DC1+                STB   A0,@DC1+
      ADDB  A1,#H'FF                ADDB  A1,#H'FF
      Branch to LOOP if A1 = 0      Skip next instruction if A1 = 0
                                    JMP   LOOP
```

Branch on What Conditions?

What are the conditions on which we will branch? We will choose the following eight branch conditions:

Branch on Zero (Z) equals 0
Branch on Zero (Z) equals 1
Branch on Carry (C) equals 0
Branch on Carry (C) equals 1
Branch on Overflow (O) equals 0
Branch on Overflow (O) equals 1
Branch on Sign (S) equals 0
Branch on Sign (S) equals 1

Branch-on-Condition instructions will be followed by single-byte displacements, which means that a forward or reverse displacement of +127 or −128 bytes is possible. This is reasonable since 90% or more of all branches will be served by this range; providing two-byte displacements would be wasteful of memory. Of course, you can always generate a longer range branch by combining an Unconditional Jump with a Branch-on-Condition instruction as follows:

Branch to THERE on Z = 0

Displacement to THERE is out of range! Substitute:

```
      Branch to HERE on Z = 1
      BR        THERE
HERE  Next instruction
```

The BR instruction is followed by a two-byte address, so it can continue execution anywhere in memory.

The Branch and Jump instruction sequence illustrated above has the same logic as a Skip-on-Condition instruction.

We will use the following eight object codes for our eight Branch-on-Condition instructions:

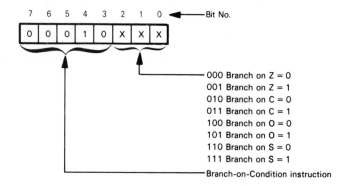

Branch-on-Condition instructions will have the format:

OP   LABEL

LABEL is the label of the instruction to be executed if the condition specified by OP is met.

The assembler will convert LABEL into a displacement by subtracting the current program counter contents from the 16-bit address value assigned to LABEL;if the result is out of range, the assembler will print an error message.

OP will be a mnemonic as follows:

BZ	Branch on Zero (Z = 1)
BNZ	Branch on Not Zero (Z = 0)
BC	Branch on Carry (C = 1)
BNC	Branch on No Carry (C = 0)
BV	Branch on Overflow (O = 1)
BNV	Branch on No Overflow (O = 0)
BP	Branch on Positive (S = 0)
BN	Branch on Negative (S = 1)

Branch If Less, Equal or Greater

The Compare instruction causes novice programmers a great deal of confusion. "Branch on Zero" and "Branch on Carry" are not nearly as meaningful as "Branch if Greater" or "Branch if Less."

Recall that the Compare instruction subtracts an operand from the contents of the specified accumulator and sets status flags based on the result of the subtraction. The following conditions can therefore be identified:

Branch on accumulator less than or equal to operand (BLE).
Branch on accumulator less than operand (BLT).
Branch on accumulator and operand equal (BE).
Branch on accumulator and operand not equal (BNE).
Branch on accumulator greater than operand (BGT).
Branch on accumulator greater than or equal to operand (BGE).

Depending on whether the accumulator contents are being interpreted as signed or unsigned binary data, the qualitative conditional branches can be determined by using the following Boolean logic:

Branch Condition	Boolean Condition	
	Signed Data	Unsigned Data
BLE	Z OR (S XOR O) = 1	C = 0 OR Z = 1
BLT	S XOR O = 1	C = 0
BE	Z = 1	Z = 1
BNE	Z = 0	Z = 0
BGT	Z OR (S XOR O) = 0	C = 1 OR Z = 0
BGE	S XOR O = 0	C = 1

For unsigned data some microprocessors invert the Carry status following a subtract or compare operation. In that case, you must exchange C = 1 and C = 0.

In order to illustrate the use of Branch-on-Condition instructions, we will take another look at how the shower temperature controller might read data being input by the thermometer.

When the thermometer is ready to output a byte of data, it tests bit 1 of I/O Port 2. If this bit is 1, thermometer logic assumes that any previous data it sent has been read and processed; therefore thermometer logic transmits a byte of data to I/O Port 0 and signals this event by setting bit 0 of I/O Port 2 to 1. Thermometer logic will also reset bit 1 of I/O Port 2 to 0, since the data at I/O Port 0 has not yet been read:

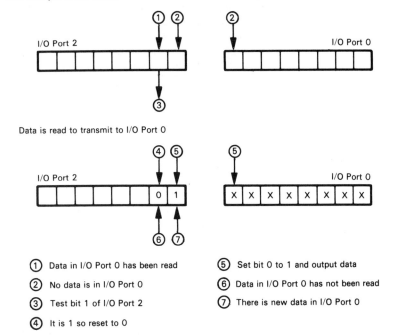

Data is read to transmit to I/O Port 0

① Data in I/O Port 0 has been read   ⑤ Set bit 0 to 1 and output data

② No data is in I/O Port 0   ⑥ Data in I/O Port 0 has not been read

③ Test bit 1 of I/O Port 2   ⑦ There is new data in I/O Port 0

④ It is 1 so reset to 0

In order to read data input by the thermometer, the microprocessor program must keep testing bit 0 of I/O Port 2 until this bit is read as 1. Then the microprocessor must read the data in I/O Port 0; but at the same time the microprocessor must reset bit 0 of the I/O Port 2 to 0, since as soon as data is read out of I/O Port 0, it becomes old data. The program must now set bit 1 of I/O Port 2 to 1; this tells thermometer logic that the data in I/O Port 0 has been read.

The following instruction sequence performs the operations described above. In addition, this instruction sequence assumes that the data byte read out of I/O Port 0 will be stored in a memory location addressed by Data Counter DC0. Auto-increment addressing is used with DC0 so that this data counter automatically addresses the next free byte of the input data buffer, ready for the next access of I/O Port 0.

```
LOOP    IN      2                      ;Clear all but 0 bit
        ANDB    A0,#H'01               ;Return to LOOP if 0 bit is 0
        BZ      LOOP                   ;New data is ready. Input status again
        IN      2                      ;Reset bit 0 to 0
        ANDB    A0,#H'FE               ;Set bit 1 to 1
        ORB     A0,#H'02               ;Restore the new status to I/O Port 2
        OUT     2                      ;Input the data byte
        IN      0                      ;Store in memory using implied, auto-
        STB     A0,@DC0+               ;increment addressing
```

Jump-to-Subroutine on Condition

A number of microprocessors have Jump-to-Subroutine instructions akin to the Branch-on-Condition instructions we have just described. Our microprocessor has one Jump-to-Subroutine instruction which was described as an Immediate instruction.

Conditional Jump-to-Subroutine instructions will usually be followed by a two-byte address, since subroutines may well reside in memory a long way away from the Jump-to-Subroutine instructions. The logic of Conditional Jump-to-Subroutine instructions is otherwise similar to the Branch-on-Condition: if the specified condition is met, the Jump-to-Subroutine occurs; if not, the next instruction is executed.

Conditional Return-From-Subroutine

Some microprocessors also have a set of Conditional Return-from-Subroutine instructions. These instructions restore to the program counter the address which the Jump-to-Subroutine instruction saved. We have no special Return-from-Subroutine instruction; we will use a Pop instruction instead (described along with the stack instructions).

Register-Register Move Instructions

There are two types of instructions that reference two CPU registers: instructions that move data from one register to another, and instructions that perform secondary memory reference type operations, but entirely within the CPU.

Register-Register Move Instructions Justified

Register-register data movement instructions can be quite limited in our microcomputer, given its register organization.

We must be able to move data between A0 and A1. Exchanging the contents of the accumulators is also frequently useful.

Moving data from the accumulators to the data counters allows program logic to create variable addresses in the accumulators, then move these addresses to a data counter, for variable implied addressing. Moving data in the reverse direction allows a data counter to be used as temporary storage for data in the accumulators. Of course, this assumes that the data counter in question is not being used for implied addressing.

Multiple Stacks

There is rarely any need to move data from one data counter to another. However, the ability to move data between the stack pointer and data counters, or between the stack pointer and accumulators is useful, since this allows a program to have more than one stack. DC2 could be used as a buffer for the stack pointer, for example; now, by exchanging the contents of DC2 and SP, two stacks could be accessed.

Computed Jump

Moving data between the accumulators and the program counter allows program logic to compute jump addresses. This is very useful in branch tables, which are illustrated later in this chapter.

We will therefore provide **Data Move and Data Exchange instructions as follows:**

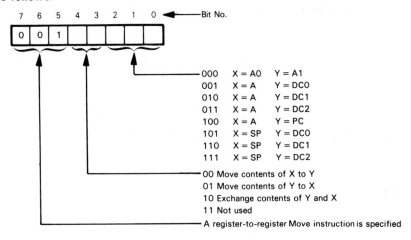

000	X = A0	Y = A1
001	X = A	Y = DC0
010	X = A	Y = DC1
011	X = A	Y = DC2
100	X = A	Y = PC
101	X = SP	Y = DC0
110	X = SP	Y = DC1
111	X = SP	Y = DC2

00 Move contents of X to Y
01 Move contents of Y to X
10 Exchange contents of Y and X
11 Not used

A register-to-register Move instruction is specified

In the description above, X = A specifies a 16-bit value formed out of the two accumulators as follows:

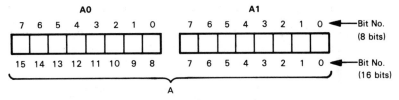

Move   **The instructions:**

          MOVB   AX,AY
          MOV   S,D

will move the register contents specified by AX or S to the register specified by AY or D. S and D must be one of the valid 16-bit pairs shown; AX and AY can only be A0 or A1. Therefore, these Moves are valid:

          MOVB   A1,A0   ;Move A1 contents to A0
          MOVB   A0,A1   ;Move A0 contents to A1
          MOV   SP,DC1   ;Move stack pointer contents to DC1

This Move is invalid:

          MOV   DC1,DC0

but the intended operation could be achieved via these two valid Moves:

          MOV   DC1,A   ;Move DC1 contents to accumulators
          MOV   A,DC0   ;Move accumulators to DC0

MOVB specifies a byte move; MOV specifies a word move. MOVB could be replaced by MOV without creating any ambiguities, but the two mnemonics make programs easier to read.

Recall the program that tests switches for any changes of state; the program uses a register-to-register Move instruction as follows:

          IN   4   ;Input new switch settings
          XORB   A0,SWITCH   ;Identify changed switches
          MOVB   A0,A1   ;Save A0 contents in A1
          ANDB   A0,SWITCH   ;Identify switches that turned off

Exchange instruction mnemonics will be:

XCHB	AX,AY
XCH	S,D

The same rules apply to S and D as described for MOVB and MOV.

Register-Register Operate Instructions

Because our microcomputer has a number of secondary memory reference instructions, it needs very few Register-Register Operate instructions; the following seven instructions, which parallel the secondary memory reference instructions, will do:

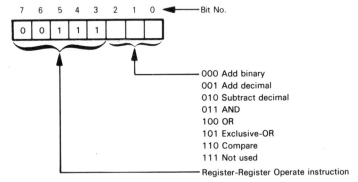

The four status flags are set or reset to reflect the results of the operation.

Because there is an A0-A1 Exchange instruction, we have only one set of Register-Register Operate instructions, where A0 is always the destination of the the result.

The Register-Register Operate instructions will use the same **mnemonics** as the secondary memory reference instructions. Only the operand fields differ. These are the mnemonics used:

Add Binary
Add Decimal
Subtract Decimal
AND
OR
Exclusive-OR
Compare

ADDB	A0,A1	Add A1 to A0 binary
ADDDB	A0,A1	Add A1 to A0 decimal
SUBDB	A0,A1	Subtract A1 from A0
ANDB	A0,A1	AND A1 with A0
ORB	A0,A1	OR A1 with A0
XORB	A0,A1	XOR A1 with A0
CMPB	A0,A1	Compare A1 with A0

These three instructions will allow A1 to be the destination of any Register-Register Operate instruction:

XCHB	A0,A1	;Exchange A0 and A1 contents
ADDB	A0,A1	;Add binary; the result is in A0
XCHB	A0,A1	;Exchange A0 and A1 contents

**Register-
Register
Operate
Instructions
Justification**

Register-Register Operate instructions are convenient to have, but not vital, since they do nothing that could not be done using Load, Store, and secondary memory reference instructions.

Register-Register Operate instructions will execute faster than equivalent secondary memory reference instructions, since secondary memory reference instructions require one data byte to be fetched from memory — and that takes time.

**Accumulator-
Data Counter
Addition**

There is one further set of Register-Register Operate instructions which will prove very useful. We will allow the contents of Accumulator A0 to be added, as a signed binary number, to any one of the data counters. This allows a data address displacement to be computed, then added to (or subtracted from) a data counter.

**Addressing
Matrices**

This instruction is particularly useful in matrix arithmetic, where doubly subscripted parameters such as:

VAL(X,Y)

may be used. If the dimension of Y is known, each increment of X may be handled by adding the dimension of Y to the data counter which is addressing VAL. This is illustrated as follows:

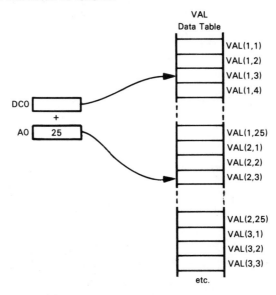

To extend this type of matrix handling, **we will also allow A0 and A1, treated as a 16-bit unit, to be added to any data counter.**
We now have these instruction codes:

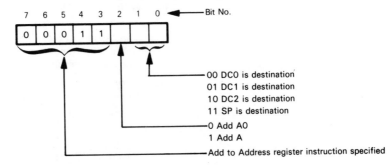

A specifies the 16-bit unit:

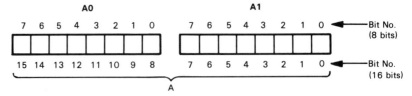

We will use these mnemonics:

```
ADDB    D,AX
ADD     D,A
```

AX is the source, and may be A0 or A1; no other options are allowed. For ADD A is the only allowed source.

D is the destination; it may be DC0, DC1, DC2, or SP; no other options are allowed.

Branch Tables **The Accumulator-Data Counter Addition instruction is also useful for creating branch tables.**

A branch table is a list of addresses, identifying a number of programs, just one of which must be executed, based on current program logic.

To illustrate a branch table we will create a table of program starting addresses. This is not a simple concept. Consider the following real, but arbitrary, numbers:

```
ADDR1    EQU     H'1247      Start of Program 1
ADDR2    EQU     H'183C      Start of Program 2
ADDR3    EQU     H'28CA      Start of Program 3
         etc.
         ORG     H'0800
BTBL     DATA    ADDR1
         DATA    ADDR2
         DATA    ADDR3
         etc.
```

Equate Directive The EQU mnemonic, you will recall, is an assembler directive; it tells the assembler what values to assign to the symbols ADDR1, ADDR2, ADDR3, etc.

Define Address Directive The DATA mnemonic is a data assembler directive; it tells the assembler to place the value provided by the operand in the next currently identified memory locations.

Origin Directive The ORG mnemonic is an assembler directive which specifies the current memory address. In this case, it defines the current memory address as 0800_{16}. In terms of a memory map, the above instructions create these six data bytes:

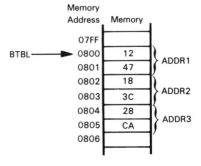

Note that the label BTBL becomes a symbol with the value 0800_{16}.

Now suppose a program number is in Accumulator A0; we can execute the program identified by the program number as follows:

```
LD      DC0,#BTBL       ;Load the beginning address for program
                        ;addresses into DC0
ADDB    DC0,A0          ;Add the table number twice, since each
ADDB    DC0,A0          ;address occupies two bytes
LDB     A0,@DC0+        ;Load the address identified by DC0
LDB     A1,@DC0
MOV     A,PC            ;Move this address to PC
```

Look at what happens:

1) The LD instruction loads 0800_{16} into DC0.
2) Suppose Accumulator A0 contains 2; the two ADDB instructions add 4 to DC0, which now contains 0804_{16}.
3) The first LDB instruction loads the contents of memory location 0804_{16} into A0, then increments DC0. Now A0 contains 28_{16} and DC0 contains 0805_{16}.
4) The second LDB instruction loads the contents of memory location 0805_{16} into A1. Now A1 contains CA_{16}.
5) The MOV instruction moves the value $28CA_{16}$ into the program counter, forcing a jump to memory location $28CA_{16}$.

When would you use a branch table? One example is given in the description of interrupt instructions.

Register Operate Instructions

Register Operate instructions modify the contents of a single register; no other register's contents are modified in any way.

Some Register Operate instructions are absolutely necessary, whereas others are nothing more than conveniences. We will therefore identify the ways in which a register's contents may be modified, then determine whether the operation is a necessity or a convenience.

Increment and Decrement **We must be able to increment and decrement registers' contents.** When a register contains a counter or index, there is the probability that the index will have to be incremented or decremented.

Complement **Since we have no binary subtract instructions, it is vital that there be an instruction to complement at least one of the accumulators.** Complementing the data counters serves no useful purpose. (See Chapter 2 for a discussion of twos complement subtraction.)

Clear Register **It must be possible to zero each accumulator.** This is a common initialization step, and precedes addition. Zeroing the Address registers is not necessary, since address 0000_{16} is seldom used to hold data or data tables.

Shift and Rotate **Shift and rotate operations are very important for two reasons: they are vital to most multiplication and division algorithms, and they are frequently used in counting operations.**

Shift A shift operation is linear:

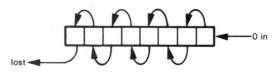

lost

0 in

A simple shift left, as illustrated above, will move each bit one position to the left; the high-order bit, having no bit to the left, will be lost. There being no bit to the right of the low-order bit, 0 will be moved into the low-order bit.

Rotate   A rotate operation is circular; the high-order and low-order bits are assumed to be adjacent:

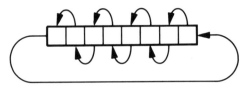

Simple Shift and Rotate   Numerous variations of shift and rotate operations are possible; you can shift or rotate left:

Simple Shift Left:

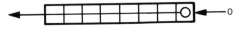

Simple Rotate Left:

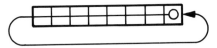

You can shift or rotate right:

Simple Shift Right:

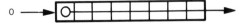

Simple Rotate Right:

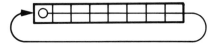

Shift and Rotate Through Carry   A right shift is equivalent to dividing by 2. A left shift is equivalent to multiplying by 2, and can be reproduced by adding the contents of a register to itself.

A shift or rotate may occur through the Carry status. We may illustrate a shift through Carry as follows:

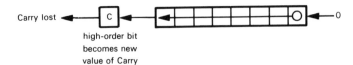

Here is a rotate through Carry:

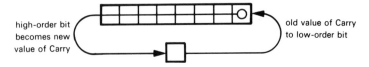

The equivalent right shift or rotate through Carry is self-evident.

Rotate with Branch Carry

Another variation branches a bit into the Carry status, but excludes the old Carry status from the rotate:

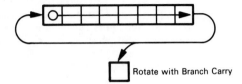

Rotate with Branch Carry

The shift with branch carry is very useful as the first in a multibyte shift operation, where an initial value of 0 must be assumed for the Carry status.

Arithmetic Shift

The shift may also be arithmetic and propagate the high-order bit (sign bit) to the right:

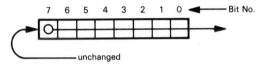

An arithmetic shift left will maintain the sign bit, and shift out of the penultimate bit into the Carry:

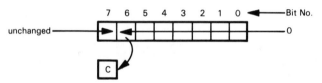

Shifting Binary Coded Decimal

A four-bit shift, left or right, is very useful in microprocessor applications which process numeric data.

As was discussed in Chapter 2, binary-coded decimal digits each occupy four bits; each byte holds two BCD digits. A four-bit shift is therefore equivalent to a single decimal digit shift, left or right; that is, it is equivalent to multiplying or dividing by ten.

The four-bit left and right shift also makes it easy to pack and unpack ASCII characters. Recall that the ASCII representation of a decimal digit appears as follows:

```
0 = 011 0000
1 = 011 0001
2 = 011 0010
3 = 011 0011
4 = 011 0100
5 = 011 0101
6 = 011 0110
7 = 011 0111
8 = 011 1000
9 = 011 1000
```

Suppose a string of ASCII digits is being read through an I/O port and must be packed in BCD format, two digits per byte as follows:

Data as read: 0011001000110110001100000110101 etc.

Data as packed: 0010 0110   1000 0101

The four-bit shift is a natural for this operation. We will settle on some shift mnemonics, then write a program to perform this BCD packing operation.

How many, and which shift/rotate instructions should we have?

Shift and rotate instructions are usually inadequately represented in microprocessor instruction sets. We will have such instructions for the two accumulators only, but we will provide shifts and rotates without Carry (simple), with Carry, and with branched Carry.

The ability to shift data counter contents would provide a 16-bit shift, but that is a luxury we will have to forego.

We will include two versions of the four-bit left and right shift. One will operate on the contents of either Accumulator A0 or A1; the other will operate on the combined unit as a 16-bit number. In each case, since we are dealing with four-bit units, the Carry will be ignored during the shift operation.

We can now summarize the Register Operate instruction object codes as follows.

For the operations which are confined to the accumulators, these are the instructions and their object codes:

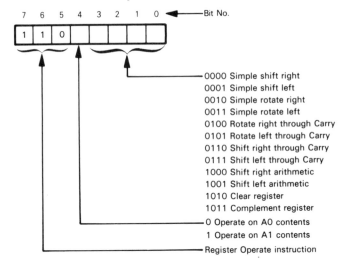

The Shift and Rotate instructions may modify the Carry and Zero statuses. The Complement instruction will affect the Zero status only.

The two 4-bit shift instructions can operate on A0, A1, or A (A0-A1 16-bit unit). Object codes for these instructions will be as follows:

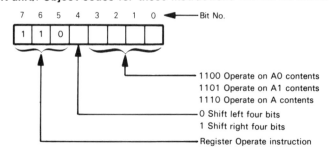

The Increment and Decrement instructions operate on the accumulators and on the Address registers; they will use these object codes:

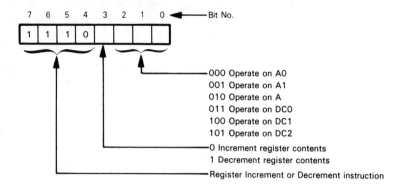

Shift and Rotate Instructions

The Shift and Rotate instructions will have these mnemonics:

SHR	Shift A0 or A1 contents right, simple
SHL	Shift A0 or A1 contents left, simple
ROR	Rotate A0 or A1 right, simple
ROL	Rotate A0 or A1 left, simple
RORC	Rotate A0 or A1 right through carry
ROLC	Rotate A0 or A1 left through carry
SHRC	Shift A0 or A1 right through carry
SHLC	Shift A0 or A1 left through carry
SHRA	Shift A0 or A1 right arithmetic
SHLA	Shift A0 or A1 left arithmetic
SHR4	Shift A0, A1 or A right four bits
SHL4	Shift A0, A1 or A left four bits

Increment Register

These are the mnemonics we will use for Register Operate instructions:

INCB	AX
INC	R

This specifies the Increment register instruction; R may be A, DC0, DC1, or DC2; AX must be A0 or A1.

Decrement Register

The Decrement register instruction will differ only in the mnemonics, as follows:

DECB	AX
DEC	R

Complement

Clear

Complement (or Negate) and Clear will apply to the two accumulators only, and will have these mnemonics:

CLRB	AX	;Clear A0 or A1
NEGB	AX	;Twos complement A0 or A1

We will now illustrate the value of Register Operate instructions with some examples of how these instructions may be used.

Consider multibyte shifts; they allow multibyte numbers to be multiplied and divided. A rotate through Carry will propagate a shift down a number of bytes, since the high-order bit of each byte propagates into the Carry status, and then into the low-order bit of the next byte. This may be illustrated for the following simple, three-byte left shift:

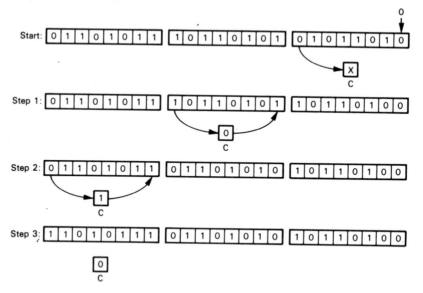

The following program performs this operation:

```
LD      DCO,#BUFA    ;Load the buffer starting address into DCO
LDB     A0,@DCO      ;Load low-order byte into A0 via DCO
SHLC    A0           ;Shift left through carry
STB     A0,@DCO—     ;Store the result back; decrement DCO
LDB     A0,@DCO      ;Shift the second byte into DCO
ROLC    A0           ;Rotate left through carry
STB     A0,@DCO—     ;Store the result back; decrement DCO
LDB     A0,@DCO      ;Load last byte
ROLC    A0           ;Rotate left through carry
STB     A0,@DCO      ;Store result back
```

The LD instruction loads the address of the low-order byte into Data Counter DCO.

The next three instructions, LDB, SHLC, and STB, accomplish step 1. First, LDB loads the low-order byte into Accumulator A0 but does not modify the address in DCO, since we will want to return the shifted result to the same address. The SHLC instruction is very useful at this point, because we do not know what the Carry status is before entering this routine. But the SHLC instruction does not care; this instruction loads 0 into the low-order bit of A0, and moves the high-order bit of A0 into the Carry status, ready to be shifted into the next byte. The STB instruction stores the shifted contents of A0 back into the memory byte from which the unshifted source came; then the address in DCO is decremented to point to the second byte.

The next three instructions, LDB, ROLC, and STB, perform step 2. These three instructions differ from the previous three instructions only in that a rotate left through carry must now be performed since the Carry status represents the high-order bit of the previous byte, which must become the low-order bit of the current byte.

Step 3 is accomplished via the last three instructions, LDB, ROLC, and STB; these three instructions differ from the three step 2 instructions only in that we do not bother to decrement the address in DC0, since there are no more bytes to be shifted.

Observe that since only three bytes are to be shifted, we do not use an instruction loop. The whole of the program above only occupies 12 bytes, three for the Load Immediate into DC0 instruction, and one for each of the remaining instructions. We could condense the three steps into one set of three repeated instructions so long as we can change SHLC to an ROLC instruction, and so long as the final STB instruction decrements DC0. The program now appears as follows:

```
          Clear Carry status, which must initially be 0
          LD        DC0,#BUFA      ;Load buffer starting address into DC0
          LDB       A1,#3          ;Load byte count into A1
LOOP      LDB       A0,@DC0        ;Load next byte into A0, via DC0
          ROLC      A0             ;Rotate left through carry
          STB       A0,@DC0—       ;Store the result back; decrement DC0
          DECB      A1             ;Decrement byte count
          BNZ       LOOP           ;Return if not end
```

We now have a program with eight instructions, versus the previous ten. But these eight instructions still occupy 12 bytes: three for the Load Immediate into DC0, two each for the Load Immediate into A1 and the Branch on Non-Zero, and one each for the remainder. When a loop has very few iterations, a branch-and-loop program structure offers few economies as compared to a once-through program structure.

Switch Testing

Next consider switch testing. The eight switches we described when justifying secondary memory reference instructions could be tested for "on" or "off" status in a program loop as follows:

1) Load 00000001 into A1. We are going to use A1 as a switch counter. Its contents will be shifted left with branch carry until a 1 appears in the Carry status, which will indicate that eight shifts have been performed.
2) Load switch settings into A0.
3) Shift A0 one bit right through carry. The low-order bit of A0 is now in the Carry status.
4) Save A0 and A1 in DC2. The Carry status still reflects the low-order bit of A0, since a Move instruction will not affect the status flags.
5) Branch on "carry true" to "switch on" program. Otherwise continue with "switch off" program.
6) When the "switch on" or "switch off" program has completed execution, reload A0 and A1 from DC2.
7) Shift A1 left one bit through carry. If Carry is set, we are done. If Carry is not set, return to step 3 above.

The program steps required to implement the above logic are as follows:

```
          LDB       A1,#1          ;Load 1 into A1
          INB       4              ;Input switch settings from I/O port 4
LOOP      SHRC      A0             ;Shift right with branch carry
          MOV       A,DC2          ;Save A0 and A1 in DC2
          BC        SWON           ;Branch on C=1 to "switch on" program
```

"Switch off" program logic appears here.

```
          MOV       DC2,A          ;Restore A0 and A1 from DC2
          SHLC      A1             ;Shift A1 left with branch carry
          BNC       LOOP           ;Continue if more switch settings to test
```

Packing ASCII Digits

Now consider the program steps needed to pack the four low-order numeric bits of ASCII numeric digits. Two numeric digits will be packed per byte, as described previously.

These steps would be required to pack digits:

Step 1 — Read in one ASCII digit and store in Accumulator A0.

Step 2 — Shift left four bits.

Step 3 — Move the contents of A0 to A1. A1 now contains the high-order digit as follows:
Original ASCII digit: 0011XXXX
After four-bit left shift: XXXX0000

Step 4 — Input the next ASCII digit to Accumulator A0.

Step 5 — Mask out the four high-order bits of A0. A0 now contains the low-order digit as follows:
Original ASCII digit: 0011YYYY
After masking high-order bits: 0000YYYY

Step 6 — Add A1 to A0. A0 now contains the high-order and low-order digits as follows:
0000YYYY + XXXX0000 = XXXXYYYY

Step 7 — Store the two packed digits in memory (we will assume the correct buffer is addressed by DC1).

Step 8 — Return to step 1 for the next two ASCII digits.

We will assume that ASCII digits are input at I/O Port 5, and bit 0 of I/O Port 6 is set to 1 by the inputting device whenever it has transmitted an ASCII digit to I/O Port 5. Other bits of I/O Port 6 are always 0.

Program steps are as follows:

```
LOOP1   INB    6           ;Input status
        SHRC   A0          ;Shift bit 0 of A0 into Carry
        BNC    LOOP1       ;If Carry is 0, input status again
        OUTB   6           ;If Carry is 1, output A0 to I/O Port 6
                           ;This clears the status
        INB    5           ;Input the next ASCII digit
        SHL4   A0          ;Shift left 4 bits
        MOVB   A0,A1       ;Save in A1
LOOP2   INB    6           ;Repeat first five instructions
        SHRC   A0          ;to input next ASCII digit
        BNC    LOOP2
        OUTB   6
        INB    5
        ANDB   A0,#H'0F    ;Mask out high-order four bits
        ADDB   A0,A1       ;Add A1 to A0
        STB    A0,@DC0−    ;Store the two packed digits
        BR     LOOP1       ;Return for next two digits
```

Stack Instructions

Push

Pop

Return-From-
Subroutine

Subroutine
Parameter Passing

Since our microprocessor has a stack, it must have **Push instructions to move registers' contents onto the stack. It must also have Pop instructions to move data off the stack and into registers.**

Push instructions will be used primarily for interrupt processing. Programming examples are given along with interrupt handling instructions.

Pop instructions are used in interrupt processing, and in order to return from a subroutine; examples of the latter use will be given shortly.

Push and Pop instructions are sometimes used to pass data (parameters) to subroutines; we will illustrate this use of Push and Pop instructions later. You cannot pass parameters to subroutines via the stack if the stack is also used by interrupt processing logic.

Our microprocessor will have Push and Pop instructions that reference the two accumulators and the five Address registers. Object codes will be as follows:

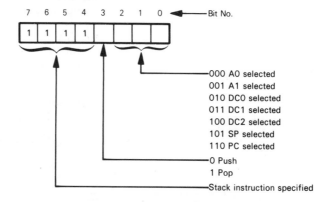

The **Push and Pop instructions will use this instruction format:**

OP   R

OP represents the instruction mnemonic; it will be PUSH or POP, for a 16-bit Push or Pop instruction, respecvely. PUSHB and POPB are used for an 8-bit PUSH or POP.

R will specify the register whose contents are to be pushed onto the stack, or which is to receive data popped from the stack. R may be DC0, DC1, DC2, SP, or PC with PUSH or POP. If A0 or A1 is specified by R, then one byte will be pushed or popped, and OP must be PUSHB or POPB.

Return
Instruction
We will allow an additional instruction mnemonic for subroutine returns. The instruction:

POP   PC

moves the two bytes at the top of the stack into the program counter, thus effecting a return from the subroutine. The mnemonic:

RET

will perform the same operation, and generate the same object code. In other words, the RET mnemonic will generate the one object code byte:

As an example of Stack instructions' use, return to the data move-ment subroutine which was described along with Immediate instructions; the subroutine will now be listed as follows:

```
MOVE    LD     DC0,#BUFA            ;Load source initial address
        LD     DC1,#BUFB            ;Load destination initial address
LOOP    LDB    A0,@DC0-             ;Move data from source
        STBNZ  A0,@DC1, LOOP        ;to destination
        RET                        ;Return from subroutine
```

Parameter Passing

In addition to adding a Return instruction, this subroutine can be made more useful if the beginning addresses for the source and destination buffers (BUFA and BUFB) are variable. Stack instructions provide one way (but not the best way) of making this possible.

Parameter Passing Instructions

Because subroutines are so frequently used, it is worth taking a look at instructions which make subroutines easier to use. Parameter passing in-structions fall into this category.

Parameter passing instructions allow parameters to follow the Jump-to-Subroutine instruction. We provide the microprocessor with a form of indirect addressing, where the two bytes at the top of the stack become the memory ad-dress from which data will be fetched. Via this address the subroutine can read the data appearing after the subroutine call.

But before we explain this concept with illustrations and examples, let us define the parameter passing instructions which our microcomputer will include.

First, there are the object codes that are to be used:

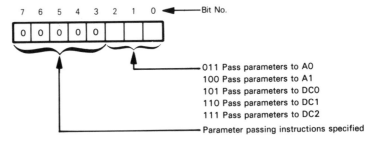

This is the format we will use for the Pass Parameter instruction:

```
LDB       AY,(SP)+@
LD        R,(SP)+@
```

R identifies one of the 16-bit registers DC0, DC1, or DC2; AY can be A0 or A1.

The operand field of the Pass Parameter instruction explains the instruction's execution logic. The contents of the addressed memory byte is loaded into A0 or A1 for LDB. The contents of the addressed memory word are loaded into DC0, DC1, or DC2 for LD. In either case, the memory address is taken from the top two bytes; the syntax (SP)@ stipulates this addressing logic, which we may illustrate as follows:

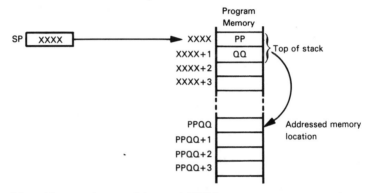

The address at the top of the stack (PPQQ in the illustration above) is incremented by 1 for LDB, or by 2 for LD. Hence, the syntax (SP)+@ in the operand field.

We will now develop a very efficient data move subroutine.

The subroutine will be called as follows:

```
CALL      MOVE        ;Call data move subroutine
DATA      BUFX        ;Specify beginning source address
DATA      BUFY        ;Specify beginning destination address
```

Recall that the DA mnemonic represents the Define Address assembler directive. Suppose these instructions reside in memory as follows:

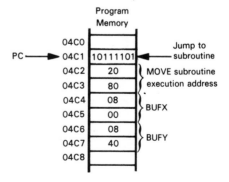

After the CALL instruction has been executed, PC will contain 2080_{16}, which is the execution address for subroutine MOVE. The previous value of PC, $04C4_{16}$, will be at the top of the stack:

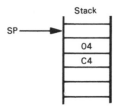

The MOVE subroutine appears as follows:

```
MOVE    LD      DC0,(SP)+@        ;Load source starting address into DC0
        LD      DC1,(SP)+@        ;Load destination starting address into DC1
LOOP    LDB     A0,@DC0+          ;Move data from source
        STBNZ   A0,@DC1,LOOP     ;to destination
        RET
```

The first LD instruction causes the microprocessor to execute the following logic:

1) The two bytes at the top of the stack are fetched into the CPU.
2) These two bytes are treated as a memory address. The contents of the memory location identified by this memory address are loaded into the high-order byte of DC0. The memory address is then incremented. The memory address was $04C4_{16}$, and memory location $04C4_{16}$ contains 08_{16}. Therefore, at the end of this step the high-order byte of DC0 contains the value 08_{16} and the memory address has been incremented to $04C5_{16}$.
3) Step 2 is repeated, with the data fetched from memory going to the low-order byte of DC0. At the end of this step DC0 contains 0800_{16}, and the memory address is now $04C6_{16}$.
4) Instruction execution is complete, so the memory address is returned to the top of the stack, which now holds $04C6_{16}$, not $04C4_{16}$.

The second LD instruction is a repeat of the first LD instruction, except that DC1 is specified as the destination; therefore, at the conclusion of the LD instruction, 0840_{16} will be loaded into DC1, and the top two bytes of the stack will hold the value $04C8_{16}$. This is the address of the next instruction to be executed following the two parameters, BUFX and BUFY. At the conclusion of the Move subroutine, the RET instruction will pop the value $04C8_{16}$ back into the program counter, thus allowing normal program execution to continue.

Interrupt Instructions

In reality we are going to talk about more than interrupt instructions. There are only three interrupt instructions; one disables all interrupts, the second enables all interrupts, and the third is a Return-from-Interrupt instruction.

How is our microprocessor going to handle interrupts?

There are many similarities between processing an interrupt and entering a subroutine. In each case, program execution temporarily branches from a main program to a secondary logic sequence, at the conclusion of which program execution returns to the main program. The difference between a subroutine and an interrupt is that a Jump-to-Subroutine is part of the scheduled mainstream logic:

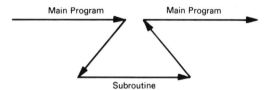

An interrupt, on the other hand, is an unscheduled event, and the main program has no way of knowing when the interrupt will occur:

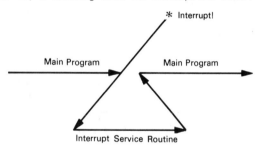

We discussed at some length, in Chapter 5, the various ways in which external devices can interrupt the microprocessor. Recall that as the interrupt protocol becomes more minicomputer-like, and more sophisticated, so also the cost and complexity of the external logic needed to meet the requirements of interrupt protocol goes up. Since we are developing an instruction set for a simple, 8-bit microprocessor, we will therefore adopt a very simple scheme. Interrupting devices will be daisy-chained on a single interrupt request line, and when the microprocessor sends out an acknowledge signal, the interrupting device will return a single byte of data to an I/O port with address FF_{16}. The microprocessor will interpret data in I/O Port FF_{16} as identifying the interrupting device.

As soon as the microprocessor acknowledges an interrupt, it will automatically do three things:

First, it will disable interrupts, thus preventing another interrupt from being processed before the current one has been adequately handled. An Enable Interrupt instruction must be executed by the program before any further interrupts can be handled.

Next, the microprocessor will save the status flags' contents by pushing them onto the stack.

Finally, the microprocessor will push the program counter contents to the top of the stack and clear the program counter. This causes program execution to continue at memory location 0.

A **Disable Interrupt** instruction can be executed at any time to prevent any interrupts from being acknowledged; this condition will last until the Enable Interrupt instruction is reexecuted.

Let us first look at the object code for the Enable and Disable Interrupt instructions:

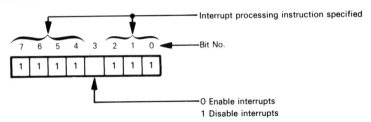

Enable Interrupt

Disable Interrupt

Return-From-Interrupt

The mnemonics for the two interrupt instructions will be:

DI

for Disable Interrupts, and

EI

for Enable Interrupts.

The Return-from-Interrupt instruction will do three things:

First it will pop the return address from the stack to the program counter.

Then it will return the status flags, which were saved on the stack automatically when the interrupt was acknowledged.

Finally the Return-from-Interrupt instruction enables interrupts.

The Return-from-Interrupt instruction's object code will be:

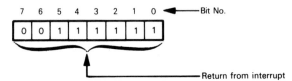

The instruction mnemonic will be:

RETI

To illustrate the use of interrupt instructions, we will show the program steps which follow an Interrupt Acknowledge.

We will also show the program steps which must be present at the end of the interrupt service routine.

Following an interrupt these steps must occur:

1) At the time of the Interrupt Acknowledge, microprocessor logic saves the status flags at the top of the stack, pushes the program counter contents onto the top of the stack, then disables interrupts. The program counter is zeroed, which means that program execution jumps to memory location 0.

2) Starting at memory location 0, there is a short program sequence which saves the contents of all microprocessor registers by pushing registers' contents onto the stack. This is necessary, since the registers may be used in any way by the program which is about to be executed.

3) After all registers' contents have been saved on the stack, the contents of I/O Port FF$_{16}$ are read, and are used to compute the starting address of the particular program which will service the identified interrupting device.

4) The program which gets executed following step 3 may optionally contain an Enable Interrupt instruction. If this instruction is present, another interrupt may be processed before the current interrupt has completed execution, as follows:

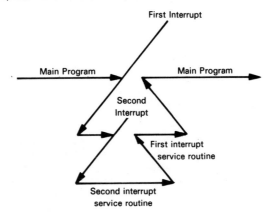

If interrupts are not enabled, then no further interrupts can be processed until their Return-from-Interrupt instruction is executed.

These are the instructions which, given our interrupt service logic, must be present beginning at memory location 0:

```
ORG     0
PUSHB   A0              ;Save all registers' contents
PUSHB   A1              ;on the stack
PUSH    DC0
PUSH    DC1
PUSH    DC2
INB     H'FF            ;Input device ID from I/O Port FF
LD      DC0,#BTBL       ;Load jump table base address
SHL     A0              ;Shift A0 left, simple, to multiply by 2
ADDB    DC0,A0          ;Add A0 to DC0
LDB     A0,@DC0+        ;Load the interrupt service routine
LDB     A1,@DC0         ;starting address
MOV     A,PC            ;Move the address to PC
```

This is what the above short program does:

Recall that the ORG mnemonic specifies the current memory address for the assembler. The ORG mnemonic above tells the assembler to start creating object code beginning at memory location 0.

The five PUSH instructions save the contents of all registers on the stack.

The INB instruction will receive a device ID at I/O Port FF. We are assuming that within the time taken for the microprocessor to execute the Push instruction, the interrupting device will have been able to place its ID number at I/O Port FF. This ID number will be in Accumulator A0.

**Branch
Tables**

The instructions from LD to MOV constitute a branch table. Branch tables were described along with the ADDB Register-Register Operate instruction. Notice in the branch table instruction sequence above that a Shift instruction has been used to multiply the contents of A0 by 2 before adding them to DC0; in the previous example, the ADDB instruction was executed twice to achieve the same end result.

The address computed by the branch table becomes the beginning of the interrupt service routine, which will now be executed to service the device which requested an interrupt. Once the interrupt service routine has completed execution, it will jump to a short routine that reverses the interrupt acknowledge steps as follows:

```
RINT    POP     DC2     ;Restore all registers' contents
        POP     DC1
        POP     DC0
        POPB    A1
        POPB    A0
        RETI
```

**Restoring
Registers
from Stack**

Observe that registers are popped from the stack in the reverse order in which they were pushed, since the stack is a last-in-first-out storage unit.

The final RETI instruction will load back into the program counter the memory address which was saved at the time of the interrupt acknowledge; then it will restore the saved status (which is on the stack following the interrupt acknowledge) to the four status flags.

If interrupts are still disabled, the RTI instruction will reenable interrupts.

Program execution will now continue at the instruction following the last one executed prior to the interrupt being acknowledged.

Status Instructions

Since we have four status flags, Sign (S), Carry (C), Overflow (O), and Zero (Z), it must be possible to set or reset these flags individually. The most common situation in which program logic will require a flag to be set is just before entering a program loop which contains a Branch-on-Condition instruction at the beginning of the loop. In the normal course of events, status flags will be set later in the loop to be tested when program logic comes back to the beginning of the loop. It must be possible to set status conditions before entering the loop, so that we can get by the Branch-on-Condition on the first pass.

There are also many multibyte arithmetic algorithms which require the Carry and Overflow statuses to be either cleared or set before starting the algorithm; subsequently, after each byte of the multibyte number is processed, carries are passed from one byte to the next via these two status flags, as described in Chapter 2.

We will therefore include these eight status instructions:

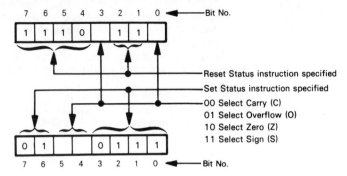

Set Status **The Set Status instruction will have this format:**

SET X

Reset Status **The Reset Status instruction will have this format:**

CLR X

In each case, X may be C, O, Z, or S, to identify one of the four status flags. No other symbol is allowed.

As an example of status instruction use, the multibyte, binary addition routine (described along with the secondary memory reference instructions) starts out by clearing the Carry status:

```
        CLR     C               ;Clear Carry status
LOOP    LDB     A0,@DC0+        ;Load next input byte
        ADDCB   A0,@DC1         ;Add binary from answer buffer
        STBNZ   A0,@DC1,LOOP    ;Store the result, increment and skip
```

Once in the loop, the binary addition instruction ADDCB sets and resets the Carry status appropriately.

Halt Instruction

Virtually every microprocessor has a Halt instruction. When this instruction is executed, the microprocessor simply stops. In a minicomputer, or in a microcomputer that has a front panel, program execution is restarted by pressing a restart button on the panel. As far as the microprocessor is concerned, the reset signal which is input to the microprocessor (this signal is described in Chapter 4) must be pulsed in order to start execution after a Halt instruction.

The Halt instruction mnemonic is:

HALT

AN INSTRUCTION SET SUMMARY

You will find that books describing individual microprocessors provide tables that summarize the microprocessor instruction set cryptically. These summary tables are very useful. Assuming that you have a general understanding of assembly languages, two or three pages tell you everything you need to know about operations performed when any instruction is executed.

We are going to summarize our hypothetical instruction set in Table 7-1. Similar tables in other Osborne/McGraw-Hill books will summarize the instruction sets for real microprocessors.

In Table 7-1, symbols are used as follows:

A0	Accumulator A0
A1	Accumulator A1
AY	Either Accumulator A0 or Accumulator A1
ADDR	A 16-bit memory address
C	Carry status
DATA	An 8-bit binary data unit
DC0	Data Counter DC0
DC1	Data Counter DC1
DC2	Data Counter DC2
DCX	Any data counter
DISP	An 8-bit signed binary address displacement
DST	Any destination register
I	Any status indicator
O	Overflow status
P	An I/O port number
PC	Program Counter
R	Any register
S	Sign status
SP	Stack Pointer
SRC	Any source register
SW	Statuses
Z	Zero status
[ ]	Contents of location enclosed within brackets. If a register designation is enclosed within the brackets, then the designated register's contents are specified. If an I/O port number is enclosed within the brackets, then the I/O port contents are specified. If a memory address is enclosed within the brackets, then the contents of the addressed memory location are specified.
[[ ]]	Implied memory addressing; the contents of the memory location designated by the contents of a register.
$\wedge$	Logical AND
V	Logical OR
$\underline{V}$	Logical Exclusive-OR
$\longleftarrow$	Data is transferred in the direction of the arrow.
$\longleftarrow \longrightarrow$	Data is exchanged between the two locations designated on either side of the arrow.

Under the heading of "Statuses" in Table 7-1, an X indicates statuses which are modified in the course of the instructions' execution. If there is no X, it means that the status maintains the value it had before the instruction was executed.

Table 7-1. A Summary of the Hypothetical Microcomputer Instruction Set

Type	Mnemonic	Operand(s)	Bytes	C	O	S	Z	Operation Performed
I/O	INB	P	1,2					[A0] ← [P] Input to A0 from I/O Port P (only 0, 1 or 2 for INB)
	OUTB	P	1,2					[P] ← [A0] Output from A0 to I/O Port P (only 0, 1 or 2 for OUTB).
Primary Memory Reference	LDB	AY,ADDR	3					[A0] ← [ADDR], [A1] ← [ADDR] Load to A0 or A1, use direct addressing.
	LDB	AY,@DCX	1					[A0] ← [[DCX]], [A1] ← [[DCX]] Load A0 or A1 using implied addressing.
	LDB	AY,@DCX+	1					[A0] ← [[DCX]], [A1] ← [[DCX]], and [DCX] ← [DCX] + 1 Load A0 or A1 using implied addressing with auto-increment.
	LDB	AY,@DCX−	1					[A0] ← [[DCX]], [A1] ← [[DCX]], and [DCX] ← [DCX] − 1 Load A0 or A1 using implied addressing with auto-decrement.
	STB	AY,ADDR	3					[ADDR] ← [A0], [ADDR] ← [A1] Output from A0 or A1, use direct addressing.
	STB	AY,@DCX	1					[[DCX]] ← [A0], [[DCX]] ← [A1] Store A0 or A1 in memory using implied addressing.
	STB	AY,@DCX+	1					[[DCX]] ← [A0], [[DCX]] ← [A1], and [DCX] ← [DCX] + 1 Store A0 or A1 in memory using implied addressing with auto-increment.
	STB	AY,@DCX−	1					[[DCX]] ← [A0], [[DCX]] ← [A1] and [DCX] ← [DCX] − 1 Store A0 or A1 in memory using implied addressing with auto-decrement.
	LDBNZ	AY,@DCX,ADDR	2					[A0] ← [[DCX]] and [DCX] ← [DCX] + 1 plus branch Load A0 or A1 using implied addressing with auto-increment and branch.
	STBNZ	AY,@DCX,ADDR	2					[[DCX]] ← [A0], [[DCX]] ← [A1] and [DCX] ← [DCX] + 1 plus branch Store A0 or A1 in memory using implied addressing with auto-increment and branch.
Secondary Memory Reference	ADDCB	AY,ADDR	3	X	X	X	X	[A0] ← [A0] + [ADDR] + [C], [A1] ← [A1] + [ADDR] + [C] Add binary with carry to A0 or A1 using direct addressing.
	ADDCB	AY,@DCX	1	X	X	X	X	[A0] ← [A0] + [[DCX]] + [C], [A1] ← [A1] + [[DCX]] + [C] Add binary with carry to A0 or A1 using implied addressing.
	ADDCDB	AT,ADDR	3	X	X	X	X	[A0] ← [A0] + [ADDR] + [C], [A1] ← [A1] + [ADDR] + [C] Add decimal with carry to A0 or A1 using direct addressing.
	ADDCDB	AY,@DCX	1	X	X	X	X	[A0] ← [A0] + [[DCX]] + [C], [A1] ← [A1] + [[DCX]] + [C] Add decimal with carry to A0 or A1 using implied addressing.
	SUBCDB	AY,ADDR	3	X	X	X	X	[A0] ← [A0] − [ADDR] − [C], [A1] ← [A1] − [ADDR] − [C] Subtract decimal with borrow from A0 or A1 using direct addressing.
	SUBCDB	AY,@DCX	1	X	X	X	X	[A0] ← [A0] − [[DCX]] − [C], [A1] ← [A1] − [[DCX]] − [C] Subtract decimal with borrow from A0 or A1 using implied addressing.

Table 7-1. A Summary of the Hypothetical Microcomputer Instruction Set (Continued)

Type	Mnemonic	Operand(s)	Bytes	C	O	S	Z	Operation Performed
Secondary Memory Reference (continued)	ANDB	AY,ADDR	3			×		[A0] ← [A0] ∧ [ADDR], [A1] ← [A1] ∧ [ADDR] AND with A0 or A1 using direct addressing.
	ANDB	AY,@DCX	1			×		[A0] ← [A0] ∧ [[DCX]], [A1] ← [A1] ∧ [[DCX]] AND with A0 or A1 using implied addressing.
	ORB	AY,ADDR	3			×		[A0] ← [A0] ∨ [ADDR], [A1] ← [A1] ∨ [ADDR] OR with A0 or A1 using direct addressing.
	ORB	AY,@DCX	1			×		[A0] ← [A0] ∨ [[DCX]], [A1] ← [A1] ∨ [[DCX]] OR with A0 or A1 using implied addressing.
	XORB	AY,ADDR	3			×		[A0] ← [A0] ⊻ [ADDR], [A1] ← [A1] ⊻ [ADDR] Exclusive-OR with A0 or A1 using direct addressing.
	XORB	AY,@DCX	1			×		[A0] ← [A0] ⊻ [[DCX]], [A1] ← [A1] ⊻ [[DCX]] Exclusive-OR with A0 or A1 using implied addressing.
	CMPB	AY,@DCX	1	×	×	×	×	Compare memory with A0 or A1 using implied addressing.
Immediate	LDB	AY,#DATA	2					[DST] ← DATA Load immediate into A0 or A1.
	LD	R,#DATA	3					[DST] ← DATA Load immediate into DC0, DC1, DC2, SP.
Immediate Operate	ADDB	AY,#DATA	2	×	×	×	×	[A0] ← [A0] + DATA + [C], [A1] ← [A1] + DATA + [C] Add binary immediate to A0 or A1.
	ANDB	AY,#DATA	2		×	×		[A0] ← [A0] ∧ DATA, [A1] ← [A1] ∧ DATA AND immediate with A0 or A1.
	ORB	AY,#DATA	2		×	×		[A0] ← [A0] ∨ DATA, [A1] ← [A1] ∨ DATA OR immediate with A0 or A1.
	CMPB	AY,#DATA	2	×	×	×	×	Compare immediate with A0 or A1.
Jump	BR	ADDR	3					[PC] ← ADDR Jump to instruction with label ADDR.
	CALL	ADDR	3					[[SP]] ← [PC], [PC] ← ADDR, [SP] ← [SP] + 1 Jump to subroutine starting at ADDR.

Table 7-1. A Summary of the Hypothetical Microcomputer Instruction Set (Continued)

Type	Mnemonic	Operand(s)	Bytes	C	O	Z	S	Operation Performed
Branch-On-Condition	BE,BZ	DISP	2					If [Z] = 1, [PC] ← [PC] + DISP Branch on Z = 1.
	BNZ	DISP	2					If [Z] = 0, [PC] ← [PC] + DISP Branch on Z = 0.
	BGE,BC	DISP	2					If [C] = 1, [PC] ← [PC] + DISP Branch on C = 1.
	BNC,BLT	DISP	2					If [C] = 0, [PC] ← [PC] + DISP Branch on C = 0.
	BV	DISP	2					If [O] = 1, [PC] ← [PC] + DISP Branch on O = 1.
	BNV	DISP	2					If [O] = 0, [PC] ← [PC] + DISP Branch on O = 0.
	BP	DISP	2					If [S] = 0, [PC] ← [PC] + DISP Branch on S = 0.
	BN	DISP	2					If [S] = 1, [PC] ← [PC] + DISP Branch on S = 0.
Move Reg-Reg	MOV	SRC,DST	1					[DST] ← [SRC] Move contents of SRC to DST.
	MOVB	SRC,DST	1					SRC = A0, A or SP. DST = A1, DC0, DC1, DC2 or PC.
	XCH	SRC,DST	1					[DST] ← [SRC]
	XCHB	SRC,DST	1					Exchange SRC and DST contents.
Register-Register Operate	ADDB	A0,A1	1	X	X	X	X	[A0] ← [A0] + [A1] + [C] Add binary A1 to A0.
	ADDD	A0,A1	1	X	X	X	X	[A0] ← [A0] + [A1] + [C] Add decimal A1 to A0.
	SUBDB	A0,A1	1	X	X	X	X	[A0] ← [A0] – [A1] – [C] Subtract decimal A1 from A0.
	ANDB	A0,A1	1			X		[A0] ← [A0] ∧ [A1] AND A1 with A0.
	ORB	A0,A1	1			X		[A0] ← [A0] ∨ [A1] OR A1 with A0.
	XORB	A0,A1	1			X		[A0] ← [A0] ⊻ [A1] Exclusive-OR A1 with A0.
	CMPB	A0,A1	1	X	X	X	X	Compare A1 with A0.
	ADD	SRC,DST	1			X		[DST] ← [DST] + [SRC] + [C]
	ADDB	SRC,DST	1					Add binary SRC to DST. SRC = A0 or A. DST = DC0, DC1, DC2 or SP.

Table 7-1. A Summary of the Hypothetical Microcomputer Instruction Set (Continued)

Type	Mnemonic	Operand(s)	Bytes	C	O	S	Z	Operation Performed
Register Operate	SHR	AY	1					Shift A0 or A1 right, simple.
	SHL	AY	1					Shift A0 or A1 left, simple.
	ROR	AY	1					Rotate A0 or A1 right, simple.
	ROL	AY	1					Rotate A0 or A1 left, simple.
	RORC	AY	1	X				Shift A0 or A1 right through carry.
	ROLC	AY	1	X				Shift A0 or A1 left through carry.
	SHRC	AY	1	X				Shift A0 or A1 right with branch carry.
	SHLC	AY	1	X				Shift A0 or A1 left with branch carry.
	SHRA	AY	1	X	X			Shift A0 or A1 right arithmetic.
	SHLA	AY	1	X	X			Shift A0 or A1 left arithmetic.
	SHR4	AY	1					Shift A0 or A1 right 4 bits.
	SHL4	AY	1					Shift A0 or A1 left 4 bits.
	SHR4	A	1					Shift A0 and A1 right 4 bits.
	SHL4	A	1					Shift A0 and A1 left 4 bits.
	INC	R	1				X	$[R] \leftarrow [R] + 1$. Increment Register (R = A0, A1, A, DC0, DC1, DC2).
Stack	PUSH	R	1					$[[SP]] \leftarrow [R]$, $[SP] \leftarrow [SP] + 1$. Push Register R contents onto stack. R = A0, A1, DC0, DC1, DC2, SP, PC.
	POP	R	1					$[R] \leftarrow [[SP]]$, $[SP] \leftarrow [SP] - 1$. Pop top of stack to Register R.
	RET		1					$[PC] \leftarrow [[SP]]$, $[SP] \leftarrow [SP] - 1$. Same as POP PC.
Param Pass	LDB	AY,(SP)+@	1					$[R] \leftarrow [[[SP]]$, $[[SP]] \leftarrow [[SP]] + 1$. Pass parameter to Register R.
	LD	DCX,(SP)+@	1					R = A0, A1, DC0, DC1 or DC2.
Interrupt	DI		1					Disable interrupts.
	EI		1					Enable interrupts.
	RETI		1					$[SW] \leftarrow [[SP]]$, $[PC] \leftarrow [[SP]]$. Return from interrupt.
Status	SET	I	1	X	X	X	X	$[I] \leftarrow 1$. Set Status I to 1 (I = C, O, Z, S).
	CLR	I	1	X	X	X	X	$[I] \leftarrow 0$. Reset Status I to 0.
	HALT		1					Halt.

7-60

MORE ADVANCED MICROPROCESSOR INSTRUCTION SET CONCEPTS

We will now examine the types of instructions found in the more powerful instruction sets of recently introduced microprocessors. These include all of the recent 16-bit microprocessors, together with some of the later 8-bit microprocessors. We will not construct a complete instruction set as we did leading up to Table 7-1; rather, we will take instructions category by category, looking at the types of operations likely to be found in more complex instruction sets.

CPU Architecture

The most recent microprocessors have a large number of programmable registers. For 16-bit microprocessors sixteen or thirty-two 16-bit registers are typical. Most registers can be used variously, as accumulators or Index registers. For example, the Z8000 assigns registers as follows:

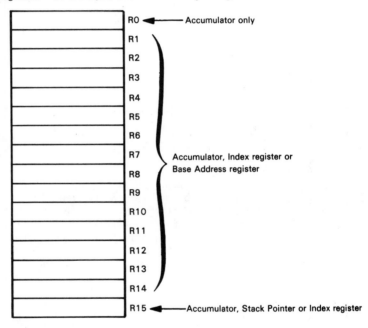

Instructions that access CPU registers or memory will usually be able to address a byte, a 16-bit word, or a 32-bit long word. Thus registers are designated by the Z8000 as follows:

15	8	7	0	← Bit No.	
B1		B0	R0	}	D0
B3		B2	R1		
B5		B4	R2	}	D1
B7		B6	R3		
B9		B8	R4	}	D2
B11		B10	R5		
B13		B12	R6	}	D3
B15		B14	R7		
			R8	}	D4
			R9		
			R10	}	D5
			R11		
			R12	}	D6
			R13		
			R14	}	D7
			R15		

The illustration above shows sixteen 16-bit registers, designated R0 through R15. The eight low-order registers, R0 through R7, alternatively function as sixteen 8-bit registers, designated B0 through B15. Eight 32-bit registers are also identified, designated D0 through D7. Thus the same physical locations are selected by 32-bit register D1, 16-bit registers R2 and R3, or 8-bit registers B4, B5, B6, and B7.

Program flexibility is slightly restricted by the 8-bit register organization illustrated above, since byte register reference instructions can access only the eight low-order 16-bit registers. It would be possible to extend byte register addressing so that the sixteen 16-bit registers could all be accessed one byte at a time, as thirty-two 8-bit registers, but five object code bits would be needed to select one of thirty-two 8-bit registers, whereas four object code bits accessed sixteen 16-bit registers. In all probability register reference object code bits will be assigned in some fashion as follows:

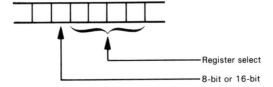

Therefore, changing the number of register bits when going from 8-bit registers to 16-bit registers would complicate CPU logic more than we could justify based on the resulting improved programming flexibility.

An alternative register organization (used by the M68000) may be illustrated as follows:

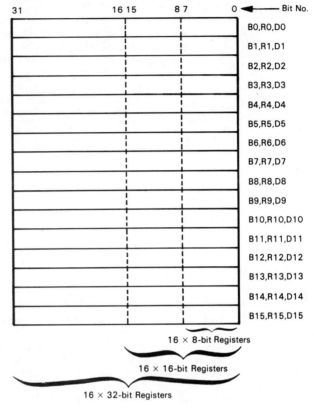

Some microprocessors require two-byte and four-byte memory units to be origined on even-addressed boundaries; others do not.

New microprocessors have instructions that access a single bit of a register or a memory location, with the ability to set, reset, or test the bit value.

It is easy for 16-bit microprocessors to support 16 general purpose registers, and have the many variations we have described for register or memory reference instructions, since the instruction object codes are typically 16 bits wide. Since 16 registers require four address bits, register-to-register instructions would use just eight of the 16 object code bits to specify instruction type.

Input/Output Instructions

Powerful microprocessor instruction sets, if they distinguish between I/O ports and memory at all, will usually have similar I/O instructions that differ little from our simple 8-bit microprocessor; however, they will not have one-byte short form I/O instructions, but they will have two-word instructions with the following object code:

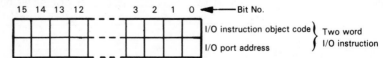

A two-word I/O instruction can address 65,536 I/O ports. No microcomputer system is likely to be so complex as to require this number of I/O ports. However, new support devices are likely to contain large numbers of internal programmable locations which may be addressed as I/O ports.

Having a large number of I/O port addresses simplifies support device addressing by allowing a single high-order address line to act as select inputs. For example, the eight high-order address lines could be used directly as eight select inputs as follows:

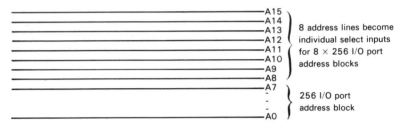

This select scheme allows 2048 I/O ports to be addressed, and we need no device select logic. Having a large I/O port address space generates economies that have nothing to do with any potential need for a large number of I/O ports.

Memory Reference Instructions

A powerful microprocessor instruction set's memory reference instructions will differ from the simple instructions we have already described in variety, rather than type. For example, if there are sixteen 16-bit registers, the instruction set will treat them equally as the data source or destination, or as an index. Likewise, byte, word, and long word instructions will all have a complete complement of addressing variations.

Such versatility can quickly consume even a 16-bit instruction set. Consider, for example, memory addressing options. If we restrict ourselves to register indirect, direct, indexed, and auto-increment memory addressing, we already have a need for a formidable number of object code bits. Addressing options consume two bits of object code. If any of the sixteen 16-bit registers can function as the indirect memory address register or the index, four object code bits are needed for this specification. Add four object code bits to specify the source register, another four object code bits to specify the destination register, one bit to specify a load or store instruction, and two bits to specify a byte, word, or long word; 13 bits have been allocated, although some combinations of the 13 bits remain unused. This may be illustrated as follows:

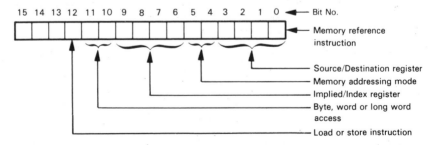

As memory addressing becomes more complex, allowing base relative addressing, base relative index addressing, and indexed addressing with or without a displacement, the number of object code bits required to specify all variations could easily exceed even a 16-bit word. Some arbitrary restrictions must then be applied to a 16-bit instruction set, much as we applied restrictions to our 8-bit instruction set.

Secondary Memory Reference Instructions

As compared to our simple 8-bit instruction set, more complex 8-bit and 16-bit microprocessors will have more options, but similar formats. These additional options will probably be available.

1) **A large variety of operations.** There will be separate add and add-with-carry instructions; there will be subtract and subtract-with-borrow instructions. Binary or decimal add and subtract instructions will be available. New 16-bit microprocessors also offer a variety of multiplication and division instructions. All Boolean operations are supported.

2) **Secondary memory reference instructions will likely operate on bytes, words, or long words.** New 16-bit microprocessors will offer 32-bit multiplication and division.

3) **Many of the operations which a simple microprocessor will perform on the contents of a CPU register, a real 8-bit or 16-bit microprocessor instruction set will also perform on the contents of a memory location.** For example, you will probably be able to shift and rotate the contents of memory bytes and words.

A powerful bit microprocessor instruction set will also increase your secondary memory reference instruction operand options. Our simple instruction set's secondary memory reference instructions required one operand to be in a CPU register and the other in memory, with the result going to the Operand CPU register. A more complex instruction set will give you the option of taking both operands from memory and returning the result to memory, or returning the result to a CPU register other than the Operand register.

Load Immediate, Jump, and Jump-to-Subroutine Instructions

Modern 8-bit and 16-bit microprocessor instruction sets allow immediate instructions to load data into memory bytes or words, addressed using the complete range of allowed memory addressing modes.

Jump-to-Subroutine and Return-from-Subroutine instructions offer a variety of addressing modes via which the subroutine can be identified. Conditional Jump-to-Subroutine and Return-from-Subroutine instructions are frequently provided. These instructions were discussed earlier for our simple instruction set.

Immediate Operate Instructions

Modern microprocessor instruction sets offer a wide variety of immediate operate instructions. **All of the arithmetic and logical operations performed by secondary memory reference instructions are also available in immediate operate versions.** Immediate operate instructions allow either registers or memory to be accessed by the immediate operand. Variations of immediate instructions allow bytes, words, or in some cases long words to be referenced, with 8, 16, or 32 bits of immediate data provided by the instruction itself. When an immediate operate instruction accesses memory, all of the available memory addressing options will likely be supported.

Branch-on-Condition Instructions

Modern microprocessor Branch-on-Condition instructions allow the condition to be specified directly from status bits, or via Boolean conditions such as the ones we summarized for our simple instruction set. Instructions frequently have two versions: one with a short 8-bit displacement and another with a long 16-bit displacement.

Register-Register Move Instructions

There is very little room for imagination in this class of instructions. **Modern microprocessor instruction sets allow the contents of any register to be moved to any other register; or the contents of any two registers may be exchanged.** But Register-Register Move instructions can do no more.

Register-Register Operate Instructions

Modern microprocessor instruction sets allow a large number of operations to be performed using operands held in registers. These will likely include all of the possible arithmetic and Boolean operations. Variations allow 8-bit, 16-bit, and in some cases 32-bit operands to be addressed out of registers.

Register Operate Instructions

The set of register operate instructions which we described for our simple 8-bit microprocessor was very complete. A modern microprocessor instruction set will include these options, but may well allow 8, 16, or in some cases 32 bits of data to be operated on out of registers.

Stack Instructions

Some new 16-bit microprocessors have two stack pointers capable of maintaining two separate stacks. But stack instructions will otherwise be limited to the Push and Pop instructions which we described for our simple 8-bit microprocessor. Sometimes Push and Pop instructions allow any CPU register to function as the stack pointer, rather than requiring a special Stack Pointer register to be used by default.

When a microprocessor allows the stack pointer to be treated as an Index register or a Base register, all of the memory reference, immediate, and operate instructions become stack instructions, since specific stack locations can be accessed by using the stack pointer as an appropriate index into the stack.

Block Move and Translate Instructions

Some new microprocessor instruction sets allow a single instruction to move a large number of data bytes or words from a source to a destination. Consider the following example:

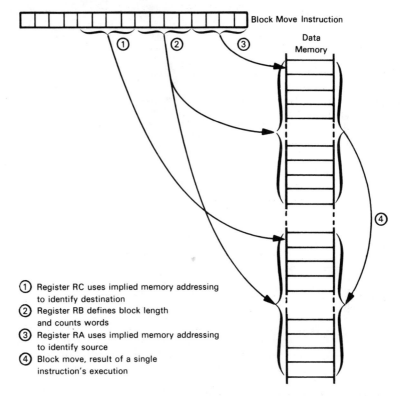

1. Register RC uses implied memory addressing to identify destination
2. Register RB defines block length and counts words
3. Register RA uses implied memory addressing to identify source
4. Block move, result of a single instruction's execution

The instruction object code illustrated above identifies three general purpose registers. One defines the length of a data block (in bytes or words). The other two provide a beginning source address and a beginning destination address. When this instruction is executed, an entire block of data is moved from a source to a destination.

A block move instruction such as the one illustrated above performs an operation that is very similar to a Direct Memory Access block data transfer.

The Z8000 microprocessor instruction set takes the block move logic a step further, allowing an I/O port to become the data source or destination. The memory address will change as the block of data moves, but the I/O port address will of course remain constant.

**Translate
Instruction**

Another variation of the Block Move instruction allows data to be translated as it is moved. A Z8000 Translate instruction, for example, uses an input data byte as an index into a table. The indexed memory location contents are output to the destination. This may be illustrated as follows:

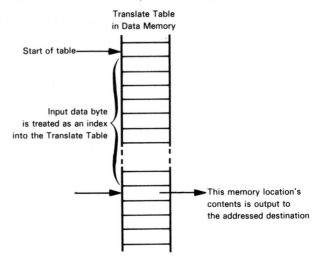

A Translate instruction which performs an operation such as the one illustrated above would be able to take an entire block of source data in ASCII code and, with the execution of a single instruction, deposit the data in a destination, translated into EBCDIC code.

Appendix A

STANDARD CHARACTER CODES

ASCII Character Codes

b4	b3	b2	b1	Row/Column	0	1	2	3	4	5	6	7
b7 →					0	0	0	0	1	1	1	1
b6 →					0	0	1	1	0	0	1	1
b5 →					0	1	0	1	0	1	0	1
0	0	0	0	0	NUL	DLE	SP	0	@	P	`	p
0	0	0	1	1	SOH	DC1	!	1	A	Q	a	q
0	0	1	0	2	STX	DC2	''	2	B	R	b	r
0	0	1	1	3	ETX	DC3	#	3	C	S	c	s
0	1	0	0	4	EOT	DC4	$	4	D	T	d	t
0	1	0	1	5	ENQ	NAK	%	5	E	U	e	u
0	1	1	0	6	ACK	SYN	&	6	F	V	f	v
0	1	1	1	7	BEL	ETB	'	7	G	W	g	w
1	0	0	0	8	BS	CAN	(	8	H	X	h	x
1	0	0	1	9	HT	EM	)	9	I	Y	i	y
1	0	1	0	10	LF	SUB	*	:	J	Z	j	z
1	0	1	1	11	VT	ESC	+	;	K	[	k	{
1	1	0	0	12	FF	FS	,	<	L	\	l	¦
1	1	0	1	13	CR	GS	-	=	M	]	m	}
1	1	1	0	14	SO	RS	.	>	N	Λ	n	~
1	1	1	1	15	SI	US	/	?	O	—	o	DEL

NUL	Null	DC1	Device control 1
SOH	Start of heading	DC2	Device control 2
STX	Start of text	DC3	Device control 3
ETX	End of text	DC4	Device control 4
EOT	End of transmission	NAK	Negative acknowledge
ENQ	Enquiry	SYN	Synchronous idle
ACK	Acknowledge	ETB	End of transmission block
BEL	Bell, or alarm	CAN	Cancel
BS	Backspace	EM	End of medium
HT	Horizontal tabulation	SUB	Substitute
LF	Line feed	ESC	Escape
VT	Vertical tabulation	FS	File separator
FF	Form feed	GS	Group separator
CR	Carriage return	RS	Record separator
SO	Shift out	US	Unit separator
SI	Shift in	SP	Space
DLE	Data link escape	DEL	Delete

ASCII Character Codes in Ascending Order

Hexa-decimal	Binary		ASCII	Hexa-decimal	Binary		ASCII
00	000	0 0 0 0	NUL	20	010	0 0 0 0	SP
01	000	0 0 0 1	SOH	21	010	0 0 0 1	!
02	000	0 0 1 0	STX	22	010	0 0 1 0	''
03	000	0 0 1 1	ETX	23	010	0 0 1 1	#
04	000	0 1 0 0	EOT	24	010	0 1 0 0	$
05	000	0 1 0 1	ENQ	25	010	0 1 0 1	%
06	000	0 1 1 0	ACK	26	010	0 1 1 0	&
07	000	0 1 1 1	BEL	27	010	0 1 1 1	'
08	000	1 0 0 0	BS	28	010	1 0 0 0	(
09	000	1 0 0 1	HT	29	010	1 0 0 1	)
0A	000	1 0 1 0	LF	2A	010	1 0 1 0	*
0B	000	1 0 1 1	VT	2B	010	1 0 1 1	+
0C	000	1 1 0 0	FF	2C	010	1 1 0 0	,
0D	000	1 1 0 1	CR	2D	010	1 1 0 1	-
0E	000	1 1 1 0	SO	2E	010	1 1 1 0	.
0F	000	1 1 1 1	SI	2F	010	1 1 1 1	/
10	001	0 0 0 0	DLE	30	011	0 0 0 0	0
11	001	0 0 0 1	DC1	31	011	0 0 0 1	1
12	001	0 0 1 0	DC2	32	011	0 0 1 0	2
13	001	0 0 1 1	DC3	33	011	0 0 1 1	3
14	001	0 1 0 0	DC4	34	011	0 1 0 0	4
15	001	0 1 0 1	NAK	35	011	0 1 0 1	5
16	001	0 1 1 0	SYN	36	011	0 1 1 0	6
17	001	0 1 1 1	ETB	37	011	0 1 1 1	7
18	001	1 0 0 0	CAN	38	011	1 0 0 0	8
19	001	1 0 0 1	EM	39	011	1 0 0 1	9
1A	001	1 0 1 0	SUB	3A	011	1 0 1 0	:
1B	001	1 0 1 1	ESC	3B	011	1 0 1 1	;
1C	001	1 1 0 0	FS	3C	011	1 1 0 0	<
1D	001	1 1 0 1	GS	3D	011	1 1 0 1	=
1E	001	1 1 1 0	RS	3E	011	1 1 1 0	>
1F	001	1 1 1 1	US	3F	011	1 1 1 1	?

ASCII Character Codes in Ascending Order (Continued)

Hexa-decimal	Binary	ASCII	Hexa-decimal	Binary	ASCII
40	100 0000	@	60	110 0000	`
41	100 0001	A	61	110 0001	a
42	100 0010	B	62	110 0010	b
43	100 0011	C	63	110 0011	c
44	100 0100	D	64	110 0100	d
45	100 0101	E	65	110 0101	e
46	100 0110	F	66	110 0110	f
47	100 0111	G	67	110 0111	g
48	100 1000	H	68	110 1000	h
49	100 1001	I	69	110 1001	i
4A	100 1010	J	6A	110 1010	j
4B	100 1011	K	6B	110 1011	k
4C	100 1100	L	6C	110 1100	l
4D	100 1101	M	6D	110 1101	m
4E	100 1110	N	6E	110 1110	n
4F	100 1111	O	6F	110 1111	o
50	101 0000	P	70	111 0000	p
51	101 0001	Q	71	111 0001	q
52	101 0010	R	72	111 0010	r
53	101 0011	S	73	111 0011	s
54	101 0100	T	74	111 0100	t
55	101 0101	U	75	111 0101	u
56	101 0110	V	76	111 0110	v
57	101 0111	W	77	111 0111	w
58	101 1000	X	78	111 1000	x
59	101 1001	Y	79	111 1001	y
5A	101 1010	Z	7A	111 1010	z
5B	101 1011	[	7B	111 1011	{
5C	101 1100	\	7C	111 1100	¦
5D	101 1101	]	7D	111 1101	}
5E	101 1110	∧	7E	111 1110	~
5F	101 1111	—	7F	111 1111	DEL

EBCDIC Character Codes

Hexa-decimal	Binary		EBCDIC	Hexa-decimal	Binary		EBCDIC
00	0000	0000	NUL	20	0010	0000	DS
01	0000	0001	SOH	21	0010	0001	SOS
02	0000	0010	STX	22	0010	0010	FS
03	0000	0011	ETX	23	0010	0011	
04	0000	0100	PF	24	0010	0100	BYP
05	0000	0101	HT	25	0010	0101	LF
06	0000	0110	LC	26	0010	0110	ETB
07	0000	0111	DEL	27	0010	0111	ESC
08	0000	1000		28	0010	1000	
09	0000	1001	RLF	29	0010	1001	
0A	0000	1010	SMM	2A	0010	1010	SM
0B	0000	1011	VT	2B	0010	1011	CU2
0C	0000	1100	FF	2C	0010	1100	
0D	0000	1101	CR	2D	0010	1101	ENQ
0E	0000	1110	SO	2E	0010	1110	ACK
0F	0000	1111	SI	2F	0010	1111	BEL
10	0001	0000	DLE	30	0011	0000	
11	0001	0001	DC1	31	0011	0001	
12	0001	0010	DC2	32	0011	0010	SYN
13	0001	0011	TM	33	0011	0011	
14	0001	0100	RES	34	0011	0100	PN
15	0001	0101	NL	35	0011	0101	RS
16	0001	0110	BS	36	0011	0110	UC
17	0001	0111	IL	37	0011	0111	EOT
18	0001	1000	CAN	38	0011	1000	
19	0001	1001	EM	39	0011	1001	
1A	0001	1010	CC	3A	0011	1010	
1B	0001	1011	CU1	3B	0011	1011	CU3
1C	0001	1100	IFS	3C	0011	1100	DC4
1D	0001	1101	IGS	3D	0011	1101	NAK
1E	0001	1110	IRS	3E	0011	1110	
1F	0001	1111	IUS	3F	0011	1111	SUB

Hexa-decimal	Binary		EBCDIC	Hexa-decimal	Binary		EBCDIC
40	0100	0000	space	60	0110	0000	—
41	0100	0001		61	0110	0001	/
42	0100	0010		62	0110	0010	
43	0100	0011		63	0110	0011	
44	0100	0100		64	0110	0100	
45	0100	0101		65	0110	0101	
46	0100	0110		66	0110	0110	
47	0100	0111		67	0110	0111	
48	0100	1000		68	0110	1000	
49	0100	1001		69	0110	1001	
4A	0100	1010	¢	6A	0110	1010	¦
4B	0100	1011	•	6B	0110	1011	,
4C	0100	1100	<	6C	0110	1100	%
4D	0100	1101	(	6D	0110	1101	—
4E	0100	1110	+	6E	0110	1110	>
4F	0100	1111	]	6F	0110	1111	?
50	0101	0000	&	70	0111	0000	
51	0101	0001		71	0111	0001	
52	0101	0010		72	0111	0010	
53	0101	0011		73	0111	0011	
54	0101	0100		74	0111	0100	
55	0101	0101		75	0111	0101	
56	0101	0110		76	0111	0110	
57	0101	0111		77	0111	0111	
58	0101	1000		78	0111	1000	
59	0101	1001		79	0111	1001	
5A	0101	1010	!	7A	0111	1010	:
5B	0101	1011	$	7B	0111	1011	#
5C	0101	1100	*	7C	0111	1100	@
5D	0101	1101	)	7D	0111	1101	'
5E	0101	1110	;	7E	0111	1110	=
5F	0101	1111	¬	7F	0111	1111	"

Hexa-decimal	Binary		EBCDIC	Hexa-decimal	Binary		EBCDIC
80	1000	0000		A0	1010	0000	
81	1000	0001	a	A1	1010	0001	~
82	1000	0010	b	A2	1010	0010	s
83	1000	0011	c	A3	1010	0011	t
84	1000	0100	d	A4	1010	0100	u
85	1000	0101	e	A5	1010	0101	v
86	1000	0110	f	A6	1010	0110	w
87	1000	0111	g	A7	1010	0111	x
88	1000	1000	h	A8	1010	1000	y
89	1000	1001	i	A9	1010	1001	z
8A	1000	1010		AA	1010	1010	
8B	1000	1011		AB	1010	1011	
8C	1000	1100		AC	1010	1100	
8D	1000	1101		AD	1010	1101	
8E	1000	1110		AE	1010	1110	
8F	1000	1111		AF	1010	1111	
90	1001	0000		B0	1011	0000	
91	1001	0001	j	B1	1011	0001	
92	1001	0010	k	B2	1011	0010	
93	1001	0011	l	B3	1011	0011	
94	1001	0100	m	B4	1011	0100	
95	1001	0101	n	B5	1011	0101	
96	1001	0110	o	B6	1011	0110	
97	1001	0111	p	B7	1011	0111	
98	1001	1000	q	B8	1011	1000	
99	1001	1001	r	B9	1011	1001	
9A	1001	1010		BA	1011	1010	
9B	1001	1011		BB	1011	1011	
9C	1001	1100		BC	1011	1100	
9D	1001	1101		BD	1011	1101	
9E	1001	1110		BE	1011	1110	
9F	1001	1111		BF	1011	1111	

EBCDIC Character Codes (Continued)

Hexa-decimal	Binary	EBCDIC
C0	1100 0000	{
C1	1100 0001	A
C2	1100 0010	B
C3	1100 0011	C
C4	1100 0100	D
C5	1100 0101	E
C6	1100 0110	F
C7	1100 0111	G
C8	1100 1000	H
C9	1100 1001	I
CA	1100 1010	
CB	1100 1011	
CC	1100 1100	⑀
CD	1100 1101	
CE	1100 1110	⑂
CF	1100 1111	
D0	1101 0000	}
D1	1101 0001	J
D2	1101 0010	K
D3	1101 0011	L
D4	1101 0100	M
D5	1101 0101	N
D6	1101 0110	O
D7	1101 0111	P
D8	1101 1000	Q
D9	1101 1001	R
DA	1101 1010	
DB	1101 1011	
DC	1101 1100	
DD	1101 1101	
DE	1101 1110	
DF	1101 1111	

Hexa-decimal	Binary	EBCDIC
E0	1110 0000	\
E1	1110 0001	
E2	1110 0010	S
E3	1110 0011	T
E4	1110 0100	U
E5	1110 0101	V
E6	1110 0110	W
E7	1110 0111	X
E8	1110 1000	Y
E9	1110 1001	Z
EA	1110 1010	
EB	1110 1011	
EC	1110 1100	⑁
ED	1110 1101	
EE	1110 1110	
EF	1110 1111	
F0	1111 0000	0
F1	1111 0001	1
F2	1111 0010	2
F3	1111 0011	3
F4	1111 0100	4
F5	1111 0101	5
F6	1111 0110	6
F7	1111 0111	7
F8	1111 1000	8
F9	1111 1001	9
FA	1111 1010	LVM
FB	1111 1011	
FC	1111 1100	
FD	1111 1101	
FE	1111 1110	
FF	1111 1111	

Appendix B

BINARY MULTIPLICATION AND DIVISION
ALGORITHMS

In this Appendix we will continue the discussion of binary arithmetic which we started in Chapter 2. We will look at some binary multiplication and division algorithms which were too complex to be included in Chapter 2, yet are useful enough to be part of any discussion of basic concepts. We will not look at means of computing trigonometric functions, logarithms, or exponentials. Whole books have been written on these more complex algorithms; theory surrounding such computations is at least as complex as the entire discussion of microprocessor fundamentals that has been presented in this book.

Simple 8-Bit Binary Multiplication

The simplest way of performing multiplication is to zero a product buffer, then add a multiplier to this product buffer the number of times given by the multiplicand. For example, to multiply 4 by 3, you might zero the product buffer, then add 4 to it three times. **Using our hypothetical instruction set, here is an appropriate instruction sequence** that multiplies any two 8-bit numbers, using multiple addition, to generate a 16-bit product:

```
         LDB     A1,#H'FF      ;Load FF into A1 to initialize DC0
         LD      DC0,#0        ;Clear DC0, which will become addition
                               ;counter
         LDB     A0,MPR        ;Load complement of multiplier into A0
         CMPB    A0,#H'FF      ;Test for 0 multiplier
         BZ      ZERO          ;Zero multiplier exit
         XCH     A,DC0         ;Move multiplier to DC0. A0 becomes low-
                               ;order product byte
         CLR     C             ;Clear the Carry status
LOOP     ADDB    A0,MPND       ;Add multiplicand to A0
         BNC     LP1
         INC     A1            ;If Carry is set, increment A1
         CLR     C             ;and clear Carry status
LP1      INC     DC0           ;Increment multiplier complement
         BNZ     LOOP          ;Return if multiplier is not zero
DONE  . . .
```

But there is a faster way of executing multiplication. We can use the fact that a binary digit is limited to having values of 0 or 1; this means that at the single digit level, multiplication degenerates to addition or no addition.

Let us explain this concept. Using common decimal notation, consider the following multiplication:

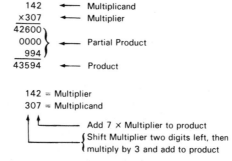

Each partial product equals the multiplicand, multiplied by one digit of the multiplier. The partial product is shifted to the left by tacking on 0s to the right. The number of 0s tacked on to the right is equal to the number of digits to the right of the current multiplier digit:

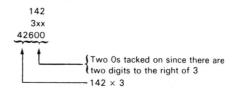

We can extend this concept to binary arithmetic, in which case the problem becomes very simple, since no binary digit can have a value other than 0 or 1. This being the case, you have only two choices: wherever a multiplier digit is 0, you do not add the shifted multiplicand to the answer; but if the multiplier digit is 1 you do add the shifted multiplicand to the answer. Here is an example:

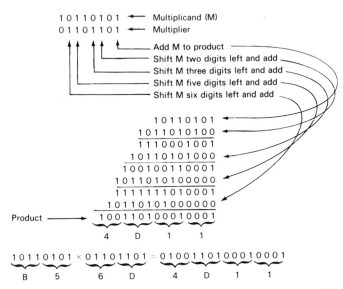

Using a "shift-and-add" technique, the following steps will multiply a one-byte multiplicand by a one-byte multiplier to produce the correct two-byte result:

1) Test the least significant bit of the multiplier. If zero, go to Step 2. If one, add the multiplicand to the most significant byte of the result.
2) Shift the entire two-byte result right one bit position.
3) Repeat Steps 1 and 2 until all 8 bits of the multiplier have been tested.

Consider B5 × 6D, the binary multiplication we just illustrated:

Multiplier = 01101101
Multiplicand = 10110101

			High-order Byte	Low-order Byte
	Start:		00000000	00000000
0 1 1 0 1 1 0 **1**	Step 1 (a)		10110101	00000000
	1 (b)		01011010	10000000
0 1 1 0 1 1 **0** 1	Step 2 (a,b)		00101101	01000000
0 1 1 0 1 **1** 0 1	Step 3 (a)		10110101	
			11100010	01000000
			01110001	00100000
	3 (b)		10110101	
0 1 1 0 **1** 1 0 1	Step 4 (a)	c → 1	00100110	00100000
			10010011	00010000
			01001001	10001000
	4 (b)		10110101	
0 1 1 **0** 1 1 0 1	Step 5 (a,b)		11111110	10001000
0 1 **1** 0 1 1 0 1	Step 6 (a)		01111111	01000100
	6 (b)		10110101	
0 **1** 1 0 1 1 0 1	Step 7 (a)	c → 1	00110100	01000100
			10011010	00100010
	7 (b)		01001101	00010001
0 1 1 0 1 1 0 1	Step 8 (a,b)		4 D	1 1

B-3

We will now write a program using our hypothetical instruction set to implement this multiplication algorithm.

Accumulator A0 will ultimately hold the most significant byte of the result. Accumulator A1 will ultimately hold the least significant byte of the result; initially A1 will hold the multiplier, which will get shifted out of A1 as the product low-order bits are rotated in from A0.

The 16-bit right shift of the result is performed by two rotate-right-through-carry instructions as follows:

Rotate A0:

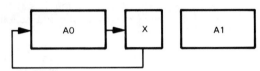

Then rotate A1 to complete the shift:

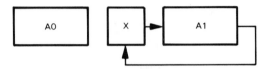

The following is a multiplication program that uses our hypothetical instruction set to implement the multiplication algorithm illustrated above.

We will establish a bit counter in DC2.

Data Counter DC0 will address the memory byte that holds the multiplicand. Here is the problem:

```
MULT    CLRB    A0              ;Clear A0 to initialize product space
        LD      DC2,#H'FFF8     ;Initialize bit counter
        LD      DC1,#0          ;Clear Data Counter DC1
        LDB     A1,MPR          ;Load the multiplier into A1
        LD      DC0,#MCND       ;Load multiplicand address into DC0
        SHLC    A1              ;Shift low-order multiplier bit into Carry
LOOP    BNC     MULT0           ;Bypass partial product addition if Carry = 0
        CLR     C               ;Clear Carry
        ADDCB   A0,@DC0         ;Add multiplicand to low-order product
                                ;byte
MULT0   RORC    A0              ;Right rotate product in A0 and A1
        RORC    A1
        INC     DC2             ;Increment bit counter
        BNZ     LOOP            ;Return for more bits
DONE    . . .
```

Simple 8-Bit Binary Division

We can perform a simple 8-bit binary division using an algorithm which is the logical inverse of the simple 8-bit binary multiplication. In order to divide an unsigned 16-bit dividend by an unsigned 8-bit divisor, we compare the 8-bit divisor with the nine high-order bits of the dividend. If the divisor is larger, then we generate a 0 high-order quotient bit. If the divisor is smaller, we subtract it and generate 1 as the high-order quotient bit. Next we left shift the 16-bit dividend and repeat the process.

Using the inverse of our multiplication example, the division problem may be defined, using hexadecimal digits, as follows:

$$B5 \overline{)\,4D11}^{\,6D}$$

Step by step, the binary division would be executed as follows:

		A0	A1	Quotient
		01001101	00010001	
Step 1a)	B5 > 010011010			0
Step 1b)	Left shift	10011010	00100010	
Step 2a)	134 − B5	1011010	1	
		00111111	10100010	01
Step 2b)	Left shift	01111111	01000100	
Step 3a)	FE − B5	1011010	1	
		00100100	11000100	011
Step 3b)	Left shift	01001001	10001000	
Step 4a)	B5 > 0100010011			0110
Step 4b)	Left shift	10010011	00010000	
Step 5a)	126 − B5	1011010	1	
		00111000	10010000	01101
Step 5b)	Left shift	01110001	00100000	
Step 6a)	E2 − B5	1011010	1	
		00010110	10100000	011011
Step 6b)	Left shift	00101101	01000000	
Step 7a)	B5 > 5A			0110110
Step 7b)	Left shift	01011010	10000000	
Step 8a)	B5 − B5	1011010	1	
		00000000	0	01101101

We have regenerated 6D as our quotient.

Simple Signed Binary Multiplication and Division

The simplest method of handling signed binary multiplication and division is to convert the problem to unsigned binary multiplication and division. Test each argument before performing a multiplication or a division. Take the twos complement of any negative argument. This will allow you to generate a positive result. If one of the two arguments is negative, then the result will be negative and must be converted to its twos complement form. Otherwise, the result will be positive and can be left as is.

Multiplying and Dividing Larger Binary Numbers

The algorithms we have described to multiply or divide 8-bit and 16-bit numbers could be extended to handle larger numbers. But if you attempted to multiply two 32-bit numbers in order to generate a 64-bit product, and you had to handle the operation in byte increments using an 8-bit microprocessor, execution times would most likely become unacceptably long.

There are, however, some simplifications which will speed up the process. These simplifications are described only for an 8-bit microprocessor, since all new 16-bit microprocessors provide multiplication and division instructions; developing program logic is therefore pointless.

Suppose an 8-bit microprocessor has to perform 32-bit by 32-bit multiplications to generate a 64-bit product. If the numbers are represented using four arbitrary hexadecimal digits, the multiplication may be illustrated as follows:

```
                          J        K        L        M
                          P        Q        R        S
        ─────────────────────────────────────────────────
                               (P × M)    0        0        0
                      (P × K)  (Q × M)    0        0
             (P × K)  (Q × L)  (R × M)    0
    (P × J)  (Q × K)  (R × L)  (S × M)
    (Q × J)  (R × K)  (S × L)
    (R × J)  (S × K)
    (S × J)
```

(X × Y) represents the 8-bit product of any two 4-bit values X and Y.

J, K, L, M, P, Q, R, and S represent any hexadecimal digits. We can reorganize the partial products into seven non-overlapping numbers as follows:

```
                    (Q × L) ─────────────────── 1
                    (P × M) ─────────────────── 2          ⎫
           (Q × K)  (R × L) ─────────────────── 3          ⎬ Seven Partial
           (R × J)  (S × K) ─────────────────── 4          ⎮ Products
    (P × K), (R × K)  (R × M) ───────── 5                  ⎭
    (Q × J)  (S × J)  (S × L) ───────── 6
    (P × J)  (P × L)  (Q × M)  (S × M) ── 7
```

Now consider generating a 256-byte lookup table which immediately gives you the 8-bit product of any two 4-bit numbers. This lookup table might be illustrated as follows:

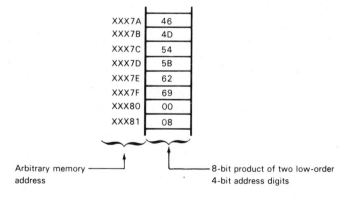

Arbitrary memory address

8-bit product of two low-order 4-bit address digits

The multiplication now degenerates into 16 lookups, which provide sixteen 8-bit numbers that you can concatenate into the seven partial products illustrated above. If partial products lie on even-byte boundaries in memory, in order to generate the final product you will add partial products 1 and 2, then left shift them four bits. Similarly, you will add partial products 5 and 6 and left shift the sum four bits. This may be illustrated as follows:

Let 0XY0 represent $(Q \times L) + (P \times M)$ and let 0 T U V W Z H 0 represent $(P \times K) (R \times K) (R \times M) + (Q \times J) (S \times J) (S \times L)$.

Finally, you need to add five numbers as follows:

		0	X	Y	0	0	0
		(Q × K)	(R × L)	0	0		
		(R × J)	(S × K)	0	0		
0	T	U	V	W	Z	H	0
(P × J)	(P × L)	(Q × M)	(S × M)				

MICROPROCESSOR ASSEMBLY LANGUAGE DRAFT STANDARD*

IEEE Task P694/D11

With the proliferation of microprocessors, the need to establish standards for the naming of microprocessor instruction sets and assemblers has become critical. This standard sets forth a set of instruction mnemonics and descriptions, provides procedures for consistently naming additional instructions, and establishes standard assembler language characteristics.

1. Scope and purpose

1.1 Scope. The intent of this standard is to name a common set of instructions used by most microprocessors, to provide rules for the naming of new instructions and the derivation of new mnemonics, and to establish assembly language conventions.

1.1.1 Limitation of scope. This standard *does not* do the following:

  a) Define programming style.
  b) Define or restrict the number of instructions.
  c) Define or restrict the type of instructions.
  d) Specify or restrict architectures.
  e) Define file media format.

1.2 Purpose. The purpose of this standard is to establish uniform requirements for instruction naming, instruction mnemonics, and assembly language grammar conventions. It is intended to be utilized as a basis for microprocessor assembler design.

1.3 Caution. This standard sets forth the functional definition and operation of typical microprocessor instructions. The repertoire of instructions is different for each microprocessor type. Likewise, the number of condition codes and the setting and resetting of conditions are microprocessor dependent. Each user of a particular microprocessor should be thoroughly familiar with its functional operation and should make no assumptions as to how the instructions are executed.

2. Applicable documents

2.1 Definitions. *IEEE Standard Dictionary of Electrical and Electronic Terms,* IEEE Std. 100-1977.

3. Definitions

3.1 Absolute address. An address value defined at assembly or load time which is not modified during program execution.

3.2 Address. An identification, as represented by a name, label, or number, for a register, location in storage, or any other data source or destination such as the location of a station in a communication network.

3.3 Arithmetic unit. A unit of a computing system that contains the circuits which perform arithmetic and logical operations.

3.4 Assemble. To prepare a machine language program from a symbolic language program by substituting absolute operation codes for symbolic operation codes and absolute or relocatable addresses for symbolic addresses.

3.5 Assembler. A utility program which translates a program written in symbolic assembly language into binary code which is executable by a computer.

3.6 Borrow. A quantity that, during subtraction, is transferred from one number place to the next less significant place (see Carry).

3.7 Carry. A quantity that, during addition, is transferred from one number place to the next more significant place; also, a condition or single bit register within a microprocessor indicating whether a transfer has occurred from the most significant place.

3.8 Complement. The complement of a number is another number in which each zero bit has been replaced by a one and each one bit has been replaced by a zero. This is generally known as one's complement and should not be confused with two's complement.

* © 1979 IEEE. Reprinted, with permission, from Computer (December 1979, pp. 96-109).

3.9 Condition. A state of being. In logic, a proposi-. tion upon which the truth of another proposition depends.

3.10 Effective address. The result of evaluation of an address mode. It is the address of the actual operand of an instruction.

3.11 Indexed addressing. The formation of an effective address by summing the contents of an index register and the address part of an instruction at execution time.

3.12 Indirect addressing. An address mode in which the address part of an instruction refers to a location containing the address of an operand.

3.13 Infix. An operator placed within the body of an expression.

3.14 Language. A set of symbolic representations, with conventions and rules, used to convey information. A system consisting of: (1) a well defined set of characters; (2) rules for combining characters with one another to form words or other expressions; (3) rules for combining words or expressions.

3.15 Link. A single bit register used to join two operands during shift operations.

3.16 LSB. Least significant bit.

3.17 Memory. Any device in which information can be stored. Normally excludes registers.

3.18 MSB. Most significant bit.

3.19 Multifunction instruction. An instruction which performs more than one operation during execution; sometimes known as a microcoded instruction or one composed of microinstructions.

3.20 Operand. Something (a quantity of data) that is operated on; also, the address of data to be operated on.

3.21 Operator. A mathematical or logical symbol denoting an operation to be performed.

3.22 Postfix. An operator appended to the end of an expression.

3.23 Prefix. An operator positioned at the beginning of an expression.

3.24 Register. A device for storing a unit of data which provides facilities for the data to be operated upon.

3.25 Relative addressing. An address mode in which the effective address is derived by adding the address part of an instruction and part or all of the contents of the program counter at execution time.

4. Instruction set

4.1 General. This section describes the functional operation of each standard instruction and provides rules for naming additional instructions. The operation described may be implemented in any microprocessor (independent of word length) with the appropriate conditions. This standard does not necessarily

define the circumstances under which microprocessor conditions are set or cleared, but implies possible usage. The grouping of instructions in this section is arbitrary, and is not intended to imply necessary relationships.

4.1.1 Instruction names. The naming of instructions shall be in accordance with the following rule:

Instruction names shall begin with an action verb.

Examples are: Add with Carry, Rotate Right, Branch if Less Than, And, Return if Zero, Shift Left, Test, etc.

Certain exceptions, the results of common usage, are noted herein.

4.1.2 Instruction mnemonics. The selection of mnemonics for instructions not contained in this standard shall be in accordance with the following rules (exceptions are noted herein):

a) The first character of the mnemonic *shall* be the first letter of the action verb.
b) Addressing modes *shall not* be embedded in the mnemonic.
c) Operand designations *shall not* be embedded in the mnemonic.
d) Conditions *shall* be embedded in the mnemonic.
e) Operand type may be indicated, where appropriate, by the last character of the mnemonic, as shown below (the default operand type is word):

B:	Byte
H:	Halfword
L:	Long (Double Word)
D:	Decimal
F:	Floating Point
1:	Bit
4:	Nibble or Digit
M:	Multiple

4.1.3 Synonymous mnemonics. Depending on the microprocessor architecture, several standard mnemonics may assemble into the same machine instruction. In those cases, all such mnemonics shall be included in the assembly language.

4.1.4 Multifunction instructions. The representation of multifunction instructions shall be by the use of two or more standard mnemonics on the same line, unless a standard mnemonic exists which describes the multifunction instruction, in which case that mnemonic shall be used in the assembly language.

4.2 Conditional instructions. Conditional instruction mnemonics shall be constructed by concatenating the generic instruction name with the condition name. An example would be "Branch if Zero" (BZ), which is formed from an abbreviated Branch (B-) and "if Zero" (-Z). When the opposite condition state is used, then the letter "N" for "Not True" or "No" shall be inserted between the instruction mnemonic and the condition mnemonic to define the false condition as in "Branch if Not Zero" (BNZ).

Conditions are generally utilized with the following instruction types:

a) Branch (B-)
b) Skip (SK-)
c) Call subroutine (CALL-)
d) Return from subroutine (RET-)
e) Increment and Branch (IB-)
f) Increment and Skip (ISK-)
g) Decrement and Branch (DB-)
h) Decrement and Skip (DSK-)

The standard condition mnemonics are defined in this section. The dash character "-" represents the instruction mnemonic letter(s) to be replaced with the generic instruction name. See Sections 4.6 through 4.9 for a listing of conditional instruction names and mnemonics.

4.2.1 Zero (-Z). The instruction is executed if the zero condition is true. Note that this condition may be the same as the Equal condition.

4.2.2 Not Zero (-NZ). The instruction is executed if the zero condition is false. Note that this condition may be the same as the Not Equal condition.

4.2.3 Equal (-E). The instruction is executed if the equal condition is true. Note that this condition may be the same as the Zero condition.

4.2.4 Not Equal (-NE). The instruction is executed if the equal condition is false. Note that the condition may be the same as the Not Zero condition.

4.2.5 Carry (-C). The instruction is executed if the carry condition is true.

4.2.6 No Carry (-NC). The instruction is executed if the carry condition is false.

4.2.7 Positive (-P). The instruction is executed if the positive condition is true.

4.2.8 Negative (-N). The instruction is executed if the negative conditon is true.

4.2.9 Overflow (-V). The instruction is executed if the arithmetic overflow condition is true.

4.2.10 No Overflow (-NV). The instruction is executed if the arithmetic overflow condition is false.

4.2.11 Greater Than (-GT). The instruction is executed if an arithmetic (signed) greater than condition exists. This condition is not equivalent to the Higher condition.

4.2.12 Greater Than or Equal (-GE). The instruction is executed if an arithmetic (signed) greater than or equal condition exists. This condition is not equivalent to the Not Lower condition.

4.2.13 Less Than (-LT). The instruction is executed if an arithmetic (signed) less than condition exists. This condition is not equivalent to the Lower condition.

4.2.14 Less Than or Equal (-LE). The instruction is executed if an arithmetic (signed) less than or equal condition exists. This condition is not equivalent to the Not Higher condition.

4.2.15 Higher (-H). The instruction is executed if an unsigned greater than condition exists. This condition is not equivalent to the Greater Than condition.

4.2.16 Not Higher (-NH). The instruction is executed if an unsigned less than or equal condition exists. This condition is not equivalent to the Less Than or Equal condition.

4.2.17 Lower (-L). The instruction is executed if an unsigned less than condition exists. This condition is not equivalent to the Less Than condition.

4.2.18 Not Lower (-NL). The instruction is executed if an unsigned greater than or equal condition exists. This condition is not equivalent to the Greater Than or Equal condition.

4.2.19 Parity Even (-PE). The instruction is executed if the even parity condition exists. This condition is the negation of Parity Odd.

4.2.20 Parity Odd (-PO). The instruction is executed if the odd parity condition exists. This condition is the negation of Parity Even.

4.3 Arithmetic instructions.

4.3.1 Add (ADD). This instruction performs an addition.

4.3.2 Add With Carry (ADDC). This instruction performs an addition and adds any previous carry to the result.

4.3.3 Subtract (SUB). This instruction performs a subtraction. (See 5.1.3 for operand order.)

4.3.4 Subtract Reverse (SUBR). This instruction performs a subtraction in reverse order. (See 5.1.3 for operand order.)

4.3.5 Subtract With Carry//Borrow (SUBC). This instruction performs a subtraction and incorporates a previous borrow into the result. The borrow may or may not be related to the carry.

4.3.6 Increment (INC). This instruction causes a one to be added to the specified operand.

4.3.7 Decrement (DEC). This instruction causes a one to be subtracted from the specified operand.

4.3.8 Multiply (MUL). This instruction performs a multiplication.

4.3.9 Divide (DIV). This instruction performs a division.

4.3.10 Compare (CMP). This instruction performs a comparison and sets the appropriate condition(s) according to the results.

4.3.11 Negate (NEG). This instruction causes the specified operand to be replaced with its arithmetic negative (two's complement).

4.3.12 Extend (EXT). This instruction extends an operand to fill a specified larger field.

4.4 Logical instructions.

4.4.1 And (AND). This instruction performs a logical "AND."

4.4.2 Or (OR). This instruction performs a logical "OR."

4.4.3 Exclusive Or (XOR). This instruction performs a logical "Exclusive OR." Note that this instruction mnemonic violates the mnemonic naming rule, but is retained in deference to common usage.

4.4.4 Not (NOT). This instruction causes the specified operand to be replaced with its one's complement (logical not).

4.4.5 Not Carry (NOTC). This instruction causes the carry condition to be complemented.

4.4.6 Shift Right (SHR). This instruction causes the specified operand to be shifted one or more places to the right (toward the LSB), with the most significant bit(s) being replaced with zero(s).

4.4.7 Shift Left (SHL). This instruction causes the specified operand to be shifted one or more places to the left (toward the MSB), with the least significant bit(s) being replaced with zero(s).

4.4.8 Shift Right Arithmetic (SHRA). This instruction causes the specified operand to be shifted one or more places to the right with the most significant bit (sign) being preserved and propagated to the right.

4.4.9 Rotate Right (ROR). This instruction causes the specified operand to be shifted one or more places to the right, with the MSB being replaced by the LSB on each shift.

4.4.10 Rotate Left (ROL). This instruction causes the specified operand to be shifted one or more places to the left, with the LSB being replaced by the MSB on each shift.

4.4.11 Rotate Right Through Carry/Link (RORC). This instruction causes the specified operand to be shifted one or more places to the right with the previous state of the link being loaded into the MSB, and the LSB being loaded into the link. Note that the link may be associated with the carry flag.

4.4.12 Rotate Left Through Carry/Link (ROLC). This instruction causes the specified operand to be shifted one or more places to the left with the previous state of the link being loaded into the LSB, and the MSB being loaded into the link.

4.4.13 Test (TEST). This instruction causes the specified operand to be tested and sets the appropriate condition(s) according to the result.

4.5 Data transfer instructions.

4.5.1 Load (LD). This instruction causes the contents of a memory location specified as the source to be transferred to a register specified as the destination.

4.5.2 Store (ST). This instruction causes the contents of a register specified as the source to be transferred to a memory location specified as the destination.

4.5.3 Move (MOV). This instruction causes the contents of a register to be transferred to another register, or the contents of a memory location to be transferred to another memory location.

4.5.4 Move Block (MOVBK). This instruction causes the transfer of a block of data.

4.5.5 Move Multiple (MOVM). This instruction causes the contents of a memory location to be copied into multiple memory locations.

4.5.6 Exchange (XCH). This instruction causes the specified operands to be exchanged.

4.5.7 Input (IN). This instruction causes the data at an input port to be transferred to a register or memory location.

4.5.8 Output (OUT). This instruction causes the contents of a register or a memory location to be transferred to an output port.

4.5.9 Clear (CLR). This instruction causes the specified operand to be replaced by zero(s).

4.5.10 Clear Carry (CLRC). This instruction causes the carry to be set to the not true or no carry state.

4.5.11 Clear Overflow (CLRV). This instruction causes the overflow to be set to the not true or no overflow state.

4.5.12 Set (SET). This instruction causes the specified operand to be replaced by one(s).

4.5.13 Set Carry (SETC). This instruction causes the carry to be set to the true or carry state.

4.5.14 Set Overflow (SETV). This instruction causes the overflow to be set to the true or overflow state.

4.6 Branch instructions.

4.6.1 Branch (BR). This instruction causes the contents of the program counter to be replaced by the effective address, thereby transferring control to the memory location specified by that address.

Note: The condition(s) for execution of the following instructions are described in Section 4.2. For brevity, only the instruction titles and mnemonics of the branch instructions are given here.

4.6.2 Branch if Zero (BZ).

4.6.3 Branch if Not Zero (BNZ).

4.6.4 Branch if Equal (BE).

4.6.5 Branch if Not Equal (BNE).

4.6.6 Branch if Carry (BC).

4.6.7 Branch if No Carry (BNC).

4.6.8 Branch if Positive (BP).

4.6.9 Branch if Negative (BN).

4.6.10 Branch if Overflow (BV).

4.6.11 Branch if No Overflow (BNV).

4.6.12 Branch if Greater Than (BGT).

4.6.13 Branch if Greater Than or Equal (BGE).

4.6.14 Branch if Less Than (BLT).

4.6.15 Branch if Less Than or Equal (BLE).

4.6.16 Branch if Higher (BH).

4.6.17 Branch if Not Higher (BNH).

4.6.18 Branch if Lower (BL).

4.6.19 *Branch if Not Lower (BNL)*.

4.6.20 *Branch if Parity Even (BPE)*.

4.6.21 *Branch if Parity Odd (BPO)*.

4.7 Skip instructions.

4.7.1 Skip (SKIP). This instruction causes the program counter to be incremented such that the execution of the next instruction(s) is skipped.

Note: The condition(s) for execution of the following instructions are described in Section 4.2. For brevity, only the instruction titles and mnemonics of the skip instructions are given here.

4.7.2 *Skip if Zero (SKZ)*.

4.7.3 *Skip if Not Zero (SKNZ)*.

4.7.4 *Skip if Equal (SKE)*.

4.7.5 *Skip if Not Equal (SKNE)*.

4.7.6 *Skip if Carry (SKC)*.

4.7.7 *Skip if No Carry (SKNC)*.

4.7.8 *Skip if Positive (SKP)*.

4.7.9 *Skip if Negative (SKN)*.

4.7.10 *Skip if Overflow (SKV)*.

4.7.11 *Skip if No Overflow (SKNV)*.

4.7.12 *Skip if Greater Than (SKGT)*.

4.7.13 *Skip if Greater Than or Equal (SKGE)*.

4.7.14 *Skip if Less Than (SKLT)*.

4.7.15 *Skip if Less Than or Equal (SKLE)*.

4.7.16 *Skip if Higher (SKH)*.

4.7.17 *Skip if Not Higher (SKNH)*.

4.7.18 *Skip if Lower (SKL)*.

4.7.19 *Skip if Not Lower (SKNL)*.

4.7.20 *Skip if Parity Even (SKPE)*.

4.7.21 *Skip if Parity Odd (SKPO)*.

4.8 Subroutine call instructions.

4.8.1 Call Subroutine (CALL). This instruction causes the program counter to be saved and replaced by the specified operand, thereby transferring control to the memory location specified by the operand.

Note: The condition(s) for execution of the following instructions are described in Section 4.2. For brevity, only the instruction titles and mnemonics of the call instructions are given here.

4.8.2 *Call if Zero (CALLZ)*.

4.8.3 *Call if Not Zero (CALLNZ)*.

4.8.4 *Call if Equal (CALLE)*.

4.8.5 *Call if Not Equal (CALLNE)*.

4.8.6 *Call if Carry (CALLC)*.

4.8.7 *Call if No Carry (CALLNC)*.

4.8.8 *Call if Positive (CALLP)*.

4.8.9 *Call if Negative (CALLN)*.

4.8.10 *Call if Overflow (CALLV)*.

4.8.11 *Call if No Overflow (CALLNV)*.

4.8.12 *Call if Greater Than (CALLGT)*.

4.8.13 *Call if Greater Than or Equal (CALLGE)*.

4.8.14 *Call if Less Than (CALLLT)*.

4.8.15 *Call if Less Than or Equal (CALLLE)*.

4.8.16 *Call if Higher (CALLH)*.

4.8.17 *Call if Not Higher (CALLNH)*.

4.8.18 *Call if Lower (CALLL)*.

4.8.19 *Call if Not Lower (CALLNL)*.

4.8.20 *Call if Parity Even (CALLPE)*.

4.8.21 *Call if Parity Odd (CALLPO)*.

4.9 Return instructions.

4.9.1 Return From Subroutine (RET). This instruction causes the previously saved contents of the program counter to be restored, thereby returning control to the routine that called the subroutine or was interrupted.

Note: The condition(s) for execution of the following instructions are described in Section 4.2. For brevity, only the instruction titles and mnemonics are given for the conditional instructions.

4.9.2 *Return if Zero (RETZ)*.

4.9.3 *Return if Not Zero (RETNZ)*.

4.9.4 *Return if Equal (RETE)*.

4.9.5 *Return if Not Equal (RETNE)*.

4.9.6 *Return if Carry (RETC)*.

4.9.7 *Return if No Carry (RETNC)*.

4.9.8 *Return if Positive (RETP)*.

4.9.9 *Return if Negative (RETN)*.

4.9.10 *Return if Overflow (RETV)*.

4.9.11 *Return if No Overflow (RETNV)*.

4.9.12 *Return if Greater Than (RETGT)*.

4.9.13 *Return if Greater Than or Equal (RETGE)*.

4.9.14 *Return if Less Than (RETLT)*.

4.9.15 *Return if Less Than or Equal (RETLE)*.

4.9.16 *Return if Higher (RETH)*.

4.9.17 *Return if Not Higher (RETNH)*.

4.9.18 *Return if Lower (RETL)*.

4.9.19 *Return if Not Lower (RETNL)*.

4.9.20 *Return if Parity Even (RETPE)*.

4.9.21 *Return if Parity Odd (RETPO)*.

4.9.22 Return With Skip (RETSK). This instruction causes the previously saved contents of the program counter to be incremented some amount and restored, thereby returning control to the routine that called the subroutine at some point after the subroutine call.

4.9.23 Return From Interrupt (RETI). This instruction returns control to the routine that was interrupted.

4.10 Miscellaneous instructions.

4.10.1 No Operation (NOP). This instruction causes the processor to take no action other than to advance to the next instruction. This instruction's name violates the naming rules, but is kept in deference to common usage.

4.10.2 Push (PUSH). This instruction causes the contents of the specified operand(s) to be transferred to the top of a stack.

4.10.3 Pop (POP). This instruction causes the contents of the top of a stack to be transferred to the designated operand(s).

4.10.4 Halt (HALT). This instruction causes the microprocessor to stop executing instructions until an external condition occurs.

4.10.5 Wait (WAIT). This instruction causes the microprocessor to stop executing instructions until an external or internal condition occurs or changes.

4.10.6 Break (BRK). This instruction causes an interrupt sequence to be initiated by the microprocessor.

4.10.7 Adjust (ADJ). This instruction makes an adjustment such that the operand or implied accumulator contents will represent the correct result, usually a binary-coded-decimal representation.

4.10.8 Enable Interrupt (EI). This instruction causes the designated interrupt(s) to be enabled.

4.10.9 Disable Interrupt (DI). This instruction causes the designated interrupt(s) to be disabled.

4.10.10 Translate (TR). This instruction references a specified table to replace an operand with value(s) selected from the table on the basis of the value of that operand.

5. Operands and syntax

5.1 Sequence of multiple operands. The terms "primary" and "secondary" are used in the specification of operand sequence. In the specification of operand sequence the primary operand shall be first, followed by one or more secondary operands in decreasing order of importance.

5.1.1 Move operands. The source of data is defined to be the primary operand. The operand sequence shall be: source, destination.

5.1.2 Load and store operands. The register being loaded or stored is defined as the primary operand. The operand sequence shall be: register, memory.

5.1.3 Arithmetic operands. In two operand instructions, the operand that is both the source and destination is the primary operand, and the second source is the secondary operand. In three operand instructions, the result is defined to be primary; therefore the destination shall be the first operand, followed by the "first" source, then the "second" source. As examples:

1) For a two operand case, SUB A, B means "subtract B from A and place result in A", $(A \leftarrow A - B)$.
2) For a three operand case, SUB A, B, C means "subtract C from B and place result in A", $(A \leftarrow B - C)$.

5.2 Operand specification. All operands are designated by either a number or a symbolic representation of that number. This is normal practice in the case of memory operands and is extended here to register operands. When multiple registers are addressable, they shall be assigned numbers consistent with the architecture of the hardware. This does not preclude the use of standard symbolic names for the registers supplied by an assembler. Numbers or user-defined names are also allowed.

5.3 Addressing modes. Addressing modes in microprocessors with more than one addressing mode shall be specified by special character(s). The special character(s) shall precede the address expression except where pre or post specification implies an operational sequence. Note that the address expression (addr) may refer to either a memory location or register. The following prefix and postfix characters shall be used to define the specified address modes:

Mode	Symbol	Example
Absolute	prefix /	/addr
Base page	prefix !	!addr
Indirect	prefix @	@addr
Relative	prefix $	$addr
Immediate	prefix #	#value
Index	enclosing parenthesis ( )	addr(index)
Register	prefix .	.addr
Auto-pre-increment	prefix +	+addr
Auto-post-increment	postfix +	addr+
Auto-pre-decrement	prefix −	−addr
Auto-post-decrement	postfix −	addr−
Indirect-pre-indexed	prefix ( ) @	addr(index)@
Indirect-post-indexed	prefix @, postfix ( )	@addr(index)

Assemblers may have the option of coercing the addressing mode for instructions that have only one addressing mode. As an example, a branch instruction which allows only relative addressing may be coded without the "$" character preceding the address designation in the operand field. Such coercion should be flagged in the assembly listing.

For microprocessors that have several address modes for a particular instruction, the assembler may select the address mode if the programmer does not specify it. The means used to indicate which address mode was selected shall be specified. The default address mode should be relative.

5.4 Expressions. An assembler should allow the use of expressions which are evaluated at assembly time.

When expression evaluation capabilities are included in the assembler, those expressions operators that are implemented shall be designated by the following infix special symbols:

Symbol(s)	Operation
+	Add
−	Subtract
•	Multiply
/	Divide (Signed)
/ /	Divide (Unsigned)
.AND.	AND
.OR.	OR
.XOR.	Exclusive OR
.NOT.	NOT
.SHL.	Left Shift
.SHR.	Right Shift
.MOD.	Modulo
••	Exponentiate
<:>	Bit Alignment

A bit alignment example: the expression A<p:q> means align bits p through q inclusive of A. Hierarchy is not specified. Parenthesis may be used to group expressions.

5.5 Constants. All numeric constants shall be representable in the base specified and shall be preceded by an alphabetic character specifying the base and an apostrophe. The following characters are reserved for the specified base:

B Binary
Q Octal
D Decimal
H Hexadecimal

Examples of numeric constants are:

B' 1001111
Q' 117
D' 79
H' 4F

An assembler should have a default option whereby one number base may be specified without the base character and apostrophe. In such cases, the default number base shall be decimal. Change of current number base shall be via the "BASE" Assembler directive.

5.5.1 Character strings. Character strings shall be enclosed with quotation marks. Two examples of character strings are:

"THIS IS A STANDARD"

"NO. TITLE PAGE"

Two consecutive quotation marks shall be used to include a quotation mark within a character string.

5.6 Location counter reference. The special symbol * shall be used to refer to the address of the first memory location of the instruction in which the symbol is used. For example:

BR *

branches to itself in an infinite loop.

6. Comments and labels

6.1 Comments. Comments may be placed after a statement on the same line, or on a separate line. Each comment shall start with a semicolon ";". Two examples are:

; THIS IS A COMMENT
    BZ NEXT ; COMMENT ON LINE

6.2 Labels. All labels shall begin with an alphabetic character in the first position of a line. At least one blank shall separate the rest of the line from the label. Instruction mnemonics and assembler directives shall not start in the first position of a line. Labels may be terminated by a colon ":" but the colon shall not be required.

7. Assembler directives

7.1 General. Assembler directives are commands to the assembler instead of instructions for the microprocessor. They direct the assembler to perform specific tasks during the assembly process.

This standard does not specify the syntax necessary to support macros or conditional assembly.

Naming of assembler directives and of assembler directive mnemonics shall follow the rules used for instructions. If the following functions are implemented, the specified mnemonic shall be used.

7.2 Originate (ORG). This assembler directive sets the current location counter to the value specified by the operand. The assembler shall initialize all location counters to zero at the beginning of the program.

7.3 Equate (EQU). This assembler directive equates a symbol to a constant, an address, or an expression.

7.4 End (END). This assembler directive informs the assembler that the end of source has been reached.

7.5 Page (PAGE). This assembler directive causes the assembler to advance the assembly listing to the top of the next page.

7.6 Title (TITLE). This assembler directive causes the assembler to advance the assembly listing to the next page and to insert the specified title into the header of that and each of the following pages.

7.7 Data (DATA). This assembler directive causes the assembler to fill the next memory location(s) with the specified value(s). A letter may be appended to the mnemonic as specified in section 4.1.2(e) to indicate data type.

7.8 Reserve memory (RES). This assembler directive reserves a block of storage locations. The number of locations reserved is specified by a constant or an expression. The content of the reserved storage location(s) may be unspecified.

7.9 Base (BASE). This assembler directive causes the assembler to change the current implied number base. See Section 5.5 for number base specification. ■

INSTRUCTION	STANDARD MNEMONIC	INTEL MNEMONIC

ARITHMETIC

	STANDARD MNEMONIC	INTEL MNEMONIC
Add	ADD	ADD
Add with Carry	ADDC	ADC
Subtract	SUB	SUB
Subtract with Carry	SUBC	SBB
Increment	INC	INC
Decrement	DEC	DEC
Negate	NEG	NEG
Multiply	MUL	IMUL
Multiply, Unsigned	MULU	MUL
Divide	DIV	IDIV
Divide, Unsigned	DIVU	DIV
Compare	CMP	CMPW
Compare, Byte	CMPB	CMPB
Compare Block	CMPBK	SCAW
Compare Block, Byte	CMPBKB	SCAB
Extend	EXT	CBW
Extend, Long	EXTL	CWD

LOGICAL

	STANDARD MNEMONIC	INTEL MNEMONIC
And	AND	AND
Or	OR	OR
Exclusive Or	XOR	XOR
Not	NOT	NOT
Shift Right	SHR	SHR
Shift Left	SHL	SHL, SAL
Shift Right Arithmetic	SHRA	SAR
Rotate Right	ROR	ROR
Rotate Left	ROL	ROL
Rotate Right Through Carry	RORC	RCR
Rotate Left Through Carry	ROLC	RCL
Test	TEST	TEST
Not Carry	NOTC	CMC

DATA TRANSFER

	STANDARD MNEMONIC	INTEL MNEMONIC
Load	LD	MOV, LEA, LES, LODS, LODW
Load, Byte	LDB	LODB
Store	ST	MOV
Store, Byte	STB	STOB
Move	MOV	MOV, LAHF
Move, Byte	MOVB	MOVB
Exchange	XCH	XHCG
In	IN	INW
In, Byte	INB	IN
Out	OUT	OUTW
Out, Byte	OUTB	OUT
Clear Carry	CLRC	CLC
Set Carry	SETC	STC
Clear Direction	CLRD	CLD
Set Direction	SETD	STD
Break	BRK	INT
Break on Overflow	BRKV	INTO
Escape	ESC	ESC
Lock	LOCK	LOCK

BRANCH

	STANDARD MNEMONIC	INTEL MNEMONIC
Branch	BR	JMP
Branch if Zero/Equal	BZ,BE	JZ,JE
Branch if Not Zero/Not Equal	BNZ,BNE	JNZ,JNE
Branch if Positive	BP	JS
Branch if Negative	BN	JNS
Branch if Overflow	BV	JNO
Branch if No Overflow	BNV	JNO
Branch if Greater Than	BGT	JNLE/JG
Branch if Greater Than or Equal	BGE	JNL/JGE
Branch if Less Than	BLT	JL/JNGE
Branch if Less Than or Equal	BLE	JLE/JNG
Branch if Higher	BH	JNBE/JA
Branch if Not Higher	BNH	JBE/JNA
Branch if Lower	BL	JB/JNAE
Branch if Not Lower	BNL	JNB/JAE
Branch if Parity Even	BPE	JNP/JPE
Branch if Parity Odd	BPO	JNP/JPO
Branch if CX Zero	BCXZ	JCXZ
Decrement and Branch if Not Zero	DBNZ	LOOP
Decrement and Branch if Not Zero and Equal	DBNZE	LOOPZ/ LOOPE
Decrement and Branch if Not Zero and Not Equal	DBNZNE	LOOPNZ/ LOOPNE

SUBROUTINE CALL

	STANDARD MNEMONIC	INTEL MNEMONIC
Call	CALL	CALL

RETURN

	STANDARD MNEMONIC	INTEL MNEMONIC
Return	RET	RET
Return from Interrupt	RETI	IRET

MISCELLANEOUS

	STANDARD MNEMONIC	INTEL MNEMONIC
Halt	HALT	HLT
Wait	WAIT	WAIT
Enable Interrupt	EI	STI
Disable Interrupt	DI	CLI
Adjust Nibble Subtract	ADJ4S	DAS
Adjust Nibble Add	ADJ4A	DAA
Adjust Byte Subtract	ADJBS	AAS
Adjust Byte Add	ADJBA	AAA
Convert Binary to Decimal	CVTBD	AAM
Convert Decimal to Binary	CVTDB	AAD
Push	PUSH	PUSH, PUSHF
Pop	POP	POP, POPF
Repeat	REP	REP
Translate	TR	XLAT

INSTRUCTION	STANDARD MNEMONIC	MOTOROLA MNEMONIC
ARITHMETIC		
Add	ADD	ADD, ABA
Add with Carry	ADDC	ADC
Subtract	SUB	SUB, SBA
Subtract with Carry	SUBC	SBC
Increment	INC	INC, INS, INX
Decrement	DEC	DEC, DES, DEX
Compare	CMP	CMP, CBA, CPX
Negate	NEG	NEG
LOGICAL		
And	AND	AND
Or	OR	ORA
Exclusive Or	XOR	EOR
Not	NOT	COM
Shift Right	SHR	LSR
Shift Left	SHL	ASL
Shift Right Arithmetic	SHRA	ASR
Rotate Right	ROR	ROR
Rotate Left	ROL	ROL
Test	TEST	BIT, TST
DATA TRANSFER		
Load	LD	LDA, LDS, LDX
Store	ST	STA, STS, STX
Move	MOV	TAB, TBA, TAP, TPA, TSX, TXS
Clear	CLR	CLR
Clear Carry	CLRC	CLC
Clear Overflow	CLRV	CLV
Set Carry	SETC	SEC
Set Overflow	SETV	SEV

	STANDARD	MOTOROLA
BRANCH		
Branch	BR	BRA, JMP
Branch if Zero	BZ	BEQ
Branch if Not Zero	BNZ	BNE
Branch if Equal	BE	BEQ
Branch if Not Equal	BNE	BNE
Branch if Carry	BC	BCS
Branch if No Carry	BNC	BCC
Branch if Positive	BP	BPL
Branch if Negative	BN	BMI
Branch if Overflow	BV	BVS
Branch if No Overflow	BNV	BVC
Branch if Greater Than	BGT	BGT
Branch if Greater Than or Equal	BGE	BGE
Branch if Less Than	BLT	BLT
Branch if Less Than or Equal	BLE	BLE
Branch if Higher	BH	BHI
Branch if Not Higher	BNH	BLS
Branch if Lower	BL	BCS
Branch if Not Lower	BNL	BCC
SUBROUTINE CALL		
Call Subroutine	CALL	BSR, JSR
RETURN		
Return from Subroutine	RET	RTS
Return from Interrupt	RETI	RTI
MISCELLANEOUS		
No Operation	NOP	NOP
Push	PUSH	PSH
Pop	POP	PUL
Wait	WAIT	WAI
Adjust Decimal	ADJ	DAA
Enable Interrupt	EI	SEI
Disable Interrupt	DI	CLI
Break	BRK	SWI

Appendix C.
Standard instruction mnemonics for Z80, 8080, and 8085.

INSTRUCTION	STANDARD MNEMONIC	ZILOG MNEMONIC	INTEL MNEMONIC
ARITHMETIC			
Add	ADD	ADD	ADD,ADI, DAD
Add with Carry	ADDC	ADC	ADC,ACI
Subtract	SUB	SUB	SUB,SUI
Subtract with Carry	SUBC	SBC	SBB,SBI
Increment	INC	INC	INX,INR
Decrement	DEC	DEC	DCX,DCR
Compare	CMP	CP,CPI,CPD	CMP,CPI
Compare, Multiple	CMPM	CPIR, CPDR	—
Negate	NEG	NEG	—
LOGICAL			
And	AND	AND	ANA,ANI
Or	OR	OR	ORA,ORI
Exclusive Or	XOR	XOR	XRA,XRI
Not	NOT	CPL	CMA
Not Carry	NOTC	CCF	CMC
Shift Right	SHR	SRL	—
Shift Left	SHL	SLA	ADD,DAD
Shift Right Arithmetic	SHRA	SRA	—
Rotate Right	ROR	RRCA,RRC	RAR
Rotate Left	ROL	RLCA,RLC	RAL
Rotate Right Through Carry	RORC	RR,RRA	RRC
Rotate Left Through Carry	ROLC	RL,RLA	RLC
Rotate Right Decimal	ROR4	RLD	—
Rotate Left Decimal	ROL4	RLD	—
Test Bit	TEST1	BIT	—
DATA TRANSFER			
Load	LD	LD	MOV,LXI, LDAX, LHLD, LDA,MVI
Store	ST	LD	MOV,STAX, SHLD, STA
Move	MOV	LD,LDI,LDD	MOV,MVI, SPHL
Move Block	MOVBK	LDIR,LDDR	—
Exchange	XCH	EX,EXX	XCHG, XTHL
Input	IN	IN,INI,IND	IN,RIM
Input Block	INBK	INIR,INDR	—
Output	OUT	OUT,OUTI, OUTD	OUT,SIM
Output Block	OUTBK	OTIR,OTDR	—
Set Bit	SET1	DET	—
Clear Bit	CLR1	RES	—
Set Carry	SETC	SCF	STC
Set Interrupt Mode	SETI	IM	—

INSTRUCTION	STANDARD MNEMONIC	ZILOG MNEMONIC	INTEL MNEMONIC
BRANCH			
Branch	BR	JP	JMP,PCHL
Branch if Zero	BZ	JP Z, JR Z	JZ
Branch if Not Zero	BNZ	JP NZ, JR NZ	JNZ
Branch if Equal	BE	JP Z, JR Z	JZ
Branch if Not Equal	BNE	JP NZ, JR NZ	JNZ
Branch if Carry	BC	JP C, JR C	—
Branch if No Carry	BNC	JP NC, JR NC	JNC
Branch if Positive	BP	JP P	JP
Branch if Negative	BN	JP M	JM
Branch if Parity Even	BPE	JP PE	JPE
Branch if Parity Odd	BPO	JP PO	JPO
Branch if Low	BL	JP C	JC
Branch if Not Low	BNL	JP NC	JNC
Decrement and Branch if Not Zero	DBNZ	DJNZ	—
CALL			
Call	CALL	CALL,RST	CALL,RST
Call if Zero	CALLZ	CALL Z	CZ
Call if Not Zero	CALLNZ	CALL NZ	CNZ
Call if Equal	CALLE	CALL Z	CZ
Call if Not Equal	CALLNE	CALL NZ	CNZ
Call if Carry	CALLC	CALL N	CC
Call if No Carry	CALLNC	CALL NC	CNC
Call if Positive	CALLP	CALL P	CP
Call if Negative	CALLN	CALL M	CM
Call if Parity Even	CALLPE	CALL PE	CPE
Call if Parity Odd	CALLPO	CALL PO	CPO
Call if Low	CALLL	CALL C	CC
Call if Not Low	CALLNL	CALL NC	CNC
RETURN			
Return	RET	RET	RET
Return if Zero	RETZ	RET Z	RZ
Return if Not Zero	RETNZ	RET NZ	RNZ
Return if Equal	RETE	RET Z	RZ
Return if Not Equal	RETNE	RET NZ	RNZ
Return if Carry	RETC	RET C	RC
Return if No Carry	RETNC	RET NC	RNC
Return if Positive	RETP	RET P	RP
Return if Negative	RETN	RET M	RM
Return if Parity Even	RETPE	RET PE	RPE
Return if Parity Odd	RETPO	RET PO	RPO
Return if Lower	RETL	RET C	RC
Return if Not Lower	RETNL	RET NC	RNC
Return from Interrupt	RETI	RETI	—
Return from Interrupt Non-Maskable	RETIN	RETN	—
MISCELLANEOUS			
No operation	NOP	NOP	NOP
Push	PUSH	PUSH	PUSH
Pop	POP	POP	POP
Wait	WAIT	HALT	HLT
Adjust Demimal	ADJ	DAA	DAA
Enable Interrupt	EI	EI	EI
Disable Interrupt	DI	DI	DI

Preliminary—Subject to Revision

INSTRUCTION	STANDARD MNEMONIC	DEC MNEMONIC
ARITHMETIC		
Add	ADD	ADD
Add with Carry	ADDC	ADC
Add Float	ADDF	FADD
Subtract	SUB	SUB
Subtract with Carry	SUBC	SBC
Subtract Float	SUBF	FSUB
Multiply	MUL	MUL
Multiply Float	MULF	FMUL
Divide	DIV	DIV
Divide Float	DIVF	FDIV
Increment	INC	INC
Decrement	DEC	DEC
Compare	CMP	CMP
Negate	NEG	NEG
LOGICAL		
Exclusive Or	XOR	XOR
Shift Right	SHR	ASR
Shift Left	SHL	ASL
Rotate Right	ROR	ROR
Rotate Left	ROL	ROL
Test Arithmetic	TESTA	TEST
Not	NOT	COM
Shift Arithmetic Long	SHAL	ASHC
Test Bit	TEST1	BIT
Or	OR	BIS
And of Not	ANDNOT	BIC
DATA TRANSFER		
Load (PSW)	LD	MTPS
Store (PSW)	ST	MFPS
Move	MOV	MOV
Exchange	XCHB	SWAB
Clear	CLR	CLR
Clear Carry	CLRC	CLC
Clear Overflow	CLRV	CLV
Clear Zero	CLRZ	CLZ
Clear Negative	CLRN	CLN
Set	SET	SET
Set Carry	SETC	SEC
Set Overflow	SETV	SEV
Set Zero	SETZ	SEZ
Set Negative	SETN	SEN
Set All Condition Codes	SETCC	SCC

	STANDARD MNEMONIC	DEC MNEMONIC
BRANCH		
Branch	BR	BR
Branch if Zero	BZ	BEQ
Branch if Not Zero	BNZ	BNE
Branch if Equal	BE	BEQ
Branch if Not Equal	BNE	BNE
Branch if Carry	BC	BCS
Branch if No Carry	BNC	BCC
Branch if Positive	BP	BPL
Branch if Negative	BN	BMI
Branch if Overflow	BV	BVS
Branch if No Overflow	BNV	BVC
Branch if Greater Than	BGT	BGT
Branch if Greater Than or Equal	BGE	BGE
Branch if Less Than	BLT	BLT
Branch if Less Than or Equal	BLE	BLE
Branch if Higher	BH	BHI
Branch if Not Higher	BNH	BLOS
Branch if Lower	BL	BLO
Branch if Not Lower	BNL	BHIS
Branch Long	BRL	JMP
Decrement and Branch Not Zero	DBNZ	SOB
CALL		
Call	CALL	JSR
RETURN		
Return	RET	RTS
Return from Interrupt	RETI	RTI
Return from Trap	RETT	RTT
Return with Skip	RETSK	MARK
MISCELLANEOUS		
No Operation	NOP	NOP
Break	BRK	TRAP
Break Emulator	BRKE	EMT
Breakpoint Trap	BRKT	BPT
Break I/O	BRKI	IOT
Wait	WAIT	WAIT
Halt	HALT	HALT

Preliminary—Subject to Revision

INSTRUCTION	STANDARD MNEMONIC	MOTOROLA MNEMONIC
ARITHMETIC		
Add	ADD	ADD,ADDA, ADDQ,ADDI
Add Decimal	ADDD	ABCD
Add with Carry/Borrow	ADDC	ADDX
Subtract	SUB	SUB,SUBA, SUBI, SUBQ
Subtract Decimal	SUBD	SBCD
Subtract with Carry/Borrow	SUBC	SUBX
Multiply, Unsigned	MULU	MULU
Multiply	MUL	MULS
Divide, Unsigned	DIVU	DIVU
Divide	DIV	DIVS
Compare	CMP	CMP,CMPA, CMPI, CMPM
Negate	NEG	NEG
Negate with Carry/Borrow	NEGC	NEGX
Negate, Decimal	NEGD	NBCD
Extend Sign	EXT	EXT
Decrement and Branch, Always	DBR	DBRA,DBF
Decrement and Branch if Equal	DBE	DBEQ
Decrement and Branch if not Equal	DBNE	DBNE
Decrement and Branch if Carry	DBC	DBCS
Decrement and Branch if no Carry	DBNC	DBCC
Decrement and Branch if Positive	DBP	DBPL
Decrement and Branch if Negative	DBN	DBMI
Decrement and Branch if Overflow	DBV	DVBS
Decrement and Branch if no Overflow	DBNV	DBVC
Decrement and Branch if Greater Than	DBGT	DBGT
Decrement and Branch if Greater Than or Equal	DBGE	DBGE
Decrement and Branch if Less Than	DBLT	DBLT
Decrement and Branch if Less Than or Equal	DBLE	DBLE
Decrement and Branch if Higher	DBH	DBHI
Decrement and Branch if not Higher	DBNH	DBLS
LOGICAL		
And	AND	AND,ANDI
Or	OR	OR,ORI
Exclusive Or	XOR	EOR,EORI
Not	NOT	NOT
Shift Right	SHR	LSR
Shift Left	SHL	LSL
Shift Right Arithmetic	SHRA	ASR
Shift Left Arithmetic	SHLA	ASL
Rotate Right	ROR	ROR
Rotate Left	ROL	ROL
Rotate Right Through Link	RORC	ROXR
Rotate Left Through Link	ROLC	ROXL
Test	TEST	TST
Test Bit	TEST1	BTST
Test and Set	TESTSET	BSET
Test and Clear	TESTCLR	BCLR
Test and Not	TESTNOT	BCHG
Check	CHK	CHK

DATA TRANSFER		
Load	LD	LEA,MOVE, MOVEA, MOVEP, MOVEQ
Load, Multiple	LDM	MOVEM
Store	ST	MOVE,MOVEP
Store, Multiple	STM	MOVEM
Move	MOV	MOVE, MOVEM, MOVEP, MOVEA, MOVEQ
Exchange	XCH	EXG,SWAP
Clear	CLR	CLR
Set	SET	ST
Set if Equal	SETE	SEQ
Set if Not Equal	SETNE	SNE
Set if Carry	SETC	SCS
Set if No Carry	SETNC	SCC
Set if Positive	SETP	SPL
Set if Negative	SETN	SMI
Set if Overflow	SETV	SVS
Set if No Overflow	SETNV	SVC
Set if Greater Than	SETGT	SGT
Set if Greater Than or Equal	SETGE	SGE
Set if Less Than	SETLT	SLT
Set if Less Than or Equal	SETLE	SLE
Set if Higher	SETH	SHI
Set if Not Higher	SETNH	SLS
BRANCH		
Branch	BR	BRA,JMP
Branch if Equal	BE	BEQ
Branch if Not Equal	BNE	BNE
Branch if Carry	BC	BCS
Branch if No Carry	BNC	BCC
Branch if Positive	BP	BPL
Branch if Negative	BN	BMI
Branch if Overflow	BV	BVS
Branch if No Overflow	BNV	BVC
Branch if Greater Than	BGT	BGT
Branch if Greater Than or Equal	BGE	BGE
Branch if Less Than	BLT	BLT
Branch if Less Than or Equal	BLE	BLE
Branch if Higher	BH	BHI
Branch if Not Higher	BNH	BLS
CALL		
Call	CALL	BSR,JSR
RETURN		
Return	RET	RTS
Return, with Restore	RETR	RTR
Return, with Exception	RETE	RTE
MISCELLANEOUS		
No Operation	NOP	NOP,PUSHEA
Push	PUSH	LINK,PEA, MOVE
Pop	POP	UNLK,MOVE
Wait	WAIT	STOP
Break	BRK	TRAP
Break On Overflow	BRKV	TRAPV
Reset	RESET	RESET

Preliminary—Subject to Revision

INSTRUCTION	STANDARD MNEMONIC	ZILOG MNEMONIC

ARITHMETIC

INSTRUCTION	STANDARD MNEMONIC	ZILOG MNEMONIC
Add	ADD	ADDB
Add, Byte	ADDB	ADDB
Add, Long	ADDL	ADDL
Add with Carry	ADDC	ADC
Add with Carry, Byte	ADDCB	ADCB
Subtract	SUB	SUB
Subtract, Byte	SUBB	SUBB
Subtract, Long	SUBL	SUBL
Subtract with Carry	SUBC	SBC
Subtract with Carry, Byte	SUBCB	SBCB
Increment	INC	INC
Increment, Byte	INCB	INCB
Decrement	DEC	DEC
Decrement, Byte	DECB	DECB
Multiply	MUL	MULT
Multiply; Long	MULL	MULTL
Divide	DIV	DIV
Divide, Long	DIVL	DIVL
Negate	NEG	NEG
Negate, Byte	NEGB	NEGB
Compare	CMP	CP
Compare, Byte	CMPB	CPB
Compare, Long	CMPL	CPL
Extend Sign	EXT	EXTS
Extend Sign, Byte	EXTB	EXTSB
Extend Sign, Long	EXTL	EXTSL
Compare	CMP	CPD,CPI,CPSD, CPSI
Compare, Byte	CMPB	CPDB,CPIB, CPSDB,CPSIB
Compare, Multiple	CMPM	CPDR,CPIR
Compare, Multiple, Byte	CMPMB	CPDRB,CPIRB
Compare Block	CMPBK	CPSDR,CPSIR
Compare Block, Byte	CMPBKB	CPSDRB, CPSIRB

LOGICAL

INSTRUCTION	STANDARD MNEMONIC	ZILOG MNEMONIC
And	AND	AND
And, Byte	ANDB	ANDB
Or	OR	OR
Or, Byte	ORB	ORB
Exclusive Or	XOR	XOR.COMFLG
Exclusive Or, Byte	XORB	XORB
Not	NOT	COM
Not, Byte	NOTB	COMB
Shift Left or Right Arithmetic	SHLRA	SDA
Shift Left or Right Arithmetic, Byte	SHLRAB	SDAB
Shift Left or Right Arithmetic, Long	SHLRAL	SDAL
Shift Left or Right	SHLR	SDL
Shift Left or Right, Byte	SHLRB	SDLB
Shift Left or Right, Long	SHLRL	SDLL
Shift Left	SHL	SLL
Shift Left, Byte	SHLB	SLLB
Shift Left, Long	SHLL	SLLL
Shift Left Arithmetic	SHLA	SLA
Shift Left Arithmetic, Byte	SHLAB	SLAB
Shift Left Arithmetic, Long	SHLAL	SLAL
Shift Right	SHR	SRL
Shift Right, Byte	SHRB	SRLB
Shift Right, Long	SHRL	SRLL
Shift Right Arithmetic	SHRA	SRA

INSTRUCTION	STANDARD MNEMONIC	ZILOG MNEMONIC
Shift Right Arithmetic, Byte	SHRAB	SRAB
Shift Right Arithmetic, Long	SHRAL	SRAL
Rotate Left	ROL	RL
Rotate Left, Byte	ROLB	RLB
Rotate Left Through Carry	ROLC	RLC
Rotate left Through Carry, Byte	ROLCB	RLCB
Rotate Left Digit	ROL4	RLDB
Rotate Right	ROR	RR
Rotate Right, Byte	RORB	RRB
Rotate Right Through Carry	RORC	RRC
Rotate Right Through Carry, Byte	RORCB	RRCB
Rotate Right Digit	ROR4	RRDB
Set if Zero	SETZ	TCC Z
Set if Not Zero	SETNZ	TCC NZ
Set if Equal	SETE	TCC EQ
Set if Not Equal	SETNE	TCC NE
Set if Carry	SETC	TCC C
Set if No Carry	SETNC	TCC NC
Set if Positive	SETP	TCC PL
Set if Negative	SETN	TCC MI
Set if Overflow	SETV	TCC OV
Set if No Overflow	SETNV	TCC NOV
Set if Greater Than	SETGT	TCC GT
Set if Greater Than or Equal	SETGE	TCC GE
Set if Less Than	SETLT	TCC LT
Set if Less Than or Equal	SETLE	TCC LE
Set if Higher	SETH	TCC UGT
Set if Not Higher	SETNH	TCC ULE
Set if Lower	SETL	TCC ULT
Set if Not Lower	SETNL	TCC UGE
Set if Parity Even	SETPE	TCC PE
Set if Parity Odd	SETPO	TCC PO
Set if Zero, Byte	SETZB	TCCB Z
Set if Not Zero, Byte	SETNZB	TCCB NZ
Set if Equal, Byte	SETEB	TCCB EQ
Set if Not Equal, Byte	SETNEB	TCCB NE
Set if Carry, Byte	SETCB	TCCB C
Set if No Carry, Byte	SETNCB	TCCB NC
Set if Positive, Byte	SETPB	TCCB PL
Set if Negative, Byte	SETNB	TCCB MI
Set if Overflow, Byte	SETVB	TCCB OV
Set if No Overflow, Byte	SETNVB	TCCB NOV
Set if Greater Than, Byte	SETGTB	TCCB GT
Set if Greater Than or Equal, Byte	SETGEB	TCCB GE
Set if Less Than, Byte	SETLTB	TCCB LT
Set if Less Than or Equal, Byte	SETLEB	TCCB LE
Set if Higher, Byte	SETHB	TCCB UGT
Set if Not Higher, Byte	SETNHB	TCCB ULE
Set if Lower, Byte	SETLB	TCCB ULT
Set if Not Lower, Byte	SETNLB	TCCB UGE
Set if Parity Even, Byte	SETPEB	TCCB PE
Set if Parity Odd, Byte	SETPOB	TCCB PO
Test	TEST	TEST
Test, Byte	TESTB	TESTB
Test, Long	TESTL	TESTL
Test Bit	TEST1	BIT
Test Bit, Byte	TEST1B	BITB
Test Multi-Micro Bit	TESTM	MBIT
Test and Set	TESTSET	TSET
Test and Set, Byte	TESTSETB	TSETB

DATA TRANSFER

Load	LD	LD,LDK,LDR, LDPS,LDA, LDAR
Load, Byte	LDB	LDB,LDRB
Load, Long	LDL	LDL,LDRL
Load Multiple	LDM	LDM
Store	ST	LD,LDR,LDPS
Store, Byte	STB	LDB,LDRB
Store, Long	STL	LDL,LDRL
Store, Multiple	STM	LDM
Move	MOV	LD,LDI,LDCTL, LDD
Move, Byte	MOVB	LDIB,LDDB
Move, Long	MOVL	LDL
Move, Multiple	MOVM	LDDR,LDIR
Move, Multiple, Byte	MOVMB	LDDRB,LDIRB
Move Block	MOVBK	LDIR
Move Block, Byte	MOVBKB	LDIRB
Input	IN	IN,IND,INI,SIN SIND,SINI
Input, Byte	INB	INB,INDB,INIB, SINB,SINDB, SINIB
Input Block	INBK	INDR,INIR, SINDR,SINIR
Input Block, Byte	INBKB	INDRB,INIRB, SINDRB, SINIRB
Ouput	OUT	OUT,OUD,OUTI, SOUT, SOUTD,SOUTI
Output, Byte	OUTB	OUTB,OUTDB, OUTIB, SOUTB, SOUTDB, SOUTIB
Output Block	OUTBK	OTDR,OTIR, SOTDR,SOTIR
Output Block, Byte	OUTBKB	OTDRB,OTIRB, SOTDRB, SOTIRB
Exchange	XCH	EX
Exchange, Byte	XCHB	EXB
Clear	CLR	CLR,RESFLG
Clear, Byte	CLRB	CLRB
Clear Bit	CLR1	RES
Clear Bit, Byte	CLR1B	RESB
Clear Multi-Micro	CLRM	CLRM
Set Bit	SET1	SET,SETFLG
Set Bit, Byte	SET1B	SETB
Set Multi-Micro	SETM	MSET

BRANCH

Branch	BR	JP,JR
Branch if Zero	BZ	JP Z, JR Z
Branch if Not Zero	BNZ	JP NZ, JR NZ
Branch if Equal	BE	JP EQ, JR EQ
Branch if Not Equal	BNE	JP NE, JR NE
Branch if Carry	BC	JP C, JR C
Branch if No Carry	BNC	JP NC, JR NC
Branch if Positive	BP	JP PL, JR PL
Branch if Negative	BN	JP MI, JR MI
Branch if Overflow	BV	JP OV, JR OV
Branch if No Overflow	BNV	JP NOV, JR NOV
Branch if Greater Than	BGT	JP GT, JR GT
Branch if Greater Than Or Equal	BGE	JP GE, JR GE
Branch if Less Than	BLT	JP LT, JR LT
Branch if Less Than Or Equal	BLE	JP LE, JR LE
Branch if Higher	BH	JP UGT, JR UGT
Branch if Not Higher	BNH	JP ULE, JR ULE
Branch if Lower	BL	JP ULT, JR ULT
Branch if Not Lower	BNL	JP UGE, JR UGE
Branch if Parity Even	BPE	JP PE, JR PE
Branch if Parity Odd	BPO	JP PO, JR PO
Decrement and Branch if Not Zero	DBNZ	DJNZ
Decrement and Branch if Not Zero, Byte	DBNZB	DJNZB

CALL

Call	CALL	CALL,CALR

RETURN

Return	RET	RET
Return if Zero	RETZ	RET Z
Return if Not Zero	RETNZ	RET NZ
Return if Equal	RETE	RET EQ
Return if Not Equal	RETNE	RET NE
Return if Carry	RETC	RET C
Return if No Carry	RETNC	RET NC
Return if Positive	RETP	RET PL
Return if Negative	RETN	RET MI
Return if Overflow	RETV	RET OV
Return if No Overflow	RETNV	RET NOV
Return if Greater Than	RETGT	RET GT
Return if Greater Than or Equal	RETGE	RETGE
Return if Less Than	RETLT	RET LT
Return if Less Than or Equal	RETLE	RET LE
Return if Higher	RETH	RET UGT
Return if Not Higher	RETNH	RET ULE
Return if Lower	RETL	RET ULT
Return if Not Lower	RETNL	RET UGE
Return if Parity Even	RETPE	RET PE
Return if Parity Odd	RETPO	RET PO
Return From Interrupt	RETI	IRET

MISCELLANEOUS

No Operation	NOP	NOP
Break	BRK	SC
Push	PUSH	PUSH
Push, Long	PUSHL	PUSHL
Pop	POP	POP
Pop, Long	POPL	POPL
Wait	WAIT	HALT
Enable Interrupt	EI	EI
Disable Interrupt	DI	DI
Request Multi-Micro	REQM	MREQ
Translate	TR	TRDB,TRIB
Translate, Block	TRBK	TRDRB,TRIRB
Translate and Test	TRTEST	TRTDB,TRTIB
Translate and Test, Multiple	TRTESTM	TRTDRB,TRTIRB

Index

OSBORNE/McGraw-Hill GENERAL BOOKS

An Introduction to Microcomputers series
by Adam Osborne
    Volume 0 — The Beginner's Book
    Volume 1 — Basic Concepts
    Volume 2 — Some Real Microprocessors (1978 ed.)
    Volume 3 — Some Real Support Devices (1978 ed.)
      Volume 2 1978-1979 Update Series
      Volume 3 1978-1979 Update Series

The 8089 I/O Processor Handbook
by Adam Osborne
The 8086 Book
by R. Rector and G. Alexy
8080 Programming for Logic Design
by Adam Osborne
6800 Programming for Logic Design
by Adam Osborne
Z80 Programming for Logic Design
by Adam Osborne

8080A/8085 Assembly Language Programming
by L. Leventhal
6800 Assembly Language Programming
by L. Leventhal
Z80 Assembly Language Programming
by L. Leventhal
6502 Assembly Language Programming
by L. Leventhal
Z8000 Assembly Language Programming
by L. Leventhal et al.
Running Wild: The Next Industrial Revolution
by Adam Osborne
The PET - CBM Personal Computer Guide
by C. Donahue and J. Enger
PET and the IEEE 488 Bus (GPIB)
by E. Fisher and C. W. Jensen

OSBORNE/McGraw-Hill SOFTWARE

Practical BASIC Programs
by L. Poole et al.
Some Common BASIC Programs
by L. Poole and M. Borchers
Some Common BASIC Programs PET Cassette
Some Common BASIC Programs PET Disk
Some Common BASIC Programs TRS-80 Cassette

Payroll with Cost Accounting - CBASIC
by Lon Poole et al.
Accounts Payable and Accounts Receivable - CBASIC
by Lon Poole et al.
General Ledger - CBASIC
by Lon Poole et al.